Physical Measurement and Analysis

by

NATHAN H. COOK

and

ERNEST RABINOWICZ

Massachusetts Institute of Technology

ADDISON-WESLEY PUBLISHING COMPANY, INC.

READING, MASSACHUSETTS · PALO ALTO · LONDON

This book is in the

ADDISON-WESLEY SERIES IN THE
ENGINEERING SCIENCES

MECHANICS AND THERMODYNAMICS

Consulting Editors

HOWARD W. EMMONS and BERNARD BUDIANSKY

Preface

This book is based on a course which the authors have been teaching for the past five years to juniors, seniors, and graduate students in the Mechanical Engineering Department at the Massachusetts Institute of Technology. The course has also been given during the past two years to 100 post-graduate students from government and industry at a special M.I.T. Summer Program.

The authors have found, as a result of their contact with graduate and undergraduate students and their consulting work with various industrial laboratories, that serious problems in regard to experimental measurements and their analysis are almost universal. We have often observed expensive research investigations actually heading in the wrong direction due to rather elementary difficulties and errors in experimental technique. The basic reason for this state of affairs is that our schools of Engineering and Science are much more proficient in preparing students to analyze and plan a research program, than in showing them how to make the meaningful measurements required of the research problem.

The aim of our presentation has been to make the students aware of the principles underlying physical measurements, stressing wherever necessary the pitfalls and limitations of such measurements. In particular, we have emphasized the dynamical and statistical points of view. The experimental apparatus described is extremely simple in nature because our desire is to emphasize the analysis of apparatus, and an understanding of possible sources of error, rather than to expose the student to a wide variety of commercial equipment.

Many of the problems appearing in the book are quite different from those found in most texts, which are generally simplified and idealized to produce short, single answers that can be obtained in 15 minutes or so. The important areas in measurement do not often generate such simplified problems. Hence the problems presented here are likely to be more realistic and considerably more difficult. However, we wish to emphasize that even in this text, each problem is still idealized. In numerous instances, typical answers are given. Due to the nature of certain problems, there is often a wide range of satisfactory answers.

While the chapter sequence represents a rather logical progression of subject matter, we have found that it is perfectly satisfactory to teach the course in an order which intermixes "Analysis," and "Methods."

For instance, we have used the chapter order 1, 4, 5, 2, 3, 6, 7, 8 most often.

We wish to express our thanks to the many people who have been helpful and critical in the preparation of this text. We are greatly indebted to Professor Milton C. Shaw, who inspired us to undertake the task of developing the course which led to this book. We wish to thank Professor George S. Reichenbach for his generous help in preparing the chapters on fluid and temperature measurement. Messrs. J. Leach, F. Anderson, R. Bowley, and R. Foster have been very helpful in the development of laboratory equipment. Mrs. Betty Foster and Miss Barbara Wollan have been most patient and helpful in typing and retyping the manuscript. Finally, we thank our students, who have thoughtfully and critically commented on the course.

Cambridge, Mass.   N. H. C.
April 1963   E. R.

Contents

Chapter 1. INTRODUCTION 1

1-1. What are experiments? 1
1-2. Types of measurement 3
1-3. Choice of suitable instruments 6
1-4. The resolution and accuracy of instruments 7
1-5. The microscope 7
1-6. The eye as a microscope lens 10
1-7. Magnification obtainable with a microscope 11
1-8. Depth of focus of a lens 12
1-9. The chemical balance 13
1-10. Theoretical limit of resolution of the balance 15
1-11. Accuracy of instruments and errors of measurement . . . 15
1-12. Errors of the caliper micrometer 16
1-13. Errors of a dynamic measuring device: the voltmeter . . . 21
1-14. Design of experiments to reduce errors 25

Chapter 2. EXPERIMENTAL STATISTICS 29

2-1. Internal and external estimates of measurement error . . . 29
2-2. External estimates of the error 30
2-3. Independence and dependence of errors 32
2-4. How to estimate the external error of a measurement . . . 35
2-5. Internal estimates of the error 36
2-6. Properties of the normal distribution 38
2-7. Use of the normal distribution to eliminate data 40
2-8. Use of the normal distribution to relate various definitions of error 41
2-9. Use of the normal distribution to estimate the extreme of a distribution 41
2-10. Use of the normal distribution to calculate the probable error in $\bar{x}$ 42
2-11. How to set up a normal distribution calculation 44
2-12. Short cuts in calculating σ 48
2-13. Testing a distribution for normalcy: the χ^2 test 49
2-14. Nonnormal distributions 53
2-15. How to draw the "best" straight line through a set of points 56

Chapter 3. DYNAMICS OF MEASUREMENT 69

3-1. First-order systems 70
3-2. Second-order systems (where input is a force) 78

3–3. Second-order systems (where input is a displacement) . . . 84
3–4. Compensating networks 87
3–5. Harmonic analysis 97
3–6. Dynamic data analysis 106

Chapter 4. DISPLACEMENT MEASUREMENT 113

4–1. Displacement measuring by mechanical means 114
4–2. Optical measuring methods 116
4–3. Fluid gages 121
4–4. Displacement measurement through electrical means . . . 124

Chapter 5. FORCE AND TORQUE MEASUREMENT 153

5–1. Preliminary requirements 153
5–2. Systems for measuring force 154
5–3. Axially loaded members 158
5–4. Cantilever beams 159
5–5. Rings 160
5–6. Torque tubes 165
5–7. General considerations 165

Chapter 6. TEMPERATURE MEASUREMENT 169

6–1. Temperature-measuring devices 170
6–2. Sources of error in thermocouples 177
6–3. Pyrometry 179
6–4. Other measuring techniques 182
6–5. Dynamics of thermal measurement 183
6–6. Velocity error 185
6–7. Radiation error 186
6–8. Temperature measurement in moving and sliding members . . 187
6–9. Sliding temperature measurement 190

Chapter 7. MEASUREMENTS ON FLUIDS 195

7–1. Flow measurement 195
7–2. Pressure measurement 204
7–3. Vacuum gages 212
7–4. Cleanliness considerations 214
7–5. Leak detection 215
7–6. Dynamics of pressure measurement 215

Chapter 8. RADIOTRACER TECHNIQUES 225

8–1. Introduction 225
8–2. The constitution of atoms 225

8–3.   Stability of nuclides: radionuclides 226
8–4.   Decay of radioactive nuclei 229
8–5.   Multiple decay 230
8–6.   Half-life of radionuclides 231
8–7.   Penetrating power of radioactive decay particles 232
8–8.   Detection of radiation 234
8–9.   The geiger counter 234
8–10. Photographic film 237
8–11. Comparison of geiger counters and photographic film as
       radioactivity detectors 238
8–12. Obtaining radioactive material 240
8–13. Quantitative aspects of irradiation 241
8–14. Amount of radioactivity required for tracer experiments . . 244
8–15. The statistics of radiotracer measurements: Poisson statistics 245
8–16. Resolution and accuracy of radiotracer counting methods . . 248
8–17. Experimental uses of radioactivity: nontracer uses 250
8–18. Tracer applications of radiotracers 252
8–19. Calibration of radioactive materials 253

APPENDIX 1. Time-variant physical quantities: the use of complex
       numbers 259

APPENDIX 2. Experiments with random numbers 265

APPENDIX 3. Illustrative experiments 272

APPENDIX 4. The use of analog computers in measurement analysis 295

APPENDIX 5. Tables of physical quantities 299

INDEX 310

To Milton C. Shaw

CHAPTER ONE

Introduction

1-1. What are experiments?

We all have in the back of our minds a stereotype concept of the experimenter. He may be a white-coated, sober-faced scientist peering through a microscope in a laboratory full of odd-shaped scientific glassware, or perhaps a somewhat harried engineer with an oil smear across his forehead, who is turning the controls of some massive engine with one hand while he records the readings obtained on various dials and gages (sometimes spelled *gauges*) with the other. The value to society of both these types of experimenters is so obvious that it seems quite unnecessary to defend the validity of experiments. However, we will do well to remind ourselves that, for some thousands of years, sensible intelligent people, leaders of thought in society, held that experiments were quite unnecessary and misleading, since an accurate model of the material aspects of the universe could be obtained either by pure reason or by appeal to divine authority. Some vestige of this attitude still persists, in all of us, when some carefully designed experiment of ours gives an unexpected result. It is now generally accepted, however, that a view of the universe based on observation and experiment has great validity, and this has endowed those activities with importance and significance.

Naturally, experiments fall into many different categories, from the very fundamental one of counting the distribution of galaxies in space to test a cosmological theory, to the much more practical one of measuring the mechanical strength of a new alloy to see if it has commercial value, to the very mundane one of weighing a letter to see how much postage it needs. However, although the aim of these experiments is so different, they do have much in common: In all cases we are measuring a quantity which we can specify more or less exactly; and whether we like it or not, in all cases the measurements tend to be affected by errors of various types. In all cases the measurements are carried out by means of instruments, which must be chosen to be suitable to the task at hand, and to carry it out in an effective manner. Lastly, these measurements are quantities which must be interpreted, so that the results of the experiment can be put to use.

The typical experiment, as we have described it above, is a process in which we have a machine or system or apparatus in action, and make a measurement or series of measurements of one quantity or one phenomenon, although in many cases several such quantities are measured simultaneously. A large number of different experiments will be described in the pages which follow. However, it must be realized that one isolated experiment is generally but one step in the study of a problem, such as a research investigation. Any complete investigation generally involves a wide variety of endeavors. Typically, the essence of the research program can be stated in the following steps.

1. STATEMENT AND DEFENSE OF THE PROBLEM

This should answer such questions as: What is the problem? Why is this investigation necessary? What do we hope to prove? Where will the results be of use? What has been done in the past on this problem?

2. PRELIMINARY ANALYSIS OF THE PROBLEM

Here some sort of mental or pictorial or mathematical model of the problem is conceived which may possibly be used to solve it. At this point, original thinking and new ideas and concepts are introduced, weighed, and combined.

3. EXPERIMENTAL ANALYSIS OF THE PROBLEM

Experiments are designed and carried out which will either verify or disprove the usefulness of the model proposed in step 2. Here we always strive for the "critical experiment" which will say "yes" or "no" to the theory being put forth.

4. EXAMINATION OF THE MODEL IN LIGHT OF THE EXPERIMENT

The experimental results, if properly obtained, should lead either to acceptance or to alteration of the model. Steps 2, 3, and 4 are generally repeated until satisfactory agreement between prediction and experiment is obtained.

The above steps sound simple and straightforward. However, this is not the case. The solution of the problem lies in obtaining the correct model, while the experiments serve as signposts pointing toward the correct model. Unfortunately, most people are completely illiterate when it comes to reading these signs. Also, in probably the majority of research work, errors creep into the experiments in such a way as to render at least partially incorrect the conclusions based on them.

One of the main tasks of the experimenter is to detect such errors, or at any rate to make himself aware of their probable existence and likely magnitude, so that corrective action can be taken. This awareness of the capabilities and limitations of his apparatus comes to the experimenter most naturally when he is working with a simple experimental setup, perhaps of his own design; indeed, history shows that many important discoveries have been made with basically *simple* pieces of experimental equipment. Today, however, a tremendous assortment of measuring equipment is commercially available, and to a researcher it is always tempting to assemble quantities of it to carry out measurements without understanding how this equipment functions. Under such circumstances, he cannot properly evaluate the meaning of the measurements. In this book, we hope to give the reader sufficient background in simple measurement systems to enable him to design and test simple systems and to understand the functioning of a variety of systems.

1-2. Types of measurement

Historically speaking, the earliest types of measurement were those based on the principle of direct comparison. If the length of a rope were to be measured, then it was placed alongside a standard length (which might be a foot or a cubit), and the standard was stepped off against the rope, as in Fig. 1-1. Similarly, to determine the weight of an object, the experimenter would take the object in one hand and a standard weight in the other and compare them (Fig. 1-2). An obvious characteristic of this direct-comparison process is that the matching of these two quantities is done by some human sense, and therefore the quantity has to be one which falls well within the capabilities of the human experimenter. A second feature of this direct-comparison process (one which is true of all experimentation, but which is not so obvious in less direct measurements) is that the quantity to be measured can be compared only with another quantity of the same dimension. An indirect measurement, for example, in which a force is transformed by a transducer into an electric signal, then amplified, and finally displayed

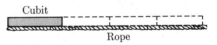

Fig. 1-1. Stepping off a standard cubit against a rope.

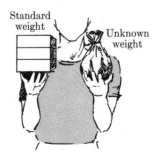

Fig. 1-2. Comparing two weights.

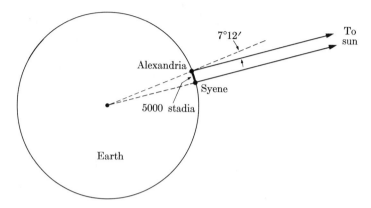

Fig. 1–3. Eratosthenes' method of calculating the earth's diameter. When the sun was overhead at Syene (Assuan), it was 7°12' from vertical at Alexandria. The baseline, Alexandria-Syene, was 5000 stadia. (One stadium ≈ 600 feet.)

on an electromagnetic recorder as a length, takes on meaning only when the performance of the recorder is calibrated against a known force, so that, overall, the unknown force is compared with a standard force. It follows from this reasoning that no experimenter should undertake a measurement, and indeed is not in a position to make a measurement, unless he can relate the quantity being measured (even though he might have to relate it indirectly) to standards of measurement, such as the standard kilogram or volt, as defined and preserved by the international and national bureaus of standards. And yet it has surprised the authors on several occasions that many students, even research students of considerable ability, can carry on long series of measurements with complex systems calibrated months earlier by others, without feeling the need or desirability of ever recalibrating their equipment, or of frequently checking the calibration.

Another feature of direct-comparison processes, which holds true for most other methods of measurement, is that the unknown and the standard must not only have the same dimension, but also be of similar magnitude. In fact, one of the triumphs of ancient science, namely, the determination of the circumference of the earth, could be accomplished only by setting up a tremendous base line on earth, some 500 miles long, from Alexandria to Syene (Fig. 1–3). One of the great failures of ancient scientists was their inability to measure the size of atoms; but the most convenient tiny yardstick for this purpose is the wavelength of an x-ray, and x-rays were not discovered until modern times.

Indirect measurements have, as is well known, largely taken over the task of measurement from direct-measuring instruments. This change is due to a number of causes, of which we will cite just a few. First, there is the fact that many of the quantities of interest to us are ones to which the human observer has little sensitivity; for example, electric quantities such as current and potential. All that can be done in such cases is to convert the electric quantity by indirect means to the deflection of the pointer of an electric meter, or some similar device, which human senses can then detect. Secondly, in many cases the measurements to be made are on a dimensional scale outside the range of human competence; for example, the distance from the earth to the sun, or the size of an atom. Last, but not least, there is the factor of convenience. Indirect measurements can often be made quickly, for twenty-four hours every day, be recorded automatically, and be applied immediately to correct some process through feedback control.

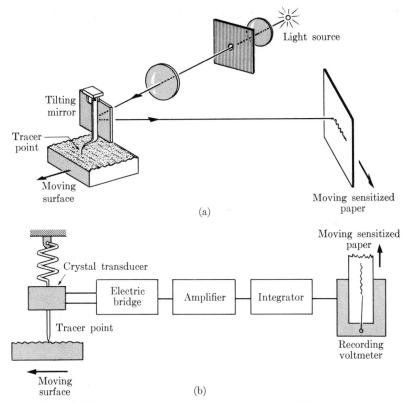

Fig. 1–4. (a) Roughness measurement using optical lever. (b) Roughness measurement using electronic amplification.

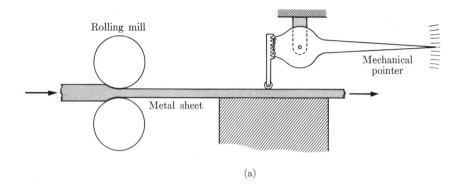

(a)

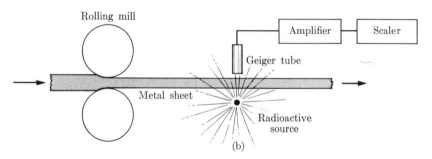

(b)

Fig. 1–5. (a) Measurement of sheet thickness using mechanical feeler. (b) Measurement of sheet thickness using beta-gage.

1–3. Choice of suitable instruments

A striking feature of the present-day technical scene is that the experimenter has available many alternative ways of performing a measurement. These often differ quite drastically in the scientific principle on which the apparatus is based, the mechanism through which this principle is applied, and the way in which the result is displayed. Two typical measurements, and alternative ways to carry them out, are shown in Figs. 1–4 and 1–5. Clearly, the experimenter must consider the factors which determine the ability of an apparatus to perform well. These are:

(1) *resolution*, (2) *accuracy*, (3) *convenience*, and (4) *cost*.

We may perhaps ignore the last two for the present, since subjective factors figure in them so strongly, and confine our discussion to the first two.

1-4. The resolution and accuracy of instruments

The *resolution* of an instrument may be defined as the smallest amount of the quantity being measured which the instrument will detect. The *accuracy* may be defined as the fractional error in making a measurement.

There is a difficulty in terminology here, in that "great" resolution or "great" accuracy actually are terms which denote a small value for these quantities. Hence, we shall use expressions such as "good" resolution to describe an instrument which will detect small quantities. Similar considerations apply to accuracy.

It should be noted that the two factors, accuracy and resolution, are sometimes quite independent, at other times closely related. Let us suppose that we are measuring wear during a sliding test, and that we propose to use either a radiotracer technique or a chemical balance to determine the amount of material worn away. The radiotracer technique has very good resolution and will detect as little as 10^{-10} gm of wear, but it is not very accurate, and even when the amount of wear is quite large, say 1 gm, the accuracy is no better than 3%. The chemical balance has much poorer resolution, with a least detectable weight of 10^{-4} gm, but 1 gm can be measured with an error of only 10^{-4} gm, giving an accuracy of 0.01%. The characteristics of the wear process (wear rates very small but very variable) match the characteristics of the radiotracer technique, namely good resolution but poor accuracy, much better than they do those of the weighing method. This sort of consideration is often a crucial factor in deciding which of alternative methods of measurement to use, because the characteristics of the instrument should match those of the quantity being studied.

We shall not in this section take up further the question of accuracy, but rather discuss exclusively the resolution of instruments. Generally speaking, this is both a simpler and a more basic problem than that of accuracy. If we considered all possible instruments, we would find that the resolution of each was determined either by fundamental factors, or by more or less trivial design factors, or by a combination of the two. In citing illustrations, we shall limit our discussion to two simple instruments which occupy extreme positions in this classification: the microscope and the chemical balance.

1-5. The microscope

Let us assume that a microscope is to be used to measure the length of some small illuminated object in its field of view by projecting an enlarged image against a calibrated scale (Fig. 1-6). Then, to find the resolution, we have to determine the smallest length which the micro-

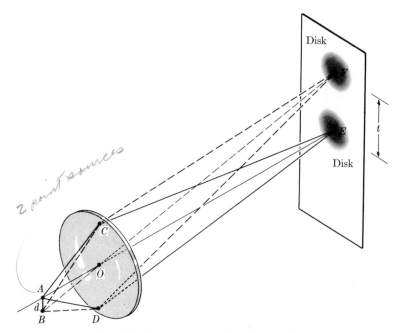

Fig. 1–6. Ray construction for a simple lens.

scope will measure. Putting the question differently, what is the smallest separation the microscope will detect between two point objects? Initially, we shall take a simple lens to represent the microscope; later, we shall see that more complicated lens systems follow the same rule.

If A is an object lying on the axis of the lens, and B is an object separated from A by a distance d, then by a simple ray construction, the images will be at E and F, and will be separated by a distance t. In practice, however, E and F will not be point images, but finite disks, and if these overlap, it becomes impossible to look at the image and tell whether there are one or two objects. This factor determines the resolution. Hence, we must determine the size of the disks constituting E and F.

As is well known, the spreading of a point image into a disk is the phenomenon of diffraction, which has its origin in the wave nature of light. This limits the distance which may be determined to those which are of the order of magnitude of one wavelength, which we shall call λ.

Referring to Fig. 1–6, we see that point A on the axis gives an image at E on the axis. How do we know that A lies on the axis? Presumably, because the distances AC and AD are equal, each being $m\lambda$, where m is an arbitrary number of wavelengths. If the image of B is not also to

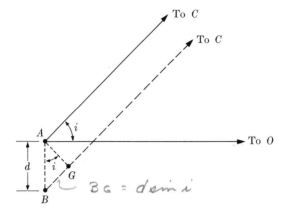

Fig. 1–7. Enlarged section of Fig. 1–6.

fall at E, it is necessary for B to lie a significant distance from the axis. This means that BC and BD must be significantly unequal, whereas AC and AD were exactly the same.

The least inequality between BC and BD which has real meaning in a situation such as this, where information is transmitted through waves, is of the order of magnitude of one wavelength. Hence we insert the condition that $BC - BD = \lambda$, or (what is the same thing) $BC - AC = \lambda/2$.

Figure 1–7 is a section of Fig. 1–6, enlarged to allow us to see clearly how to impose the above condition. Note that if d is small, we may assume that AC and BC are parallel. Then

$$BC - AC = BG = d \sin i.$$

But

$$BC - AC = \frac{\lambda}{2}.$$

Hence

$$d_r = \frac{\lambda}{2 \sin i}. \tag{1–1}$$

This is the basic formula for the resolution, or the least resolved distance d_r, of a lens. In deriving it we have not had to consider the geometry of the image side of the lens system; consequently our formula is equally applicable to simple lenses, compound lenses, and microscope systems.

One small addition must be made. It is known that in a medium of refractive index n, the wavelength of light is reduced to λ/n, and hence for objects A and B immersed in a liquid, we have

$$d_r = \frac{\lambda}{2n \sin i}. \tag{1–2}$$

To get the best resolution, the d_r must be as small as possible, which means making λ as small as possible, and n and $\sin i$ as large as possible. Using violet light ($\lambda = 4 \cdot 10^{-5}$ cm), an immersion oil ($n = 1.6$), and a well-designed lens system ($\sin i = 0.95$), we get d_r as small as 1.3×10^{-5} cm. If the objective is not of the immersion type, we get $d_r = 2.2 \times 10^{-5}$ cm.

The quantity $n \sin i$ is widely known as the numerical aperture, or N.A., of a microscope objective, and is almost always shown engraved on the objective itself.

It is interesting to note that it is not difficult to find inexpensive lenses which have the best resolution possible for lenses of that numerical aperture, or indeed to find cheap microscopes which have lenses with N.A. values of 0.9 in air or 1.4 in oil. The fine microscopes may be far superior in such features as achromatism, freedom from distortion, size of the field of view, etc., but differences in their resolution are slight.

1–6. The eye as a microscope lens

It is of interest to consider the eye as a lens, and to evaluate its performance. Referring to Fig. 1–8, we see that d_r is given by the formula

$$d_r = \frac{\lambda}{2 \sin i} = \lambda \, \frac{\text{viewing distance}}{\text{pupil diameter}}. \tag{1–3}$$

To get the greatest resolution, we need the smallest viewing distance and the largest pupil diameter. Most people cannot focus properly at viewing distances closer than 25 cm, and in good light the pupil diameter is about 0.4 cm. Hence

$$d_r = \frac{5 \times 10^{-5} \times 25}{0.4} = 3 \times 10^{-3} \text{ cm}. \tag{1–4}$$

Experimentally, values of 7×10^{-3} cm have been determined.

The next point we may consider is the structure of the detecting system of the eye, namely the retina. The retina has sensitive elements,

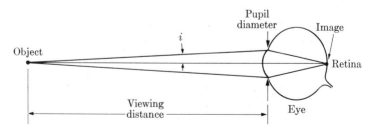

Fig. 1–8. The eye as a simple lens.

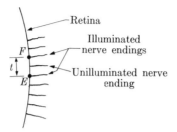

Fig. 1–9. Schematic view of detecting elements in the retina.

nerve endings, each of which detects the presence or absence of light in its vicinity and communicates this information to the brain. Since t is only $\frac{1}{8}$ of d (corresponding to a ratio of 1 to 8 between the retina-pupil and pupil-object distance), t is 4×10^{-4} cm. This happens to be precisely the spacing of the detecting elements in the eye. Thus we may say that the eye is a very efficient system, in that the *spacing* of the detecting elements, which clearly is one factor which sets a limit to the resolution, is precisely the same as the distance which (according to optical theory) is the other factor limiting the resolution.

The overall performance of the eye, as we saw above, is only half as good as it should be, for this reason: In order to make sure that images such as E and F in Fig. 1–9 are separate, it is necessary that one unilluminated nerve ending in the retina is present between the illuminated detectors at E and F. This fact doubles the minimum resolved distance d_r which the eye can see.

1–7. Magnification obtainable with a microscope

We have previously stated that the best resolution of a microscope is 1.3×10^{-5} cm, and that the resolution of the human eye is 7×10^{-3} cm. The ratio, namely 500, is the utmost in the way of real magnification that an object viewed in a microscope need be given in order for all of its visible features to be perceivable. Magnifications of 750, 1000, and even 2000 are frequently used, however, which make it possible for the human observer not to have to work at the limit of his eye's resolution. However, much of the magnification is "empty."

To get higher real magnifications, we must use illumination of shorter wavelength, as in the electron microscope, in which the wavelength is about 10^{-10} cm. Most electron microscopes have N.A. values of about 10^{-3}, giving a resolution of about 10^{-7} cm. Hence, useful magnifications of up to 100,000 become possible.

1–8. Depth of focus of a lens

The depth of focus of a lens may be calculated in a simple way. According to the principle of stationary time, if an object A gives rise to an image E, then the light paths ACE, AOE, and ADE must all take equally long periods of time (see Figs. 1–10 and 1–11).

If we consider another object a distance s from the first one, then its light path GOE will be longer by a distance s than that of the first object, while its light path GCE will be longer by a distance $s \cos i$. Hence, the distances GOE and GCE will differ by an amount equal to $s - s \cos i$. To calculate for what distance s the object at G will no longer form an image at E, we apply the same considerations as before, namely that for a blurring to become noticeable:

$$s - s \cos i = \lambda,$$

$$s - s(1 - \sin^2 i)^{1/2} = \lambda,$$

$$s - s + \frac{s \sin^2 i}{2} - \cdots = \lambda,$$

$$s = \frac{2\lambda}{(\text{N.A.})^2} \quad \text{(approx.)} \tag{1–5}$$

The depth of focus of a lens depends on the inverse square of the numerical aperture, while the resolving power depends on the inverse of the numerical aperture.

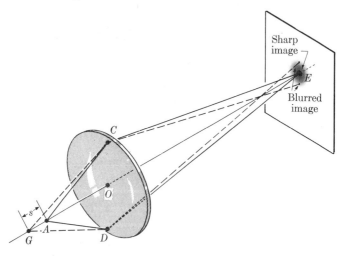

Fig. 1–10. Ray construction of a simple lens, showing defocusing owing to axial displacement.

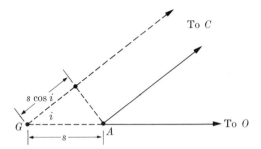

Fig. 1–11. Enlarged section of Fig. 1–10.

All in all, the whole question of the resolution of optical elements can be readily calculated theoretically, and theory seems to be in close harmony with what is observed in practice.

1–9. The chemical balance

We now proceed to study the mode of action of the chemical balance, in an attempt to discover its best theoretical resolution.

Figure 1–12 shows a schematic diagram of a chemical balance. A beam and pointer system is suspended at O, while a weight $W + \Delta W$ is placed on the balance pan attached to A, and a weight W is placed at B. This causes the beam to take up an angle θ with the horizontal; C, the midpoint of AB, is a distance x below O, while D, the center of mass of the beam-and-pointer system, is a distance y from O.

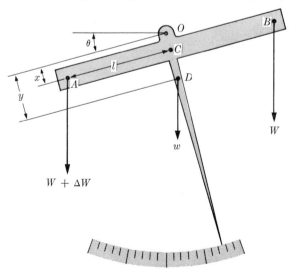

Fig. 1–12. Schematic illustration of the chemical balance.

To calculate the equilibrium, we equate the moments of the three vertical forces about O. The horizontal distance of A from O is $l \cos \theta - x \sin \theta$, the horizontal distance of B is $l \cos \theta + x \sin \theta$, while the distance of D from O is $y \sin \theta$. Hence we have

$$(W + \Delta W)(l \cos \theta - x \sin \theta) = wy \sin \theta + W(l \cos \theta + x \sin \theta)$$

or

$$\Delta W(l \cos \theta - x \sin \theta) = wy \sin \theta + 2W x \sin \theta. \qquad (1\text{–}6)$$

If θ is very small, we have $\cos \theta = 1$, $\sin \theta = \theta$, and hence we can write

$$\Delta W l = (wy + 2Wx + \Delta W x)\theta,$$

$$\frac{\theta}{\Delta W} = \frac{l}{wy + 2Wx}, \qquad \text{since} \qquad \frac{\Delta W}{W} \to 0. \qquad (1\text{–}7)$$

The quantity $\theta/\Delta W$ represents the sensitivity of the balance, namely the deflection per small load imbalance. It will be seen that the sensitivity is a function of W, the load to be measured, unless we make $x = 0$. If, however, we arrange A, O, and B to be colinear, we have

$$\boxed{\frac{\theta}{\Delta W} = \frac{l}{wy},} \qquad (1\text{–}8)$$

which is independent of W. This is the basic sensitivity equation of the chemical balance.

This equation tells us that for best sensitivity we need a balance with a long beam (l large), the beam to have small weight (w small), and a small distance y between the point of suspension of the beam and its center of mass. It is essential that the arms be rigid, or their deflection under load will introduce an unwanted x value, representing the non-colinearity of the three points of support. These requirements are contradictory, since a very long beam cannot be both light and rigid. Also, it would have a large moment of inertia and the balance would have a very long period of swing, which is undesirable. However, Eq. (1–8) tells us nothing about the resolution of the balance, since there seems to be hardly any limitation on the extent to which optical-lever techniques may be refined to measure small angles of deflection.

In fact, the resolution of the balance is determined by other factors, the perfection of the knife edges at the points of support, the stability of the arms, the frictional properties of the knife-edge-flat system, etc. Any change in the length of the arms, either as a result of local fluctuations of temperature or of aging effects in the beam material is very detrimental, as is any wear or deformation which changes the profile of the knife edges.

The best balances can weigh 1000 gm with a resolution of 10^{-5} gm, and an accuracy of one part in 10^8. Since l is about 20 cm, this means that the effective length of the arms must stay defined to better than $2 \cdot 10^{-7}$ cm. When we remember that metals show thermal expansion coefficients of 1000 parts in 10^8 per degree of change in temperature, and that many metals undergo spontaneous changes in length of the order of several hundred parts in 10^8 per year due to aging, we can see that the performance of good balances is quite remarkable.

1–10. Theoretical limit of resolution of the balance

The theoretical limit for the resolution of a balance is set by the fact that it cannot be brought absolutely to rest; but under the action of gas molecules bombarding it, the balance suffers Brownian motion. By the kinetic theory of gases, the balance will have on the average an amount $kT/2$ of kinetic energy and an amount $kT/2$ of potential energy. We may calculate the effect of this on its performance as follows.

The potential energy of the balance will lead to an angular displacement θ, and hence the weight of the beam will be lifted by a distance $y - y \cos \theta$. Hence we write

$$\frac{kT}{2} = w(y - y \cos \theta) = \frac{wy\theta^2}{2}, \quad \text{(approx.)} \quad (1\text{--}9)$$

Now $kT/2$ is about 4×10^{-14} erg at room temperature, while w is of the order of 100 gm or 10^5 dynes, while y might be 10^{-3} cm. Hence

$$\theta^2 = 8 \times 10^{-16}, \quad \text{and} \quad \theta = 3 \times 10^{-8} \text{ rad.}$$

But

$$\theta = \frac{l\,\Delta W}{wy}.$$

By substitution we find that

$$\Delta W_r = 3 \times 10^{-10} \text{ gm.} \quad (1\text{--}10)$$

In practice, the resolution of balances is nowhere near this figure; hence the resolution is based on incidental rather than fundamental considerations.

1–11. Accuracy of instruments and errors of measurement

We shall now consider the accuracy of instruments, since the performance of an instrument is often judged by assessing the degree of *accuracy* with which a measurement may be carried out when using that instrument. In defining the accuracy, we postulate that if the instrument is used to measure a quantity which is actually 20.0 units of some dimension, say amperes, and the instrumental reading is 19.6, then the accuracy is to within four parts in 200, or 2%. The accuracy is limited by the *error of measurement*, which in this case is 2%, or 0.02.

Since the types of instruments in common use cover such a wide range, and their errors are so numerous and diverse, there is some difficulty in apprehending all the causes which limit experimental accuracy. Perhaps the easiest approach is to consider the performance of two simple instruments: one a direct-reading device, the other an indirect one.

1–12. Errors of the caliper micrometer

The caliper micrometer is an instrument for taking measurements, with fairly high accuracy, of the dimensions of small, rigid objects. Figure 1–13 shows the micrometer being used to measure the diameter of a bearing ball. The ball is placed between the anvils of the micrometer, and the knurled thimble is turned until the anvils tighten on the ball and a light but definite contact is made. The dimensions of the ball are then read off, to the nearest $\frac{1}{40}$ of an inch by the scale on the barrel of the micrometer, and to $\frac{1}{1000}$ of an inch by the divisions of the thimble of the micrometer; if greater accuracy is required, direct interpolation of the divisions on the thimble will allow the size to be read off to within $\frac{1}{10000}$ of an inch.

As we shall see, this simple micrometer is subject to a large number of errors. The student may wonder why it continues to be in wide use. The answer is that other instruments, almost all instruments, also have many and diverse errors, and that it is not the number of errors which is significant, but their overall magnitude. From this point of view, the micrometer may be considered to be an instrument capable of quite a high degree of accuracy, since the various error-inducing mechanisms

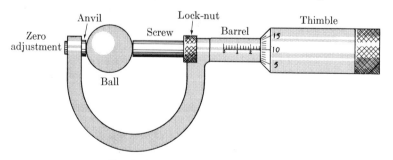

Fig. 1–13. The caliper micrometer.

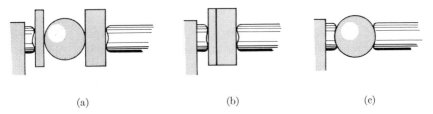

Fig. 1–14. Detecting an error (if it exists) in anvil profile.

which we describe below do not appear to operate too severely. In discerning each type of error, we shall not only give estimates of its magnitude where possible, but also give some idea of how it may be detected and reduced or eliminated.

(a) *Zero error.* It often happens that the micrometer is out of adjustment, so that when the anvils are brought together with no ball between them, a reading different from zero is obtained. This error may be eliminated by either adjusting a screw on the micrometer, or else, still more simply, by subtracting the zero error from every other reading obtained with the micrometer. Thus if the zero error is -0.0006 in., and a ball measures 0.2003 in., then the true value of the ball's diameter is

$$0.2003 - (-0.0006) = 0.2009 \text{ in.}$$

(b) *Anvil shape in error.* If the anvils of the micrometer are not flat, as they are supposed to be, but have an irregular outline as a result of wear, then even if there is no zero error, an incorrect value will still be obtained when a ball is measured with the micrometer. This error might be detected by a series of measurements in which we use two flat bars as auxiliary elements, as shown in Fig. 1–14. We measure (a) a unit of two flat bars with a ball in between; (b) the two flat bars by themselves; and (c) the ball by itself.

The difference between measurements (a) and (b) is the true value of the diameter of the ball, and should agree with measurement (c). It may be noted that, in an experiment such as this, where the desired value is obtained as the difference between two quantities measured on the same instrument, we do not have to concern ourselves with the zero error, since this drops out. Thus, if the zero error is e, then the true value of the thickness of the combination of two bars and one ball is $a - e$. The true thickness of the two bars alone is $b - e$. Their difference is the correct value of $a - b$.

Error in anvil shape is a difficult thing to allow for, especially to allow for accurately. If error exists to any extent, the micrometer should be replaced.

(c) *Error in the screw.* The performance of the micrometer depends, of course, on the perfection of the screw, since the geometry of the instrument is such that any error (even a small one) in pitch of the screw is converted into a large error in the reading of the micrometer. The best way of checking for errors in the screw is to measure the ball with one of a number of flats of different thickness, to measure the flats alone, and to subtract the measurements. If the various values, representing different measurements of the ball diameter, differ appreciably, then error in the screw is to be suspected.

It will be realized that if the screw is variable, it becomes very difficult to judge which value is best. All that can be done is to take an average of all of the values, and hope that this has averaged out the error. This process, known as randomizing, is one in which we take a number of independent measurements, hoping that the plus error of one will, to some extent, cancel out the minus error of another.

If the screw has an error, then simple repeat measurements of the ball diameter will not detect or reduce it, since the same error will affect all of the readings. However, by proper design of the experiment, as outlined above, the screw error can be changed from a *systematic* one to a *random* one, which thus becomes subject to reduction by averaging.

It is the aim of the skillful experimenter to so design his experiments that systematic errors will be kept to a minimum, and those errors which do occur will be random.

(d) *Error due to temperature differences.* If the temperature of the ball differs from that of the micrometer, because they have been held in the hand for different periods of time, then the length measured will be subject to error, owing to thermal expansion. Expansion coefficients of metals are of the order of $10 \times 10^{-6}/°F$; so for a 1-in. ball with a temperature which differs by $10°F$ from the temperature of the micrometer, there is an error of 1.0×10^{-4} in.

There may be similar errors, even when the temperature of the ball and micrometer are the same, if the temperature differs from that at which the micrometer was calibrated, and the ball and the micrometer have different coefficients of thermal expansion.

This type of error is characterized by the fact that the absolute error increases proportionately with the size of the ball, while many of the other errors are the same, no matter how large the ball might be.

(e) *Error due to torque variations.* One of the features of the caliper micrometer is that the thimble must be turned until a light but definite resistance to further turning is observed. Obviously, different observers use different amounts of torque, and thus get somewhat different read-

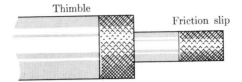

Fig. 1–15. Friction slip at end of micrometer thimble (optional).

ings. This factor constitutes a systematic component of error. More-over, the same observer applies somewhat different values of torque, and obtains somewhat different readings, from one occasion to another. Simple tests with a micrometer soon convince the experimenter that errors of about three ten-thousandths of an inch occur very readily from this cause.

This error may be greatly reduced through the provision of a friction slip mechanism, which limits the applied torque to a predetermined value, as shown in Fig. 1–15. Only small variations in the torque due to variations in the frictional resistance to slip, and to dynamic inertia effects of the thimble, now remain to produce some error due to torque variation.

(f) *Error due to dust particles.* If any dust particles get trapped be-tween the anvils of the micrometer and the ball, the readings for diam-eter of the ball may be seriously in error. This error may be detected by repeated testing. If dust particles are present on only a few occa-sions, it will be found that most of the readings cluster around one value, while a few readings are much higher. If these high readings can be identified as being due to dust particles, they may be eliminated.

(g) *Reading errors.* Reading errors can arise if the indicating line (in this case on the barrel) is not in the same plane as the scale (in this case on the thimble), and the observer's eye is not placed normal to the surface of the micrometer opposite the line on the barrel (Fig. 1–16).

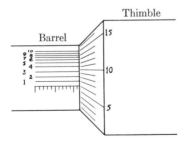

Fig. 1–16. Vernier scale on micrometer barrel (optional).

Errors of this type are known as *parallax* errors. A different error arises if the observer misjudges the fractional indication on the scale. All observers are subject to making these errors, in greater or lesser degree. Any one observer tends to make the same error over and over again, and it is often referred to as *personal* error.

The parallax error can be almost eliminated if the observer, after estimating a reading with the micrometer in the normal position, then turns the micrometer upside down. This brings the parallax error into the opposite position, and averaging will eliminate error.

The error due to misjudgments of fractions is greatly reduced by provision of a vernier scale on the micrometer barrel (Fig. 1–16).

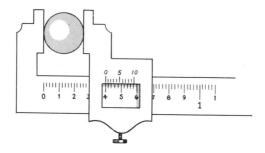

Fig. 1–17. The vernier caliper. The scale of this instrument is more foolproof than that of the caliper micrometer.

(h) *Gross error.* If the number of divisions on the micrometer is misjudged, or the way the instrument operates is misunderstood, then there may be a gross error in the reading. The effect of this is usually that it leads to an answer which is way out of line. To detect this error, it often helps to take a measurement with another instrument of lower accuracy but greater simplicity, such as the vernier caliper (Fig. 1–17), as a check on the readings of the caliper micrometer. It is unlikely that the same error would be made with two instruments of quite different type.

(i) *Summary.* This completes our evaluation of the errors of the caliper micrometer. We have discussed this instrument in some detail because, although the errors we have enumerated are to some extent characteristic of this instrument alone, very similar types of errors occur in many other instruments, even some of very different function. The reader is urged always to analyze the function of his instruments in order to pinpoint possible sources of error, to estimate their likely magnitude, and to plan ways of combating them.

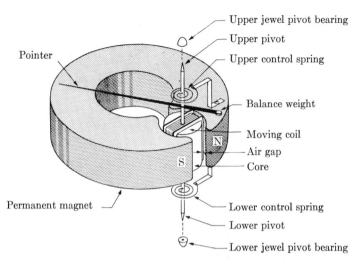

Fig. 1–18. The moving-coil galvanometer, heart of the voltmeter.

1–13. Errors of a dynamic measuring device: the voltmeter

In the example above we considered errors in performance of a caliper micrometer by analyzing possible sources of error and the way they would show up in the performance of the instrument. We now turn to an instrument of a rather different type: the voltmeter (Fig. 1–18). This instrument differs from the micrometer mainly in that it is a dynamic device, the reading of which may fluctuate continually; while the micrometer is a static device, which goes through a cycle, produces a reading, and then must go through another cycle to produce another reading.

In analyzing the performance of the voltmeter, we shall first examine the performance of the instrument, and then try to explain the reasons for this behavior in terms of the physical process occurring in the voltmeter. This method of analysis is opposite to that employed in the case of the micrometer, where we considered physical processes and deduced their effect on the instrument's performance. The two methods may be considered as alternative ways of analysis. Often it is advisable to combine both methods. That is to say, we might first measure the performance of the instrument and try to explain the results in terms of physical processes, then use the explanation to deduce other performance characteristics, test these experimentally, and continue the process until a satisfactory and comprehensive body of knowledge is available.

In order to test the performance of the voltmeter, we must have available a number of devices capable of producing constant, steady

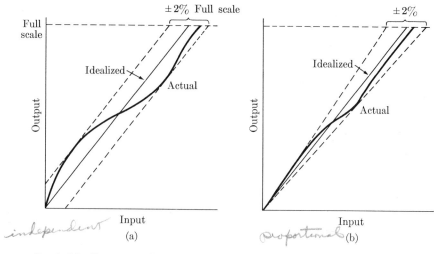

Fig. 1–19. Two ways of specifying limits for departure from linearity. (a) Independent linearity. (b) Proportional linearity.

voltages of known amounts (for example, lead cells such as are used in automobile batteries); these are connected to the voltmeter and its performance studied.

(a) *Linearity.* In the majority of measuring devices we wish, for the sake of convenience, to have output proportional to input; i.e., the relationship between input and output should be *linear.* No device is truly linear, and the deviation from linearity is an important concept. The solid line in Fig. 1–19 shows a plot of output versus input for a nominally linear voltmeter.

In commercial instruments, the maximum departure from linearity is often specified. Two ways of specifying linearity, namely in terms of independent and of proportional linearity, are in use (see Figs. 1–19a and 1–19b). In Fig. 1–19(a), the maximum deviation from linearity is independent of the input and is based on a percentage of the "full scale" or "maximum linear range" output. Thus 2% linearity means that the output will be within two parallel lines spaced ±2% of the full-scale output from the idealized line. For an input of 10% full scale (F.S.), if the deviation is 2% F.S., the actual deviation of the input from the expected value according to the output is up to 20%. In Fig. 1–19(b), a much more stringent linearity specification is shown. When "2% proportional linearity" is specified, it means that the true input is never more than 2% away from the recorded input, regardless of the magnitude of the input.

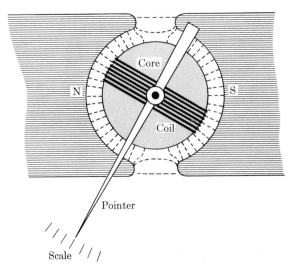

Fig. 1–20. For linearity of the moving-coil voltmeter, it is necessary that the magnetic field, shown by dashed lines, be uniform around the circumference of the core.

We shall now move on to consider the reason for the lack of linearity in voltmeters. In the typical voltmeter based on a moving coil milliammeter, the device is linear only if the magnetic field encountered by the moving coil is constant for all angles of twist (Fig. 1–20), and the restoring spring is linear, or if the nonlinearity of one is canceled out by the nonlinearity of the other. This is a difficult thing to arrange, and in any case the strength and uniformity of magnetic fields and the elastic properties of springs tend to change with time, so that even if a new voltmeter is quite linear, a voltmeter that has seen extensive use may be less linear.

Although the voltmeter may be satisfactorily linear, it may read high or low (Fig. 1–21). This is not a very serious error, since it may be detected by one calibration and then allowed for in all calculations. A high or low reading arises from the changing of the strength of the magnetic field, or from the change of the value of the resistance in series with the milliammeter resistance.

(b) *Repeatability error.* If we subject an instrument to an identical input many times, there will be some variation of the output. This deviation, which may be in absolute units or a fraction of the full scale, is called the *repeatability* of the system. Repeatability should not be confused with linearity, for here we actually make a plot of output versus input and note the scatter caused by repetition of various inputs, as shown in Fig. 1–22.

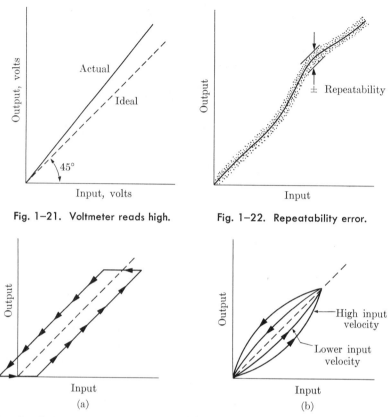

Fig. 1–21. Voltmeter reads high.

Fig. 1–22. Repeatability error.

Fig. 1–23. Hysteresis loops due to (a) solid friction, (b) viscous damping.

Repeatability error in voltmeters is generally quite low, unless hysteresis error is present. Generally speaking, it is only when the voltmeter acts as the output of some other, perhaps mechanical, system that repeatability error becomes significant.

(c) *Hysteresis.* When testing for repeatability, we often find that the output of a given input is less when the input is increasing than it is when the input is decreasing. This effect is usually caused by solid contact or Coulomb friction within the system, and gives rise to a *hysteresis loop* whenever the input is cycled as shown in Fig. 1–23. The deviation due to Coulomb friction does not depend on the *magnitude* of the rate of change of the input, only upon the sign ($\pm$) of the rate of change. Hysteresis effects are best eliminated by taking readings both for ascending and descending values of the input, and then taking an arithmetic average.

Another effect due to friction is *damping*. When the system has hydrodynamic or viscous friction, the friction force is a function of the magnitude of the rate of change of input. Hence, the greater the input velocity, the greater the deviation. As the input velocity goes to zero, so does the deviation, and the steady-state deviation is zero. Because of the steady-state or zero-velocity error introduced with Coulomb friction, we tend to avoid this as much as possible. Viscous damping, while causing "lags," gives rise to no steady-state errors, and we will see in later chapters that viscous friction can even be most beneficial.

(d) *Drifting.* One of the features of instruments is the fact that their output characteristics change with time. This is true of static instruments such as the micrometer, in which case it may be due to changes in the temperature of the micrometer with time, particularly while it is in use, but it shows up most clearly in dynamic instruments such as the voltmeter. Here again the change is often caused by temperature effects which, for example, change the value of the resistance and thus affect the calibration sensitivity.

Electronic instruments involving electron tubes are particularly liable to drifting during the fifteen minutes or so after the instrument is first switched on. The best remedy is to switch the instrument on at least a half hour before the experiment is due to begin.

1–14. Design of experiments to reduce errors

In the preceding sections we have concerned ourselves with ways of reducing errors of various kinds one at a time. In this section we consider ways of reducing errors *en masse*. We shall consider two techniques.

(a) *Use of null measurements.* Here we attempt to measure, not the output for a given input, but rather ways of counteracting the input so that there is no output. Typical ways of doing this are encountered in bridge methods for measuring characteristics of electrical components where, for example, the resistance is opposed by another, variable, resistance so that no output voltage is produced. This technique eliminates problems due to nonlinearity and those due to drifting and zero error. Moreover, it becomes possible to design special instruments of good resolution and small zero error, but of poor linearity, especially for null measurements.

Turning from electric circuitry, we find that null measurements are seen in such applications as the chemical balance or a chemical titration.

(b) *Use of partial balancing.* One of the difficulties encountered in null measurements is that of balancing the system, and sometimes having to rebalance it continuously. A good solution is to balance out the major portion of the signal, and to measure separately the small fraction which remains. This approach is frequently used in experiments with strain gages, where the unbalanced voltage is amplified and displayed directly.

Especial usefulness and great accuracy can be achieved when the opposing element is a standard, i.e., is free from errors, so that the residual signal can be added directly to the standard. This approach is used in the measurement of frequencies by the method of beats against a standard frequency, in direct reading of chemical balances, and in interference measurements based on the method of exact fractions.

PROBLEMS

1. A student uses a chemical balance to weigh a specimen. He knows that the two arms of the balance are not equally long, but that when the balance is unloaded it registers zero. He first weighs his specimen by itself, and then weighs the specimen with 10, 20, 30 gm weights in the same pan. The results are as follows.

Measured weight of specimen alone = 16.479 gm

Measured weight of specimen + 10 gm = 26.536 gm

Measured weight of specimen + 20 gm = 36.588 gm

Measured weight of specimen + 30 gm = 46.648 gm

Assuming that the weights used are accurate, calculate as accurately as you can, the length ratio of the arms of the balance and the weight of the specimen. Estimate the probable uncertainties in your estimate. [*Ans.* Ratio = 1.0055; weight = 16.390 gm ± 0.001 gm]

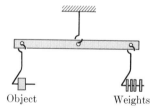

Object   Weights

Figure 1–24

2. In order to make a simple balance, a student takes a yardstick, bores three holes in it as shown in Fig. 1–24, and fashions the suspending wire and the weight-carrying hooks out of $\frac{1}{16}$-in. diameter coat-hanger wire. If the friction coefficient between wire and wood is 0.25, estimate the limit of resolution of the balance when used to weigh an object of about 1 lb. Does this problem have any relevance to the limit of resolution of the chemical balance?

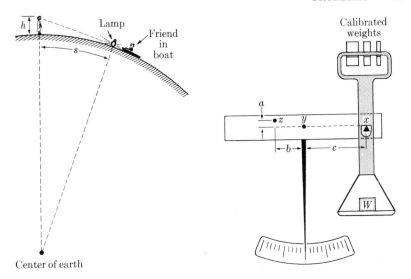

Figure 1–25   Figure 1–26

3. It is proposed to obtain a photomicrograph of the surface of a $\frac{1}{8}$-in. diameter bearing ball containing fine scratches. It is required that as much of the surface of the ball as possible be in focus. The scratches are about 5×10^{-4} cm wide. Discuss the numerical aperture of the objective you would use, and calculate the size of the region of the ball which would appear in focus. Would you take your photograph in red light ($\lambda = 6 \times 10^{-5}$ cm) or in blue light ($\lambda = 4 \times 10^{-5}$ cm)? [*Ans.* N.A. = 0.08; circle of diameter 0.17 cm in focus; blue light]

4. An ancient Greek discovers a new way of measuring the diameter of the earth (see Fig. 1–25). He stands at the seashore at night, and a friend in a boat rows from the shore, towing a floating lamp. The distance s is measured to the point where the lamp just disappears from view, because it has dropped below the horizon. Derive the relation between h, s, and the diameter of the earth. Does this method contravene the rule that to measure a quantity we need a yardstick of comparable magnitude? Estimate the probable errors of the method if the height of the Greek is 6 ft, there are 6-in. high waves in the sea, there is an error of 5% in measuring s, and the lamp has a diameter of 1 ft.

5. A single pan chemical balance consists of a beam of weight w with center of mass at z, which is freely suspended at y, as shown in Fig. 1–26. The pan is suspended at x. The pan and the calibrated weights above it have a total weight W_t. When a weight W ($W < W_t$) is added to the pan, enough calibrated weights are removed so that the balance beam, which was originally horizontal, becomes horizontal again. Calculate the resolution of the balance $\theta/\delta W$ in terms of such variables as are relevant. How does the best attainable resolution of the single pan balance compare with that of the ordinary double pan balance?

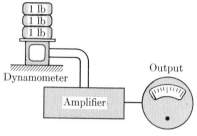

Figure 1–27

6. A student measures the deflection as a function of load of a dynamometer, using a number of weights as shown in Fig. 1–27. He gets the following readings. Calculate the best possible value for the sensitivity of the dynamometer system and estimate the probable error.

Load	Deflection, in.
0	0
1	0.27
2	0.44
3	0.69

REFERENCES

SCHENK, HILBERT, JR., *Theories of Engineering Experimentation*, McGraw-Hill Book Co., New York, 1961. A straightforward discussion of the analytical and statistical aspects of experiments.

WILSON, E. BRIGHT, JR., *An Introduction to Scientific Research*, McGraw-Hill Book Co., New York, 1952. This book, available in a paperbound edition, is an extremely readable and thought-provoking account of the theory and practice (and pitfalls) of the experimental aspect of research.

CHAPTER TWO

Experimental Statistics

2-1. Internal and external estimates of measurement error

The aim of every experiment of the type described in this text is to arrive at some conclusion in regard to some physical quantity. In a few cases this conclusion is qualitative, of the yes or no type (e.g., yes, strain-gage transducers are very linear), or it may be related to a graphical entity (e.g., the shape of a geiger counter plateau). In such cases the discussion of the accuracy of the experiment must be in terms of the probability that the conclusion is correct.

However, in the vast majority of cases the experiment produces a numerical quantity, which we shall denote by x. Owing to uncertainties of various kinds, among them the possible imperfection of the theory on which the experiment is based, the imperfection of the instrument used for the measurement, or the imperfection of the observer, the measured quantity is not the correct quantity q; there is an error e, namely $q - x$. Strictly speaking, this error e should be written in the form $\pm(q - x)$ since, although the error is generally considered a positive quantity, it is just as possible that it may be negative.

If the measured value of x is to be put to any use, it is essential that we have some conception of the likely value of the error e. In fact, since

$$q = x \pm e, \qquad (2\text{-}1)$$

it is clear that if we know nothing about e, then a measurement of the value of x tells us nothing about the correct quantity q. The experimenter should acquire the habit of never making a measurement, or calculating any experimental parameter, without having some concept of the error likely to be associated with that measurement. In some cases the absolute value e of the error is of interest; but normally the relative or fractional error ϵ, namely e/q, is of most value.

There are two ways of estimating the error that is likely to be associated with the measured quantity x. The first of these we may call the external estimate ϵ_E, based on our knowledge of the experiment and our assessment of its limitations, and in some cases, on our knowledge of experimental work carried out by others. Secondly, there is the internal estimate ϵ_I, based on analysis of the data obtained during the experiment. We may be confident that the experiment is under control when the two estimates agree, to within an order of magnitude at least. When they do not, there is a strong hint of possible trouble, which generally is due to systematic errors in our measurements.

2–2. External estimates of the error

In every experiment there are several steps involved in measuring a quantity. Let us consider a typical experiment to measure a small displacement. First, the change of position of the surface of some component is transformed into a change of electrical resistance, then the change of resistance is transformed into a change of voltage, the voltage change is amplified, and finally the amplified voltage is fed into a voltmeter and produces the displacement of a pointer. In some situations, we may know that the proportional errors likely to be associated with the various steps are ϵ_a, ϵ_b, ϵ_c, ϵ_d (Fig. 2–1). If the aim of the experiment is to measure the gain of this system, then we wish to know what error we may expect to result from the combination of these four terms. We write the performance of the four separate stages in the form

$$\frac{\Delta R}{\Delta x} = a(1 \pm \epsilon_a),$$

$$\frac{\Delta V_{\text{in}}}{\Delta R} = b(1 \pm \epsilon_b),$$

$$\frac{\Delta V_{\text{out}}}{\Delta V_{\text{in}}} = c(1 \pm \epsilon_c),$$

$$\frac{\Delta y}{\Delta V_{\text{out}}} = d(1 \pm \epsilon_d).$$

$$(2\text{--}2)$$

Then we have

$$q = \frac{\Delta y}{\Delta x} = abcd(1 \pm \epsilon_a)(1 \pm \epsilon_b)(1 \pm \epsilon_c)(1 \pm \epsilon_d). \qquad (2\text{--}3)$$

Clearly, the worst possibility is for all four errors to be in the same direction, i.e., all positive or all negative. In this case the resultant error, assuming that all the errors are much less than one, is

$$\epsilon_E = \epsilon_a + \epsilon_b + \epsilon_c + \epsilon_d. \qquad (2\text{--}4)$$

This situation is quite rare where the errors ϵ_a to ϵ_d are due to independent causes, because there is then only a rather small chance that all four errors are in the same direction.

A second possibility is that there is no resultant error at all, which can happen if the four terms happen to cancel out. This is also unlikely.

Fortunately, there is a general way of treating problems involving combinations of errors, which tells us just what error we may expect as a result of the combination of errors. Let us write Eq. (2–3) in its most general form:

$$q = F(a, b, c, d). \tag{2-5}$$

Then we have

$$dq = \sum_{n=a}^{d} \left(\frac{\partial F}{\partial n}\right) dn. \tag{2-6}$$

We may consider the variation in q to be produced by errors in the quantities a to d, the magnitude of these errors being e_a to e_d. Thus we write

$$e_E = \sum_{a}^{d} \left(\frac{\partial F}{\partial n}\right) e_n. \tag{2-7}$$

We cannot evaluate e_E directly, since we do not know how the error terms, some of which are likely to be positive and others negative, will add up. However, we can solve this difficulty by evaluating e_E^2:

$$e_E^2 = \sum_{n=a}^{d} \left(\frac{\partial F}{\partial n}\right)^2 e_n^2 + \sum_{n=a, m=a}^{d} \left(\frac{\partial F}{\partial n}\right)\left(\frac{\partial F}{\partial m}\right) dn\, dm, \tag{2-8}$$

where $m \neq n$.

If the error components e_a to e_d are independent and symmetrical in regard to positive and negative values, then the cross-product terms will tend, on the average, to disappear, and hence

$$e_E^2 = \sum_{a}^{d} \left(\frac{\partial F}{\partial n}\right)^2 e_n^2. \tag{2-9}$$

This is the general form of the expression for the resultant error in terms of its components.

In the case we are considering, we have

$$F(a, b, c, d) = abcd = q, \tag{2-10}$$

and $\partial F/\partial n$ is in all cases equal to q/n. Hence

$$e_E^2 = q^2 \sum_{a}^{d} \frac{e_n^2}{n^2}. \tag{2-11}$$

After, dividing throughout by q^2 and taking the square root, we have

$$\epsilon_E = (\epsilon_a^2 + \epsilon_b^2 + \epsilon_c^2 + \epsilon_d^2)^{1/2}. \tag{2-12}$$

The expected error is considerably smaller than the worst possibility considered above, as may be seen by considering the case when

$$\epsilon_a = \epsilon_b = \epsilon_c = \epsilon_d, \qquad (2\text{-}13)$$

in which the worst case, considered in Eq. (2–4), would give an error of $4\epsilon_a$, while the most probable error, as given in Eq. (2–12), is $2\epsilon_a$.

2–3. Independence and dependence of errors

In deriving Eq. (2–9), and Eq. (2–12) which was based on it, we assumed that the various error components were independent; that is to say, we assumed that if for example ϵ_a were positive, there was no way that this fact could influence ϵ_b, ϵ_c, or ϵ_d. We may consider the effect of having errors dependent on each other in terms of a simple example; namely, an experiment to determine the density of a sintered block of aluminum oxide. To do this, we measure the dimensions of the block, and thus calculate its volume. We then weigh the block, and the formula for its density is

$$\text{density } \rho = \frac{\text{mass } m}{\text{length } l \times \text{width } w \times \text{height } h}. \qquad (2\text{-}14)$$

The error in the density will be determined by the error in measuring the mass e_m, the error in measuring the length e_l, and the error in measuring the other terms e_w and e_h. If these are independent, we apply Eq. (2–9):

$$\rho = F(m, l, w, h) = \frac{m}{lwh}, \qquad (2\text{-}15)$$

where

$$\frac{\partial F}{\partial m} = \frac{1}{lwh}, \qquad \frac{\partial F}{\partial l} = -\frac{m}{l^2 wh},$$

$$\frac{\partial F}{\partial w} = -\frac{m}{lw^2 h}, \qquad \frac{\partial F}{\partial h} = -\frac{m}{lwh^2}. \qquad (2\text{-}16)$$

Hence we write, from Eq. (2–9),

$$e_E^2 = \frac{e_m^2}{l^2 w^2 h^2} + \frac{e_l^2 m^2}{l^4 w^2 h^2} + \frac{e_w^2 m^2}{l^2 w^4 h^2} + \frac{e_h^2 m^2}{l^2 w^2 h^4}, \qquad (2\text{-}17)$$

or, dividing each term by ρ^2 or $m^2/l^2 w^2 h^2$, and taking square roots, we have

$$\epsilon_E = (\epsilon_m^2 + \epsilon_l^2 + \epsilon_w^2 + \epsilon_h^2)^{1/2}. \qquad (2\text{-}18)$$

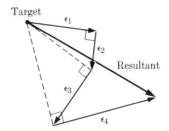

Fig. 2–1. Effect of four independent errors. Each error is likely to be at right angles to the resultant of the earlier errors.

This relationship has the same form as Eq. (2–12), and a little thought will show that this must be the case, since we could have transformed Eq. (2–3) into the form of Eq. (2–14) merely by redefining the constants b, c, and d in Eq. (2–2).

Now it is reasonable to suppose that any error ϵ_m in the balance used for the weighing process will be quite unrelated to errors involved in the length determinations. However, the errors in the length measurements are not likely to be independent. Let us assume that the error arises primarily from the fact that the ruler used for the measurements has shrunk since it was calibrated. Then all the measured values l, w, and h will be too large in the same proportion, and the proportional errors ϵ_l, ϵ_w, ϵ_h will be positive and equal. Thus the total proportional error in the volume ϵ_v will be given approximately by

$$\epsilon_v = (1 + \epsilon_l)(1 + \epsilon_w)(1 + \epsilon_h) - 1 = \epsilon_l + \epsilon_w + \epsilon_h. \qquad (2\text{–}19)$$

This error must now be combined with the independent error in the mass, and so we have

$$\epsilon_E = [\epsilon_m^2 + (\epsilon_l + \epsilon_w + \epsilon_h)^2]^{1/2}. \qquad (2\text{–}20)$$

There is a simple way in which we can visualize equations such as (2–18), (2–19), and (2–20). Let us say that the experiment is like an arrow aimed at a target, and that the first error-producing term ϵ_1 causes the arrow to miss the target in an arbitrary direction (Fig. 2–1). If the second error-producing term ϵ_2 is positively related to the first, it will be in the same direction, producing a total error of $\epsilon_1 + \epsilon_2$. If it is independent, it could be in the same direction as ϵ_1, in the opposite direction, or in any other direction. The most random direction is at right angles; this produces a total error of $(\epsilon_1^2 + \epsilon_2^2)^{1/2}$. Further random errors tend to be at right angles to the resultant of ϵ_1 and ϵ_2, producing

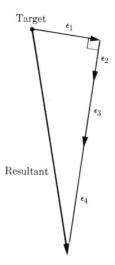

Fig. 2–2. If any of the errors are known to be in the same direction, they will combine additively, producing a larger resultant.

Eq. (2–18). Any correlated errors add up in one straight line, as in Fig. 2–2, and in Eq. (2–20).

This model of the way in which errors combine is closely analogous to the process which describes the motion of particles undergoing random excitations (the random-walk problem), and analogous equations apply. For example, after n random excitations of comparable magnitude, a particle is likely to be distant from its initial point by a distance proportional to $n^{1/2}$.

The important practical point which emerges from this discussion of dependent and independent errors is that, since situations in which the errors are dependent give greater total errors than do situations in which the errors are independent, it is helpful to design the experiment so that the errors are independent. Thus, we might make measurements of the linear dimensions of our alumina block with three different rulers, preferably of different type, so that they would be expected not to be subject to errors of the same sign. This point is particularly important in that it is contrary to most people's intuitive experience.

This simple example of a density measurement has brought up one point which is fundamental to all calculations based on experiments. Although the numbers obtained from the experiment can often be handled without considering in detail the nature of the experiment, it is true that a better, more accurate, analysis is obtained if the experiment and the data are considered together. Thus the question as to whether one or three rulers is used is significant, but this significance does not show up when we examine the numerical data. The procedure which has attained rather frequent usage, in which a group of engineers spends a lengthy period of time, often of the order of years, in compiling a set of data, and then gives all the data to an independent group of statisticians, often works out quite poorly.

2–4. How to estimate the external error of a measurement

As we have seen above, in order to estimate the external error in a measurement we must consider the error in each separate step, and combine the errors as in Eq. (2–9). However, no general method can be given for reliably discovering the error of a step in a measurement process. Often we may make informed guesses. Thus if we know the limiting resolution of the process, then the probable relative error will be no less than the quotient of the resolution to the quantity being measured; but of course the error may be greater. In other cases, we may know that the theory of the process applies only approximately to the experiment, and estimate the likely error as a result of this disagreement. Yet again, we may have had previous experience with this type of measurement, and have found that our measurements did not quite agree with the correct answer. All of these alternatives could be valid criteria for estimating the external error of a measurement.

Another approach, often used with commercial equipment, is to consult the manufacturer's literature which accompanies the instrument. This literature often provides estimates of the error. If this information is not available, it is often helpful to look at the read-out of the instrument, which is generally a calibrated scale of some kind. The error in reading the scale is usually about $\frac{1}{10}$ of one division, and it is the custom of many instrument designers to arrange matters in such a way that this $\frac{1}{10}$ of one division is approximately equal to the error of the instrument as a whole. Accordingly, the error of a commercial instrument may be assumed to be between $\frac{1}{5}$ and $\frac{1}{10}$ of one division of the read-out scale. The reader is warned, however, that sometimes quite inaccurate or even worthless instruments are provided with impressive-looking high-precision read-outs.

Often it is possible to estimate the probable error of some, but not all, stages of a measurement process. In this connection it is helpful to know that, from Eq. (2–12), if one step has a much smaller error than some of the others, it may be ignored. Similarly, if one step has a very much larger error than the others, only it need be considered.

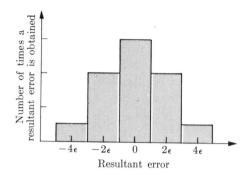

Fig. 2–3. Hypothetical experiment which yields a binomial distribution.

2–5. Internal estimates of the error

It is advisable, when carrying out an experiment, to rely not on one measurement of a quantity, but rather to carry out repeated measurements. These repeat measurements will not produce identical values of the quantity being measured, and the variation among the measurements allows us to make an estimate of the accuracy of the experiment as a whole; this is known as the internal estimate ϵ_I.

In order to derive this internal estimate, we have to consider how the variation between individual readings comes about.

Suppose that we carry out an experiment in which a large number of factors contribute to the observed variation of the readings. When we carry out the first measurement, it may happen that the individual error-generating factors are so arranged that a high reading is obtained. The next time, a low reading may result. The time thereafter, as many factors may be inducing a higher reading as are inducing a lower reading. A question of great importance is this: Suppose that we take a very large number of readings; how will the readings be arranged? This can best be visualized in terms of a diagram in which we plot various possible values of readings, varying by a constant increment, along the abscissa, and the number of times actual readings were obtained, between specified limits, on the ordinate, as indicated in Fig. 2–3. This plot of number of readings as a function of value of reading will be referred to hereafter as a histogram. Our question then is: What will be the shape of the histogram?

To answer this question, we may refer back to our earlier discussion, where we had four possible error-causing mechanisms, giving errors ϵ_a, ϵ_b, ϵ_c, and ϵ_d. To simplify the discussion, let us assume that the individual errors are equal, and that each is equally likely to take on

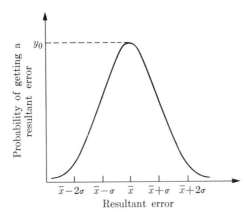

Probability of getting a resultant error

$\bar{x}-2\sigma$ $\bar{x}-\sigma$ $\bar{x}$ $\bar{x}+\sigma$ $\bar{x}+2\sigma$

Resultant error

Fig. 2–4. The normal distribution.

positive or negative values of exactly ϵ. Then there are 2^4, (16), possible, equally likely, different configurations of the errors. Only one of these, namely

$$+\epsilon_a, \quad +\epsilon_b, \quad +\epsilon_c, \quad +\epsilon_d$$

will be such that all the errors are positive, giving a total error of 4ϵ at a probability level of one in 16; while four configurations, namely

$$+\epsilon_a, \quad +\epsilon_b, \quad +\epsilon_c, \quad -\epsilon_d$$
$$+\epsilon_a, \quad +\epsilon_b, \quad -\epsilon_c, \quad +\epsilon_d$$
$$+\epsilon_a, \quad -\epsilon_b, \quad +\epsilon_c, \quad +\epsilon_d$$
$$-\epsilon_a, \quad +\epsilon_b, \quad +\epsilon_c, \quad +\epsilon_d$$

give one error negative and three positive, for a total error of 2ϵ at a probability level of four in 16. In fact, the individual probabilities are merely the individual terms of the binomial expansion $(\frac{1}{2} + \frac{1}{2})^4$. This situation is plotted in Fig. 2–3.

This general picture may be extended by considering the total error as made up of a large number of components rather than just four, and not necessarily making them equal. Further, we allow the error ϵ_a and the other similar components to take on a range of possible values all of the order of magnitude ϵ_a, rather than just the values $+\epsilon_a$ or $-\epsilon_a$. Then it may be shown that the actual distribution of the resultant errors, as plotted on a frequency diagram, is the curve

$$F(x) = y_0 e^{-(x-\bar{x})^2/2\sigma^2} \tag{2-21}$$

where y_0, $\bar{x}$, and σ are three constants. This distribution is shown in

Fig. 2–4. This curve is known as the normal, or Gaussian, frequency distribution, or normal error distribution (or merely *normal distribution*), and occupies a central place in statistical theory.

Equation (2–21) is usually derived by considering the limit of a binomial distribution as the number of error-causing terms becomes very great and their individual magnitude becomes very small. The calculation is rather tedious and we shall not reproduce it here; but an experimental demonstration of the way that random errors combine to produce a resultant with a shape similar to that of the normal distribution is given in Appendix 2. A complete discussion of all the conditions under which the normal distribution is obtained is to be found in Whittaker and Robinson (1946).

2–6. Properties of the normal distribution

The normal distribution is specified in terms of three constants: the maximum height y_0, the value of x (called $\bar{x}$) at which the maximum occurs, and a quantity σ, which determines the lateral spread of the function. The area under the curve between x and $x + \delta x$ represents the number of data points which fall between these limits, so that the total area under the curve denotes the total number of readings in the distribution. However, frequently the normal distribution is redefined so that the area under the curve between x and $x + \delta x$ is taken to be the probability that a data point falls between these limits. In this case the area under the curve is unity, and a rather difficult integration shows that the curve has the exact shape

$$y = \frac{1}{\sigma\sqrt{2\pi}} e^{-(x-\bar{x})^2/2\sigma^2} \qquad (2\text{–}22)$$

Most of the uses of the normal distribution revolve about the fact that the three constants have such simple and clear meanings. Thus $\bar{x}$ is the arithmetic average of all the readings, while σ is the root-mean-square deviation (or standard deviation) defined by the equation

$$\sigma = \left(\frac{\sum (x - \bar{x})^2}{N}\right)^{1/2}, \qquad (2\text{–}23)$$

where N is the total number of data points.

By analogy with dynamics, we may consider the normal distribution as a two-dimensional object rotated about its central y-axis, and then σ is its radius of gyration. Thus σ denotes the distance from the center to an average data point. The height of the normal distribution is not of

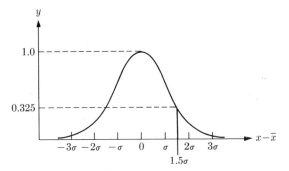

Fig. 2–5. A table of ordinates of the normal curve has, for $(x - \bar{x})/\sigma = 1.5$, a value 0.325.

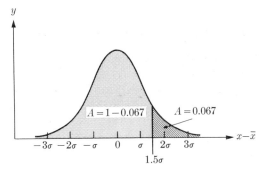

Fig. 2–6. A table of areas of the normal curve has, for $(x - \bar{x})/\sigma = 1.5$, a value of 0.067.

such fundamental significance, since it is adjusted to make the total area of the curve equal to the number of data points, or to unity, depending on whether we plot numbers or probabilities on the distribution curve.

An unfortunate aspect of the normal distribution is that its shape is rather difficult to evaluate. Hence for quantitative work it is customary to consult tables of the normal distribution, which are to be found in most compilations of mathematical functions (for example, the *Handbook of Physics and Chemistry*). The two types of table used most frequently are: (1) a table of ordinates of the normal curve, as a function of $(x - \bar{x})/\sigma$ (see Fig. 2–5), and (2) a table of the integral of the normal curve, from the end of one tail up to a value of $(x - \bar{x})/\sigma$, as a function of $(x - \bar{x})/\sigma$ (see Fig. 2–6). Slightly modified forms of this table, for example giving the area of both tails, or the area from the center up to $(x - \bar{x})/\sigma$, are also found.

By consulting a table of the integral of the normal curve, we find that

68% of the readings lie within $\bar{x} \pm \sigma$,

95% of the readings lie within $\bar{x} \pm 2\sigma$,

99.7% of the readings lie within $\bar{x} \pm 3\sigma$,

99.994% of the readings lie within $\bar{x} \pm 4\sigma$.

Hence we may predict that the chances are better than 2:1 (actually 68:32) that a reading will be within $\bar{x} \pm \sigma$; about 20:1 that a reading will be within $\bar{x} \pm 2\sigma$; about 350:1 that it will be within $\bar{x} \pm 3\sigma$, and about 15,000:1 that it will be within $\bar{x} \pm 4\sigma$.

2–7. Use of the normal distribution to eliminate data

One of the most difficult decisions an experimenter has to make is whether, or when, to throw out a piece of experimental data. Clearly, some data are properly to be ignored, if something went wrong with the experiment while a certain piece of datum was being taken, or if a gross reading error was made in recording the data. Trouble seldom arises if these situations are spotted and taken care of during the experiment. However, it is often difficult to decide some time later, with only the data themselves on hand, whether a reading should be eliminated. In this situation, the normal distribution is helpful.

For data obeying a normal distribution, there is a probability of only one in 350 that a data point will lie outside $\bar{x} \pm 3\sigma$. In a typical experiment in which, let us say, 25 readings are taken, there is consequently a probability of only one in 14 that *any* reading further from the average than 3σ will be obtained. Hence, all that is necessary in a situation such as this is to calculate $\bar{x}$ and σ, see if the data appear to match the appearance of the normal distribution, and if they do, to eliminate points outside $\bar{x} \pm 3\sigma$. If only about ten readings are taken, then perhaps points outside $\bar{x} + 2.5\sigma$ might be candidates for removal. Often it is not clear whether the distribution is normal or not, and hence the experimenter does not know whether it is valid to apply the 3σ criterion. In that case it may be advisable, on removing an extreme point on one side of the distribution, also to remove the corresponding extreme point on the other side. This procedure is often a good compromise in arriving at a good value of $\bar{x}$ when it is difficult to decide whether the deletion of a point is justified or not. After points have been deleted, it is of course necessary to recalculate $\bar{x}$ and σ for the remaining points.

2–8. Use of the normal distribution to relate various definitions of error

In Chapter 1, and again earlier in this chapter, we discussed the accuracy of a measurement in terms of the error associated with that measurement, assuming tacitly that the error was likely to be a constant quantity. In most cases, of course, the error varies from measurement to measurement, and we may select from one of the following definitions of the representative error.

The probable error is the error likely to be exceeded in half the measurements, and not reached in the other half.

The mean deviation, or mean error, is the arithmetic mean of all the deviations from the average, considered independent of sign.

The limit of error is an error so large that it is most unlikely that an error of this magnitude will ever be observed.

For a normally distributed set of points, the probable error is 0.67σ, the mean error is 0.80σ, and while the limit of error is really indeterminate, it is often taken to be 4σ. For comparative purposes it does not matter which type of error is used, so long as it is used consistently. However, the simplest and best representation of the error is probably the *root-mean-square error*, or *standard error*, namely σ itself. It should be noted that the relationship between the various types of error, as outlined above, can be established only when the histogram of data points is known.

2–9. Use of the normal distribution to estimate the extreme of a distribution

Strictly speaking, the normal distribution has no extreme points, and ranges from $+\infty$ to $-\infty$, with a finite (if very small) probability for the occurrence of any data point in between. This of course does not correspond to the actual situation, where normally maximum and minimum values are defined by the nature of the experiment. In practice, this is not a serious discrepancy, because the probability of getting extreme values is vanishingly small.

One of the most important uses of the normal distribution is that of determining the extreme value of a quantity which may be expected in practice. For example, an airframe designer might test 30 aluminum tensile specimens, and discover that the variation in their tensile strength follows a normal distribution. He now wants to use the normal distribution to calculate the strength of this material. In many design situations, it is the minimum rather than the average which is of interest, since it is the minimum strength which must be used in the design calculations if safe operation of the airplane is to be assured. Unfortunately, while the average of a normal distribution is well defined, the minimum does not, strictly speaking, exist. All that can be done is to accept a very small but finite probability, say one in a million, of having an experimental data point below the limit of strength, and then to find what value of x corresponds to this probability (for the ratio of one in a million, the value is $\bar{x} - 5\sigma$). The advantage of this use of the normal distribution is that, after a relatively small number of tests (say 20 to 50) we can make evaluations and predictions at the million-to-one probability level. (For the danger of this procedure, see Section 2–14.)

2–10. Use of the normal distribution to calculate the probable error in $\bar{x}$

A valuable concept of statistics is that every collection of data may be considered a sample from an infinite pool (often called population) of similar data. Thus if we make N measurements of the diameter of a bearing ball with a micrometer, this is a sample of N data from the infinite number which we would get if we kept on making similar measurements forever. The question we now consider is: Given that our N measurements have given a certain value of $\bar{x}$ and of σ, what can we say about the average q of all the infinite population of measurements? We define q as the "correct" or "best" value. In order to find the value of q we must determine the probable error in $\bar{x}$.

We may define $\bar{x}$ as being a function of N measurements:

$$\bar{x} = F(x_1 \cdots x_i \cdots x_N) = \frac{\sum x_i}{N}. \tag{2-24}$$

We now use Eq. (2–9), bearing in mind that the error in each of the x_i terms is likely to be about σ. This gives us

$$(e_{\bar{x}})^2 = \sum_{i=1}^{N} \left(\frac{\partial F}{\partial x_i}\right)^2 \sigma^2. \tag{2-25}$$

Since $\partial F/\partial x_i$ is seen from Eq. (2–24) to be equal to $1/N$, we have

$$e_{\bar{x}} = \left[\sum \left(\frac{1}{N}\right)^2 \sigma^2\right]^{1/2} = \left(\frac{N\sigma^2}{N^2}\right)^{1/2} = \frac{\sigma}{N^{1/2}}. \tag{2-26}$$

This equation must be corrected slightly, since we do not know the magnitude of the real error in the x values. We do know that the apparent error, as measured from $\bar{x}$, is σ, on the average; however, $\bar{x}$ is not the correct quantity q, but is removed from it by a small distance. Hence the error in the x quantities, as measured from the true average, is somewhat greater than σ. Consequently we write

$$e_{\bar{x}} = \frac{\sigma}{(N - 1)^{1/2}}. \qquad (2\text{-}27)$$

This equation means that if the original experiment of measuring N quantities were repeated a large number of times, the various values of $\bar{x}$ would cluster about their average (the true value q) with a standard deviation equal to $\sigma/(N - 1)^{1/2}$. Hence we write the equation for q in the form

$$q = \bar{x} \pm \frac{\sigma}{(N - 1)^{1/2}}. \qquad (2\text{-}28)$$

This important formula constitutes the real justification for carrying out repeat readings. If one reading is likely to differ from the true reading by an amount equal to σ, then the average of ten readings will be in error only by $\sigma/3$, and the average of 100 readings will be in error by $\sigma/10$. Each time we wish to reduce the error by a factor of two, we have to increase the number of readings by a factor of four.

It must be emphasized that there are limits to the extent to which this error-reduction process can be extended. Of the two types of error considered in Chapter 1, systematic and random, it is only the random component of error that is reduced by repeated readings. Hence it is useless to increase the number of readings beyond the point where the random component of error has become small in comparison with the systematic component of error.

This concept is difficult to apply in practice, since there is often no way of detecting the presence of systematic error. Certainly a study of the histogram of values obtained during the experiment is of no help, since the variations in the readings are due only to random errors, and all the readings share the same systematic error. All that can be done is to evaluate the experiment, as was done in Chapter 1, and compute likely errors from external considerations, which constitutes an estimate of e_E. Then we may compute the likely error from the readings themselves by using Eq. (2-28), and this constitutes an evaluation of e_I. If e_I is much smaller than e_E, then the presence of systematic errors is to be feared. Under these circumstances, the value of e_E represents more reliably the limitations of the experiment.

Sometimes the presence of systematic errors does not show up until the measurements are repeated using a different method which is not subject to the same systematic errors. As we mentioned earlier, a comparison of differing experimental results constitutes one of the external methods of estimating the errors of an experiment.

Many experimental results contained in the scientific literature, some of them associated with experimenters of great eminence, were at one time thought to be highly accurate, but later work showed up the presence of systematic error in unusually large amounts. Often we use the different words *accuracy* and *precision* to cover these situations. An *accurate* series of measurements is one whose result is close to the correct value (small systematic error), while *precise* measurements agree well among themselves (small random error), but may involve appreciable amounts of systematic error.

2–11. How to set up a normal distribution calculation

If the number N of data points is small (under 20), it is easy enough to sum all the values of x and to divide by N to obtain $\bar{x}$, and then, by subtraction, to determine the various values of $x_i - \bar{x}$. Their root mean square constitutes σ.

If the number of data points is large (over 20) it is easier to collect the data points into a number of groups, defining the group boundaries so that the data are contained in from 6 to 20 groups. The number of data in each group will be denoted by n_i. The reader should carefully note the distinction between N, the total number of data points in our distribution, and n, the number of data points in each group. Then we define x, not by the formula

$$\sum n_i x_i = N\bar{x}, \qquad (2\text{--}29)$$

which would give rise to large numbers, but by an alternative definition in which we treat $\bar{x}$ as the centroid of the distribution, which is the point about which the first moment of all the data, namely $\sum n_i(x_i - \bar{x})$, is zero.

The calculation is set up in such a way that σ is determined at the same time as $\bar{x}$.

To give a concrete example: In an experiment a certain friction coefficient was determined 162 times, the results being as shown in Table 2–1. We proceed to calculate the average friction coefficient and the standard deviation of the distribution, and to draw the normal distribution.

To set up the calculation, we first change our x variables, using numbers from 0 to as high as we have to go. In the process of doing this, we have changed the x variable from a range of 0.0025 per group to a range of 1.0 per group, an amplification of a factor of 400. We then

TABLE 2–1

RESULTS OF A FRICTION EXPERIMENT

Range of friction values	No. of readings within the range
0.0800–0.0825	1
0.0825–0.0850	1
0.0850–0.0875	0
0.0875–0.0900	2
0.0900–0.0925	2
0.0925–0.0950	4
0.0950–0.0975	9
0.0975–0.1000	22
0.1000–0.1025	18
0.1025–0.1050	25
0.1050–0.1075	23
0.1075–0.1100	15
0.1100–0.1125	7
0.1125–0.1150	12
0.1150–0.1175	8
0.1175–0.1200	8
0.1200–0.1225	2
0.1225–0.1250	2
0.1250–0.1275	1
	Sum = 162

take a guess at the position of the centroid, which in this case corresponds to the point for which $x = 9$. We denote this as $\bar{x}'$. Then we proceed to calculate the first and second moments of the individual readings about the apparent centroid $\bar{x}'$. This is shown in Table 2–2.

After setting up Table 2–2, we must first find the true average. Our first guess is $\bar{x} = 9$, and we find that the total first moment about this position is $249 - 144 = 105$.

Using the formula

$$\Delta x = \frac{\sum n_i(x_i - \bar{x}')}{N} , \qquad (2\text{–}30)$$

where Δx is the difference between the true and approximate averages (i.e., $\bar{x} - \bar{x}' = \Delta x$) we find that

$$\Delta x = \frac{105}{162} = 0.65. \qquad (2\text{–}31)$$

TABLE 2–2

SETTING UP A CALCULATION OF $\bar{x}$ AND σ

Original x	New x	n_i	$x_i - \bar{x}'$	$n_i(x_i - \bar{x}')$	$n_i(x_i - \bar{x}')^2$
0.08125	0	1	-9	-9	$+81$
.08375	1	1	-8	-8	$+64$
.08625	2	0	-7	0	0
.08875	3	2	-6	-12	$+72$
.09125	4	2	-5	-10	$+50$
.09375	5	4	-4	-16	$+64$
.09625	6	9	-3	-27	$+81$
.09875	7	22	-2	-44	$+88$
.10125	8	18	-1	-18	$+18$
.10375	9	25	0	Sum $= -144$	0
.10625	10	23	$+1$	$+23$	$+23$
.10875	11	15	$+2$	$+30$	$+60$
.11125	12	7	$+3$	$+21$	$+63$
.11375	13	12	$+4$	$+48$	$+192$
.11625	14	8	$+5$	$+40$	$+200$
.11875	15	8	$+6$	$+48$	$+288$
.12125	16	2	$+7$	$+14$	$+98$
.12375	17	2	$+8$	$+16$	$+128$
.12625	18	1	$+9$	$+9$	$+81$
				Sum $= 249$	Sum $= 1651$

Hence the true average is at $x = 9.65$. Comparing this with the original friction values, we find that it corresponds to a value of friction coefficient f of $0.10375 + 0.65 \times 0.0025 = 0.10537$.

Next we turn to the calculation of σ. The calculated second moment, namely 1651, was found about the point $x = 9$ rather than the correct point $x = 9.65$. We adjust for this, using the parallel axis theorem:

$$\sum n_i(x_i - \bar{x})^2 = \sum n_i(x_i - \bar{x}')^2 - N(\Delta x)^2$$
$$= 1651 - 162 \times 0.65^2 = 1651 - 68 = 1583. \qquad (2\text{–}32)$$

This correction is usually so small (4% in our case, which becomes 2% when we take square roots) that it may be ignored. Another correction, called Shepard's correction (to allow for the fact that we lumped our original readings into ranges instead of considering each point

TABLE 2–3

SETTING UP A NORMAL DISTRIBUTION CALCULATION

x	$x - \bar{x}$	$\dfrac{x - \bar{x}}{\sigma}$	Ordinate y_i	n Expected $y_i \times \dfrac{162}{7.82} = 20.7$	n Observed
0	−9.65	−3.09	+0.011	0.2	1
1	−8.65	−2.77	+0.022	0.5	1
2	−7.65	−2.45	+0.049	1.0	0
3	−6.65	−2.13	+0.103	2.1	2
4	−5.65	−1.81	+0.194	4.0	2
5	−4.65	−1.49	+0.330	6.8	4
6	−3.65	−1.17	+0.504	10.4	9
7	−2.65	−0.85	+0.708	14.4	22
8	−1.65	−0.53	+0.869	18.0	18
9	−0.65	−0.21	+0.978	20.2	25
10	+0.35	+0.11	+0.994	20.6	23
11	+1.35	+0.43	+0.912	18.9	15
12	+2.35	+0.75	+0.755	15.6	7
13	+3.35	+1.07	+0.564	11.7	12
14	+4.35	+1.39	+0.381	7.9	8
15	+5.35	+1.71	+0.232	4.8	8
16	+6.35	+2.04	+0.125	2.6	2
17	+7.35	+2.36	+0.062	1.3	2
18	+8.35	+2.68	+0.028	0.6	1
			Sum = 7.821	Sum = 161.6	Sum = 162

separately), may generally also be ignored. Then

$$\sigma = \left[\frac{\sum n_i (x_i - \bar{x})^2}{N}\right]^{1/2} = \left(\frac{1583}{162}\right)^{1/2} = 9.77^{1/2} = 3.12.$$

Since our displacements x are greater by a factor of 400 than the original values, our final result is that σ is 3.12/400 or 0.0078. Thus the average friction value is 0.10537, and the standard deviation of individual points about this average is 0.0078.

Our third step is the calculation of the probable error in $\bar{x}$ (often referred to as its *standard error*). This, by Eq. (2–27), is given by

$$e_{\bar{x}} = \frac{\sigma}{(N-1)^{1/2}} = \frac{0.0078}{(161)^{1/2}} = 0.00061. \qquad (2\text{--}33)$$

Thus we write $f = 0.10537 \pm 0.00061$. (*Note:* Although we have found

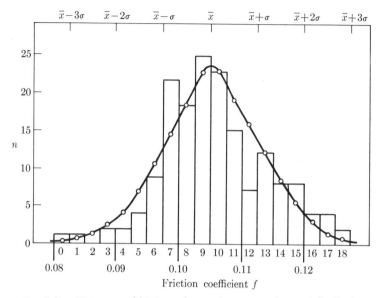

Fig. 2-7. Histogram of friction values and superposed normal distribution.

that $f = 0.10537 \pm 0.00061$, we would not normally report the result in this form, unless this was an important piece of datum, about to be combined and evaluated with other similar data. A value of 0.1054 ± 0.0006 would suffice for most purposes. In situations where no estimate of the error is to be given, answers are often written using the notation 1.054×10^{-1}, with one numeral before the decimal point, and in this form it is clear how many significant figures the answer has, even when the last significant figure is zero.)

We then proceed to calculate the constants of a normal distribution which has the same value of N, $\bar{x}$, and σ as that given originally. We do this by converting values of x into values of $(x - \bar{x})/\sigma$, and then consult a table of ordinates of the normal curve, as given in most statistical tables (Table 2-3). This gives the third column. In the fourth column, we multiply the third column by the ratio of number of readings to total height of the ordinates, to increase the height of the distribution so that its total area is N. Lastly the calculated values of n are compared with the observed values of n, and the two are plotted as in Fig. 2-7.

2-12. Short cuts in calculating σ

For many purposes an approximate value of σ is sufficient. This value can be calculated quite adequately by either of two methods.

(a) *Using the mean deviation.* The mean deviation, which we shall denote by $|\sigma|$, is defined as being the average of all the deviations, added irrespective of sign. Thus, in our notation, we have

$$|\sigma| = \frac{\sum n_i |x_i - \bar{x}|}{N}.$$ (2–34)

From Table 2–2, the sum of the negative deviations is 144 and the sum of the positive deviations is 249; hence the total deviation is 393. (Strictly speaking, the deviation should be calculated about the middle point of the distribution, or *median*, and not about the estimate $\bar{x}'$ as we have done; but the difference is not great.) By applying Eq. (2–34), we find that

$$|\sigma| = 393/162 = 2.43 \text{ (which is equivalent to } 2.43/400 = 0.0061).$$

For data which obey a normal distribution, we have, approximately,

$$\sigma = \tfrac{5}{4} \times |\sigma|.$$ (2–35)

In our case $\tfrac{5}{4}$ of 0.0061 gives 0.0076. This compares well with the correct value of 0.0078.

(b) *Using the range between the highest and lowest sextiles.* If we arrange the data in order of increasing size, then we may estimate σ in a number of ways by calculating the range, either between the highest and lowest data points, or between specified data points on the high and low sides. The best of these estimates uses the data point which is one-sixth of the way from the bottom and the one which is one-sixth of the way from the top of the distribution. For our friction distribution of 162 points, one-sixth amounts to 27 data points. Taking the distribution of Table 2–1, we find that counting 27 points from the top brings us one-third of the way into the range from 0.0975 to 0.1000; for example, to 0.0984. Counting 27 points from the bottom brings us halfway into the range from 0.1125 to 0.1150, to 0.1138. The difference between these numbers is 0.0154. As we saw earlier, the range between the first and the last one-sixth of a distribution is equal to 2σ. Hence σ is equal to 0.0077. This value, too, is very close to the correct value of 0.0078.

2–13. Testing a distribution for normalcy: the χ^2 (chi-squared) test

A number of special tests of a distribution may be used to see whether it is normal or not. We shall not discuss any of these special tests here, however, but rather introduce the χ^2 function. This is an important general way of examining data to see if they fit some hypothesis.

TABLE 2–4

SETTING UP A χ^2 CALCULATION

x	n_o	n_e	$|n_o - n_e|$	$(n_o - n_e)^2$	$(n_o - n_e)^2/n_e$
0–4	6	7.8	1.8	3.24	0.41
5	4	6.8	2.8	7.88	1.16
6	9	10.4	1.4	1.96	0.20
7	21	14.4	6.6	43.6	3.03
8	18	18.0	0	0	0
9	25	20.2	4.8	23.0	1.14
10	23	20.6	2.4	5.8	0.28
11	15	18.9	3.9	15.2	0.81
12	7	15.6	8.6	74.0	4.74
13	12	11.7	0.3	0.9	0.08
14	8	7.9	0.1	0.1	0.01
15	8	4.8	3.2	10.2	2.13
16–18	5	4.5	0.5	0.25	0.56
				Sum =	14.55 = χ^2

The χ^2 test is applied by comparing the number of times n_o an event was observed to happen with the number of times n_e that the event would be expected to happen if the hypothesis were true. Then we define χ^2 as

$$\chi^2 = \sum \frac{(n_o - n_e)^2}{n_e}. \tag{2–36}$$

In this case, our hypothesis is that the data (for example, the values of friction coefficients discussed in previous sections) fit the normal distribution. We have already calculated (see Table 2–3), for a distribution with the same N, $\bar{x}$, and σ, the expected values of n for various values of x. Since we also know the observed values of n, we are in a position to apply Eq. (2–36). For this purpose, we regard the "events" as being the number of readings within each of the various groups, and for each group we know how many "events" should have occurred (n_e), and how many did occur (n_o). The only point that needs comment is that it is necessary to group together the thinly populated regions at both ends of the distribution, so that no group has associated with it a value of n_e less than about five. Table 2–4 sets out the calculation.

To apply the criterion, we compare the value of χ^2 with that applicable to the number of values that were summed to produce χ^2. These are called "degrees of freedom." In this case there are 13 rows in Table 2–4,

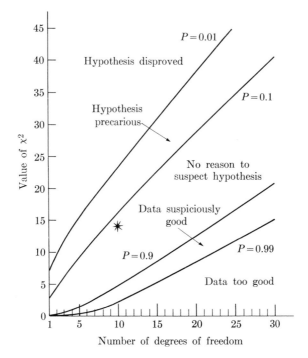

Fig. 2–8. Plot of the probability of getting values greater than values specified, as a function of number of degrees of freedom.

thus giving 13 degrees of freedom. From these, however, it is necessary to subtract three, because the data were fitted to a distribution with three constants, N, $\bar{x}$, and σ. Had the distribution been one with another number of constants, then that number would have been subtracted from the number of rows. This whole procedure seems rather mysterious, but all it means is that if we use a function with many adjustable constants, we will naturally get a better fit of our data, hence smaller $n_o - n_e$ values, hence a smaller value of χ^2. To compensate for this, we reduce the number of degrees of freedom correspondingly.

We now enter our value of χ^2, namely 14.55, and of our number of degrees of freedom, namely ten, into Fig. 2–8, where their position is marked by a star. We can see that our value falls into the middle group, "no reason to suspect hypothesis," and in this case the hypothesis is that our data follow a normal distribution. As usual in statistical tests, we cannot prove a hypothesis, but merely fail to disprove it. The various lines in Fig. 2–8 have been set up so that the line between "no reason to suspect hypothesis" and "hypothesis precarious" occurs at a probability level of 10%, so that there is only one chance in ten that if the data do fit the hypothesis, a value of x^2 as large as this would have been observed. The border of the "hypothesis disproved" region has been set at a probability level of 1%.

An interesting feature of the x^2 function is that too good agreement, leading to too low values of x^2, is also an occasion for comment. The comment here is that the data may have been "adjusted," subconsciously or otherwise. The warning lines have been entered at the 90% and at the 99% level. Thus there is a chance of as much as 99 in 100 that in an unprejudiced test of a hypothesis, a value of x^2 higher than that found on the upper boundary of the "data too good" region would have been observed.

Some further comments on the x^2 test are in order. First, it applies only to the *number of times* certain measurements are obtained, not to the *magnitude* of the measurements themselves. In fact, by applying dimensional analysis we can readily see that, since x^2 has the dimensions of n^2/n or n itself, then, if n is not a number but a length, let us say, the value of x^2 is not unique, but depends on the dimensions which are used to define the length.

Secondly, the x^2 test supplements a serious deficiency of human judgment. The human observer judges shape, and when he assesses the situation to determine whether the data points in Fig. 2–7 fit a normal distribution, he compares the shape of the histogram with the shape of the normal distribution. Suppose that the number of data points in Fig. 2–7 were increased by a factor of 10 to 1620, and the same distribution of points were obtained. Then the new Fig. 2–7 would look the same, and to the human eye the fit would look as good. However, in Table 2–4, too, the values of n_o and n_e would all be greater by a factor of 10, so that $(n_o - n_e)^2/n_e$ would be greater by a factor of 10. A x^2 value of 145.5, with 10 degrees of freedom, would be well within the "hypothesis disproved" region. For very large collections of data, in fact, the x^2 test is extremely sensitive in detecting slight departures from an assumed hypothesis. Conversely, it is much less useful for small collections of data.

It follows from what we have said above that the x^2 criterion cannot be applied to data that is presented in the form of percentage, i.e., 11% of the data were of one kind, 19% of another kind, etc. It is necessary to know the exact number of data points associated with each of the percentages.

Lastly, we may point out one feature of the x^2 test which has general application. We can see by inspection of Fig. 2–8 and confirm by examination of Table 2–4 that, if a hypothesis is true, x^2 is of the same order of magnitude as the number of degrees of freedom, and each individual term $(n_o - n_e)^2/n_e$ will be of the order of magnitude of one, which we write ≈ 1. Hence we have

$$\frac{(n_o - n_e)^2}{n_e} \approx 1,$$
$$(n_o - n_e) \approx \pm n_e^{1/2},$$
$$n_o = n_e \pm \approx n_e^{1/2}. \tag{2-37}$$

Whenever we expect to obtain the value n_e, we are likely to observe that number $\pm$ a number of the order of magnitude of $n_e^{1/2}$. If we toss a coin 1000 times, we expect 500 heads, but in practice we are likely to be "off" by a number of the order of magnitude of $\sqrt{500}$ or 22. If we toss a coin 100,000 times, we expect 50,000 heads, and may be off by about 220. As the number of tests increases, the total error increases as $n_e^{1/2}$, while the fractional error decreases as $n_e^{-1/2}$.

2–14. Nonnormal distributions

We have discussed in some detail the properties of normal distributions. We now turn to the discussion of nonnormal distributions, and consider three main types.

(a) *Distribution nearly normal but skewed.* This type frequently arises when the data fit the normal distribution well if the data are plotted a certain way, but not if they are plotted a different way. In this case, all we need do is to replot the data so as to change over to the normal distribution.

A typical example is seen in Fig. 2–9, which shows a histogram of 95 values of Vickers microhardness, for a lead-zinc composite material.

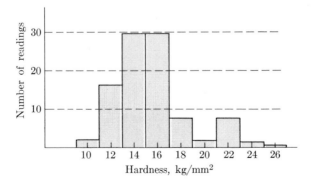

Fig. 2–9. Histogram of microhardness of a lead-zinc composite.

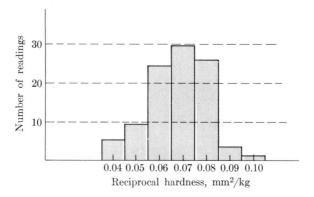

Fig. 2–10. Plot of reciprocal hardness for data of Fig. 2–9.

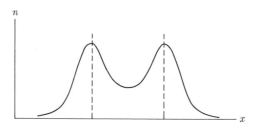

Fig. 2–11. Frequency distribution in the presence of frictional hysteresis.

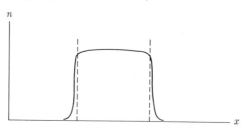

Fig. 2–12. A truncated frequency distribution.

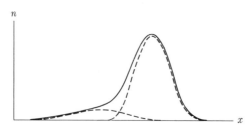

Fig. 2–13. Frequency distribution which is the sum of two separate normal distributions.

The microhardness is defined as the ratio of load (in this case 25 gm) to area when a diamond of square pyramid shape is pressed into the surface of a material. It will be seen that this histogram looks fairly normal, but it has a long tail on the high hardness side.

If now we replot the data so that the reciprocal of the hardness is our abscissa (Fig. 2–10), a distribution is obtained which looks much more normal. In this case there seems to be no theoretical reason why the reciprocal of the hardness should give a normal distribution, while the hardness itself does not; but often facts such as this can be used to develop theories of the processes by which statistical variations are produced.

(b) *Distribution quite unnormal.* This type arises from the failure of one of the assumptions on which the normal distribution is based, namely that (1) there should be a fairly large number of independent error-causing mechanisms of comparable magnitude, and (2) these mechanisms should be such that positive and negative errors are of comparable frequency, while very large errors are very highly unlikely.

Of these two assumptions, it is the first that is often found not to be valid, since in many situations one type of error predominates, and its characteristics determine the shape of the histogram. Thus, Fig. 2–11 shows the effects of frictional hysteresis (compare Fig. 1–23), where essentially two different readings are obtained, depending on whether the sliding direction of the measuring device before sliding ceased was positive or negative. Figure 2–12 shows a situation where the ends of the distribution are cut off because the recording instrument had a limited range. This type of distribution also arises in manufacture, when testing has led to the removal of the ends of the distribution.

(c) *Normal distribution with pronounced tail (or tails).* This type, which in its appearance often resembles the skewed distribution discussed above, is the most awkward of all to encounter, and often arises when the data are not homogeneous, but contain two quite different components. If we refer back to our discussion of the test of aluminum tensile specimens, we might suppose that 1% of the test specimens had a crack or flaw within the test region, and that these gave quite different readings. This would then give two separate statistical distributions, with the overall distribution the sum of these (Fig. 2–13). This distribution may cause much difficulty in practice, because of the fact that our airframe designer, while taking his 20 to 50 measurements, is likely never to encounter a flawed specimen, and hence is not made aware of the possible presence of these specimens of low strength.

Practical distributions are often of this type in which two normal distributions are superposed. As regards calculations of the standard deviation, probable error of the mean, and other properties determined mainly by the bulk of the readings, they may be treated mathematically as normal distributions and the results obtained will be reasonably reliable. However, when questions of the limit of error or minimum value arise, the presence of the tail or tails must be taken into account.

When the presence of a tail or tails is suspected, and, indeed in all cases in which the shape of the distribution is unknown, we may resort to a type of treatment known as *nonparametric statistics*. This treatment considers that, after we have carried out N tests, there is an equal likelihood of $1/(N + 1)$ that the next test will give a value between any two adjacent values yet attained, or higher or lower than the most extreme value so far obtained; but no statement can be made as to probabilities of less than one in $N + 1$. Thus, after 50 tests, we may say that the probability of finding specimens weaker than the weakest specimen yet tested is less than one in 51, but can say nothing further about the likelihood of finding specimens far weaker than this. On the other hand, when we know that our distribution is normal, we may make statements about specimens of very low strength, and state that the probability of encountering them is very small; for example, less than one in a million. For a more complete account of nonparametric statistics see McClintock and Argon (1962).

The distribution of Fig. 2–13 may be considered as arising from not observing the second criterion, which must be obeyed if a normal distribution is to result. In this case the probability of finding very large errors is small, but not vanishingly small.

2–15. How to draw the "best" straight line through a set of points

A standard problem which arises in experimental work is that of drawing a straight line through a set of points. Usually, all that is required is the slope of the line, though sometimes the position of the line is also needed.

It is best to discuss this problem in terms of a concrete example. Thus, in tests using a coil spring, the data shown in Fig. 2–14 were obtained. We wish to draw the best straight line through the twelve points, which are perhaps more widely scattered than is common.

(a) *Graphical method.* It is possible to draw a fairly good straight line through the points using a transparent ruler or other straight edge, which makes it easy to judge when the experimental points lie uniformly about the line. However, for accurate work this method has a number of shortcomings, one being that different observers draw the line rather differently; another being that an observer will tend to draw

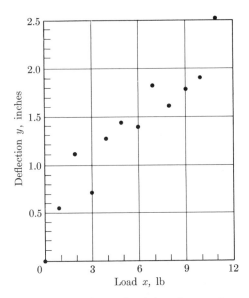

Fig. 2–14. Deflection-load data for a spring.

the line appreciably differently if the data are plotted to a different scale, say with the vertical dimension elongated. At this point the reader is invited to draw his "best" straight line on Fig. 2–14 and to calculate its slope, in order to compare it with the data which follow.

Another disadvantage of the graphical method is that it provides no notion of how good the straight line is, i.e., no estimate of the error of the slope is readily available.

(b) *Method of sequential differences.* To determine the slope of the line which best represents our twelve points, we may consider adjacent points in turn, and calculate the slope as derived from each pair. Thus we obtain eleven estimates of the slope, and take the mean of the eleven values as the "best" value of the slope. From the deviation of individual slopes from the mean slope, we may estimate the standard error of the slope. This calculation is laid out in Table 2–5.

It will be seen that the average slope is 0.232. We now proceed to the calculation of σ. If we subtract 0.23 from the various values of the slope, we obtain (neglecting signs) 0.33, 0.32, 0.62, 0.33, 0.07, 0.26, 0.17, 0.44, 0.05, 0.09, and 0.40. The total deviation is the sum of these, namely 3.08, and the mean deviation is 0.28. Hence, the standard deviation may be estimated from Eq. (2–35) as $\frac{5}{4} \times 0.28$ or 0.35. The standard error in the slope is $0.35/\sqrt{10}$ or 0.111. Hence, we quote the slope as 0.234 ± 0.111.

TABLE 2–5

CALCULATION OF SLOPE BY SEQUENTIAL DIFFERENCES

Load, lb, x	Spring deflection, in., y	Difference Δy, $y_{n+1} - y_n$	Difference Δx, $x_{n+1} - x_n$	Slope, $\Delta y / \Delta x$
0	0.00	+0.56	1	+0.56
1	0.56	+0.55	1	+0.55
2	1.11	−0.39	1	−0.39
3	0.72	+0.56	1	+0.56
4	1.28	+0.16	1	+0.16
5	1.44	−0.03	1	−0.03
6	1.41	+0.40	1	+0.40
7	1.81	−0.21	1	−0.21
8	1.60	+0.18	1	+0.18
9	1.78	+0.14	1	+0.14
10	1.92	+0.62	1	+0.62
11	2.55			Sum = 2.55
				Mean = 0.232

TABLE 2–6

CALCULATION OF SLOPE USING EXTENDED DIFFERENCES

x	y	$\Delta y = (y_{n+6} - y_n)$	$\Delta x = (x_{n+6} - x_n)$	$\Delta y / \Delta x$
0	0.00	1.41	6	0.235
1	0.56	1.25	6	0.208
2	1.11	0.49	6	0.082
3	0.72	1.06	6	0.117
4	1.28	0.64	6	0.107
5	1.44	1.11	6	0.185
6	1.41			Sum = 0.934
7	1.81			Mean = 0.166
8	1.60			
9	1.78			
10	1.92			
11	2.55			

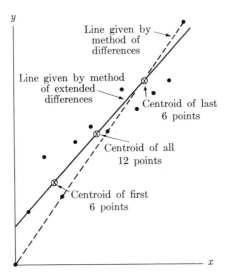

Fig. 2–15. Straight lines given by the method of differences and of extended differences.

One obvious fault of this method is that the value of the average is based entirely on the difference between the first and last reading of the spring deflection, since, for constant Δx values, the process of summing the fifth column automatically eliminates all values of y except the first and last. Thus, we are saying, in effect, that the best straight line is that joining the first and last points on the figure (see Fig. 2–15), and the other values are used only for determining the standard error of the average.

Unfortunately, the first and last points of a straight line plot are usually the most suspect. In the present case, for example, it is possible that if the spring is not initially straight, but kinked, the first application of the load will both straighten and deflect it, thus giving an unusually large extension. The application of the final increment of load, on the other hand, may initiate plastic deformation, thus again producing erroneous readings. It would be much more satisfactory to be able to use the intermediate readings which are less likely to be affected by systematic error. This may be done by adapting the method of differences to handle extended differences.

(c) *Method of extended differences.* In this method the readings are divided into two equal groups, namely high values and low values of x, and corresponding points in the two groups are differenced. The calculation is set out in Table 2–6.

In order to estimate the standard error of the mean slope, we subtract the various estimates of the slope from 0.166, and get values of 0.069, 0.042, 0.084, 0.011, 0.059, and 0.019. Their mean is found to be 0.047. Then, according to Eqs. (2–35) and (2–33), the standard error in the slope is $\frac{5}{4} \times 0.047 \times (1/\sqrt{5})$, namely, 0.027. Thus we write the slope as 0.166 ± 0.027 in./lb.

It should be carefully noted that the probable error is appreciably less than in the previous example, because of the fact that in Table 2–6 we calculated the deflection as the average of six independent applications of 6 lb, i.e., 36 lb in all, while in the previous case, we calculated the effect of applying 11 lb only. Clearly, the calculation based on 36 lb is likely to be better. Also, we have used all our data points, not just the end two.

So far we have merely determined the slope of our straight line, not its position. To do this, we must find a point through which the line should pass. The best point for this purpose is the centroid of all the points, namely the point $x = \sum x/12$, $y = \sum y/12$. From the data of Table 2–6, we calculate that this is the point $x = 5.5$, $y = 1.35$ (Fig. 2–15).

It may be shown that this procedure of extended differences, as just outlined, is equivalent to drawing a line connecting the centroid of the highest six points with the centroid of the lowest six points (see Fig. 2–15).

To sum up, the method of extended differences has the advantages of ease and simplicity, gives good results no matter whether errors arise in the x or y coordinates, and is to be recommended for ordinary calculations. However, in situations where we know which coordinate is giving rise to experimental errors it is inferior to the famous method of least squares, which we discuss next.

(d) *Method of least squares.* In this method we assume that all the scatter in the points is due to errors in measuring y, and that the best straight line is that which minimizes the sum of the squares of the errors in the y direction. For discussion of the validity of this postulate, which at first sight appears to be a very arbitrary one, see Whittaker and Robinson (1946) and Baird (1962). (It may be worth pointing out that use of the mean to represent a statistical distribution, as we have done earlier in this chapter, represents an application of the principle of least squares, since the radius of gyration of a body is least about an axis passing through its center of mass.)

If we consider that any straight line we might draw has the equation

$$y = mx + c, \tag{2–38}$$

then if point i, with coordinates x_i and y_i, lies on the line, we would have

$$y_i = mx_i + c.$$

If the point does not lie on the line, then the y coordinate of the point is in error by a distance e_{yi}, and we have

$$y_i = mx_i + c + e_{yi}. \tag{2-39}$$

According to the theory of least squares, the best straight line through a set of points is that which minimizes $\sum e_{yi}^2$.

To apply the least squares criterion, we rewrite Eq. (2–39) in the form

$$\sum_i e_{yi}^2 = \sum_i (y_i - mx_i - c)^2. \tag{2-40}$$

If $\sum e_{yi}^2$ is a minimum, then the differentiation of the right-hand side with respect to the adjustable constants m and c must be zero. Thus we get, as our conditions

$$\sum x_i(y_i - mx_i - c) = 0, \tag{2-41}$$
$$\sum (y_i - mx_i - c) = 0. \tag{2-42}$$

To apply these conditions, we first write the 12 original data points as 12 equations which do not agree (called *equations of condition*), namely,

$$
\begin{aligned}
0.00 &= 0m + c \\
0.56 &= 1m + c \\
1.11 &= 2m + c \\
0.72 &= 3m + c \\
1.28 &= 4m + c \\
1.44 &= 5m + c \\
1.41 &= 6m + c \\
1.81 &= 7m + c \\
1.60 &= 8m + c \\
1.78 &= 9m + c \\
1.92 &= 10m + c \\
2.55 &= 11m + c.
\end{aligned}
\tag{2-43}
$$

We sum these equations, column by column, to obtain

$$16.18 = 66m + 12c. \tag{2-44}$$

Next we multiply each of the 12 equations above by its value of x, i.e., the first equation by 0, the second by 1, the third by 2, etc.; this gives

$$
\begin{aligned}
0.00 &= 0m + 0c \\
0.56 &= 1m + 1c \\
2.22 &= 4m + 2c \\
2.16 &= 9m + 3c \\
5.12 &= 16m + 4c \\
7.20 &= 25m + 5c \\
8.46 &= 36m + 6c \\
12.67 &= 49m + 7c \\
12.80 &= 64m + 8c \\
16.20 &= 81m + 9c \\
19.20 &= 101m + 10c \\
28.05 &= 121m + 11c.
\end{aligned}
\tag{2-45}
$$

Summing the equations gives

$$
114.46 = 506m + 66c. \tag{2-46}
$$

The two summed equations are called "normal equations," which may be solved to find m and c.

If we multiply Eq. (2–44) by 11, and Eq. (2–46) by 2, we obtain

$$
177.98 = 726m + 132c \quad \text{and} \quad 228.94 = 1012m + 132c. \tag{2-47}
$$

Subtraction gives

$$
286m = 50.96, \quad \text{or} \quad m = 0.178. \tag{2-48}
$$

Substituting this into Eq. (2–44) gives

$$
c = 0.369. \tag{2-49}
$$

The reader is warned that in very many cases the two normal equations are rather similar, so that solving for m and c involves taking the small differences between two large numbers. Hence, it is advisable to carry one or two more decimal places in the calculation than seems to be necessary.

In order to calculate the standard error in m, we must find the values of e_y^2. This calculation is laid out in Table 2–7.

The formula for the standard error of e_y for equally spaced readings of the error-free variable is

$$
\text{Standard error} = \frac{(n\sum e_y^2)^{1/2}}{(n-2)[n\sum x^2 - (\sum x)^2]}, \tag{2-50}
$$

TABLE 2-7

CALCULATION OF VALUES OF e_y^2

x	$0.178x$	$y_{\text{calc}} = 0.178x + 0.369$	y_{meas}	$|e_y|$	e_y^2
0	0	0.369	0	0.37	0.1369
1	0.178	0.547	0.56	0.01	0.0001
2	0.356	0.725	1.11	0.39	0.1521
3	0.534	0.903	0.72	0.18	0.0324
4	0.712	1.081	1.28	0.20	0.0400
5	0.890	1.259	1.44	0.18	0.0324
6	1.068	1.437	1.41	0.03	0.0009
7	1.246	1.615	1.81	0.20	0.0400
8	1.424	1.793	1.60	0.19	0.0361
9	1.602	1.971	1.78	0.19	0.0361
10	1.780	2.149	1.92	0.23	0.0529
11	1.958	2.327	2.55	0.22	0.0484
				Sum =	0.6083

where n is the number of points on the plot, namely 12, $\sum e_y^2$ is 0.608, $\sum x^2$ is found from Eq. (2–46) to be 506, while $\sum x$ from Eq. (2–44) is 66. Substituting, we find the standard error to be 0.0206. Thus, our answer for m is 0.178 $\pm$ 0.021.

The answer obtained above is generally considered to be the "best." However, it is not well known that this superiority of the least squares method is based on the assumption that all the error is concentrated in the y coordinate, i.e., in our case, that all the weights were correct but the displacements were not read correctly. However, it is possible, particularly in situations where the load was indirectly applied, that the loads were not exactly 0, 1, 2, etc., lb, but had experimental error. As the extreme case, let us consider the possibility that the displacements were read perfectly correctly, but that all the error is due to loading error.

In this case it is clear that we should minimize, not $\sum e_y^2$, but rather $\sum e_x^2$. To do this, we rewrite Eq. (4–39) in the form

$$x_i - \frac{y_i}{m} + \frac{c}{m} = e_{xi}, \qquad (2\text{-}51)$$

and the least squares criterion becomes

$$\sum e_x^2 = \sum \left(x - \frac{y}{m} + \frac{c}{m} \right)^2. \qquad (2\text{-}52)$$

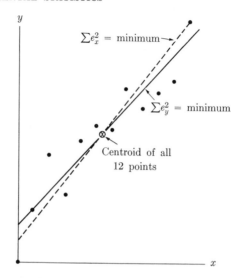

Fig. 2–16. Comparison of the two least squares solutions.

Then our conditions for zero after differentiation with respect to c and m become

$$\frac{1}{m}\sum\left(x_i - \frac{y}{m} + \frac{c}{m}\right) = 0, \qquad (2\text{–}53)$$

$$\frac{1}{m^2}\sum(y_i - c)\left(x_i - \frac{y_i}{m} + \frac{c}{m}\right) = 0. \qquad (2\text{–}54)$$

Multiplying Eq. (2–53) by m^2, (2–54) by m^3, and removing the term $\sum c(mx_i - y_i + c)$ from (2–54), since it is zero, we obtain as our two final equations

$$\sum(mx_i - y_i - c) = 0, \qquad (2\text{–}55)$$

$$\sum y_i(mx_i - y_i + c) = 0. \qquad (2\text{–}56)$$

Equation (2–55) we have already met as Eq. (2–42). Equation (2–56) is analogous to Eq. (2–41), but by no means identical with it. In fact, if we multiply each of equations (2–43) by its coefficient in y, and sum them, we obtain

$$26.957 = 114.46m + 17.18c, \qquad (2\text{–}57)$$

and, if we combine this with (2–44) we obtain

$$m = 0.202, \qquad c = 0.24.$$

This value differs quite significantly from the previous "best" answer (Fig. 2–16).

PROBLEMS

1. A student measures the thickness of a coating which covers half of a plane surface by focusing the microscope at the stations 1–8, equally spaced as shown in Fig. 2–17, and measuring the vertical displacement of the microscope for each station (See table). Note that the surface is not horizontal. Calculate as well as you can the thickness of the coating, and estimate the numerical aperture of the microscope objective used.

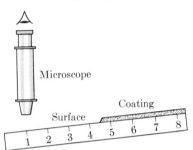

Figure 2–17

Station	Vertical adjustment reading (10^{-4} cm)
1	0
2	2
3	4
4	9
5	28
6	31
7	37
8	37

2. A class has measured the static friction coefficient of steel on a certain piece of wood 300 times using a method known to be free of systematic error. Their results are given in the following table. Two other students propose

Friction coefficient	N
0.20–0.22	3
0.22–0.24	35
0.24–0.26	128
0.26–0.28	120
0.28–0.30	13
0.30–0.32	1

two different methods (unspecified) for measuring the static coefficient of steel on the piece of wood. One of them makes but one measurement using his method and obtains a value for the friction coefficient of 0.281. The other obtains ten measurements using his method; these are 0.262, 0.240, 0.267, 0.299, 0.270, 0.287, 0.256, 0.274, 0.282, 0.279. State whether there is enough evidence to show that either, or both, of these methods has systematic errors which are not present in the original method. Discuss this evidence. [*Ans.* The student making 10 measurements is not consistent with the one making 300.]

3. Early in a baseball season, the position of the individual clubs of the American Baseball League is as follows. Use a χ^2 analysis to evaluate whether the position of the individual teams is determined by chance alone, or whether differences in skill seem to exist. [*Ans.* No reason to suspect a difference in skill. (Proof: New York won the pennant that year!)]

Club	Games won	Games lost
Detroit	9	2
Minnesota	8	3
Boston	6	5
New York	6	5
Cleveland	6	5
Chicago	5	6
Baltimore	5	6
Kansas City	4	7
Washington	4	7
Los Angeles	2	9

4. Three students measure the sizes of the same 10 particles in a microscope. Their values for the particle diameter are as follows. Comment on these measurements, paying particular attention to these points: (a) Comparing each student with the others, is there any evidence that systematic

Particle	Student 1	Student 2	Student 3
1	10.4	10.6	10.5
2	81.7	81.8	81.0
3	3.7	3.7	3.5
4	52.8	53.0	53.0
5	71.0	70.9	71.0
6	17.3	17.7	17.3
7	14.1	14.3	14.0
8	33.6	33.4	33.5
9	1.1	1.3	1.0
10	6.9	7.0	7.0

errors of measurement are present? How great are these errors? [*Hint:* Consider differences such as $(d_{\text{student 1}} - d_{\text{student 2}})$, and calculate their mean and standard error.] (b) Which student appears to be the most accurate, and which the least accurate, based on the limited amount of data available? [*Hint:* Is there evidence that any student is a slovenly observer, or that one student reads systematically higher or lower than the others?]

5. Using a micrometer, a student determines the size of a bearing ball twenty times. He finds the average to be 0.5006 in., and the standard deviation of the individual readings from this average to be 0.0006 in.

A second student repeats this experiment and measures the same ball twenty times with the same micrometer. He gets a value of 0.5001 in., with the standard deviation of individual readings from this average of 0.0005 in. (a) Do you regard this value as consistent with that obtained by the first student? (b) The first student now decides to measure twenty different balls from the same batch, and obtains a value for the diameter of 0.5008 in., the rms deviation of individual readings from the average being 0.0009 in. How much of this scatter may be attributed to real differences in size between the balls? [*Ans.* (a) No; (b) 0.0007]

6. Four students each measure the length of a line six times. Their results are as follows. Calculate the average and standard deviation of each student's results. State which student's results are clearly inconsistent with which other student's results. [*Ans.* Students 3 and 4 clearly not consistent.]

Student 1	Student 2	Student 3	Student 4
0.202	0.204	0.201	0.202
0.198	0.203	0.198	0.208
0.203	0.201	0.204	0.211
0.207	0.203	0.195	0.209
0.204	0.204	0.199	0.207
0.204	0.203	0.203	0.205

REFERENCES

Most of the material of this chapter is covered, often more thoroughly, in most elementary books of statistics. A number of moderately priced volumes of this type are listed below. Many other suitable texts exist.

BAIRD, D. C., *Experimentation, an Introduction to Measurement Theory and Experimental Design*, Prentice-Hall, Englewood Cliffs, N. J., 1962.

BEARS, Y., *Introduction to the Theory of Error*, Addison-Wesley Publishing Co., Reading, Mass., 1953. This book contains a good account of the possible limitations of the least-squares method.

BROOKS, C. E. P., and N. CARRUTHERS, *Handbook of Statistical Methods in Meteorology*, Her Majesty's Stationary Office, London, 1953. A very comprehensive account of statistical methods used in analyzing the weather (as tricky an engineering problem as any). This book discusses simplified, approximate, methods as well as the lengthy elegant ones.

MORONEY, M. J., *Facts from Figures*, Penguin Books, London, 1951. Mathematically simple, illustrative examples derived largely from economics.

TOPPING, J., *Errors of Observation and Their Treatment*, Reinhold, New York, 1955.

Statistical Tables

ARKIN, H., and R. R. COLTON, *Tables for Statisticians*, Barnes and Noble Inc., New York, 1950.

Handbook of Chemistry and Physics, Chemical Rubber Publishing Co., Cleveland. New edition annually. The mathematical section of this book is also issued separately as *C.R.C. Standard Mathematical Tables*.

Special Topics

BIRGE, R. T., "The Calculation of Errors by the Method of Least Squares," *Phys. Rev.*, **40**, 207–227, 1932. This paper discusses very thoroughly the distinction between internal and external consistency. (Birge's definition of external estimate of error is rather more restricted than ours.)

McCLINTOCK, F. A., and A. S. ARGON, eds., *An Introduction to the Mechanical Behavior of Materials*, Massachusetts Institute of Technology, 1962. Chapter 25, entitled "The Statistical Aspects of Experiments on Materials" constitutes a useful comparison of normal and nonparametric statistics.

WHITTAKER, E., and G. ROBINSON, *The Calculus of Observations*, Blackie, Glasgow, reprinted 1946. This classical treatise has especially valuable discussions of the conditions under which normal distributions arise, and of the theoretical basis for the principle of least squares.

CHAPTER THREE

Dynamics of Measurement

In *all* measuring instruments, time is required for the instrument to indicate a change in the measured quantity. Thus, for any instrument, if the measured quantity varies rapidly enough, there will be a substantial *dynamic error* in the readings. Whenever measurements of fluctuating variables are to be made, it is necessary to determine the response characteristics of the instrument in order to know the meaning of the measurements.

Although a measured quantity will not generally vary in a simple analytical fashion with time, we can learn much about an instrument by observing its response to simple time function inputs. Knowing a system's response to simple inputs, we can do a good job of predicting its response to most any input. There are two general types of variations that are of interest.

(1) Transient variations where a single occurrence can constitute a measurement, such as measuring the body temperature of a sick person, the pressure wave due to a bomb blast, or accelerations experienced by rocket components.

(2) Sustained vibrations that are cyclic in nature such as vibrations in a machine caused by motor imbalance.

If each instrument is to be completely analyzed, many different types of response will be encountered. However, the characteristics of many instruments are *close* enough to one of two general types, that are represented by first- and second-order linear differential equations, that we shall analyze these two types. The response characteristics so developed will represent to a very good approximation those of many instruments. The differences, if any, which exist between the response predictions to follow and the actual response will be due to the fact that our analytical model is not a completely true representation of fact. We shall *assume* that all springs involved are *linear*, i.e., displacement is proportional to force over the entire range of displacements encountered. We shall assume that all damping, or *friction* is *viscous*, i.e., the friction force is proportional to relative velocity between the moving members. We shall also assume that all mass can be lumped in a single *point mass* rather than considering it in its true distribution. These assumptions greatly facilitate analysis of the system behavior. Moreover, because instrument designers want to understand their products, the tendency is to design instruments to satisfy these assumptions as closely as possible. This does not mean that such instruments are, by virtue of their behaving as linear systems, the most ideal type; it simply means that we can understand them more easily.

In the analyses to follow we will discuss a particular mechanical system, where we are interested in its position x, as a function of time t, when acted upon by a force F, which is some function of time (F_t). The results we obtain will hold for many other systems (thermal, electric, hydraulic, etc.) which obey the same initial differential equations. Hence, by letting x and F represent different quantities, many systems are analyzed. A different approach would be to analyze a general first- or second-order differential equation without reference to reality, and then apply the analysis to various situations. However, the writers feel that much is gained by having a physical system in mind, analyzing that system, learning its characteristics, and then applying the results, by analogy, to other systems.

3–1. First-order systems

Figure 3–1 shows schematically a simple first-order system where a force F_t acts on a spring k and a dashpot c. The system has negligible mass, which is equivalent to saying that the acceleration forces will be negligible compared with the spring and viscous forces. If we let x represent the displacement from the *static* position, the force in the spring is kx, the force in the damper or dashpot is $c\,dx/dt$ (or $c\dot{x}$). As the system is in equilibrium, we can write

$$c\dot{x} + kx = F_t \tag{3-1}$$

or dividing by k,

$$\tau\dot{x} + x = \frac{F_t}{k}, \tag{3-2}$$

where $\tau = c/k \equiv$ "time constant" of the system. Equation (3–2) is the general first-order equation that we will consider.

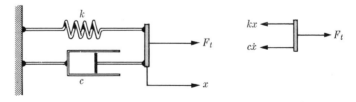

Fig. 3–1. Schematic drawing of a first-order mechanical system.

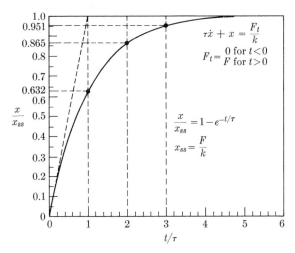

Fig. 3–2. Response of a first-order system to "step" input.

(a) *Transient inputs.* If the force F_t is 0 for $t < 0$ and F for $t > 0$, we term the force or input to the system a step input. Equation (3–2) then becomes

$$\tau\dot{x} + x = \frac{F}{k} \quad (t > 0) \tag{3–3}$$

when integrated by the usual technique and noting that when $t = \infty$, $x = F/k \equiv x_{ss}$ (the steady-state value of x), we obtain

$$\frac{x}{x_{ss}} = 1 - e^{-t/\tau}. \tag{3–4}$$

Equation (3–4) is plotted in Fig. 3–2. We note that the initial slope of the curve is unity, and that $x/x_{ss} = 95\%$ at $t/\tau = 3$.

The *dynamic error* at any time is the difference between the ideal (no lag) reading and the actual reading. In this case, an ideal instrument would give a step response, i.e., $x = 0$ for $t < 0$, and $x = x_{ss}$ for $t > 0$; hence the error is $x_{ss} - x$. The error is 100% at $t = 0$ and has reduced to 5% at $t/\tau = 3$.

The response to many other inputs can be calculated. Two are listed below, when F_t is linearly increasing, and when F_t is parabolically increasing.

For $F_t = C_1 t$ (ramp input),

$$\frac{xk}{C_1\tau} = \frac{t}{\tau} - (1 - e^{-t/\tau}). \tag{3–5}$$

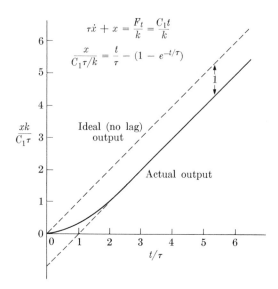

Fig. 3–3. Response of a first-order system to "ramp" input.

For $F_t = C_2 t^2$ (parabolic input),

$$\frac{xk}{C_2 \tau^2} = \left(\frac{t}{\tau}\right)^2 - 2\left(e^{-t/\tau} + \frac{t}{\tau} - 1\right). \tag{3-6}$$

Of particular interest is Eq. (3–5), the response to a ramp-type input, because (as will be demonstrated later) many complex inputs can be analyzed in terms of a number of ramp inputs. Figure 3–3 is a plot of Eq. (3–5). It is clear that for $t/\tau > 4$, the actual dimensionless output lags behind the ideal output by unity. Thus, for $t/\tau = 5$, the error is 20%, for $t/\tau = 10$, the error is 10%, and for $t/\tau = 20$, the error is reduced to 5%, etc. Hence, the error η is equal to τ/t.

Because the systems we will analyze are represented by *linear* differential equations, the solutions can be superposed. For instance, if we were to subject a first-order system to a square pulse of any duration, we could obtain the response by superposing the responses due to two step inputs, one positive and one negative. The response to a pulse of magnitude F and duration 1.5τ is shown in Fig. 3–4. In like manner, the response to any input made up of straight line sections can be determined through superposition of various ramp and step inputs.

If the duration Δt of a pulse becomes small compared with the time constant τ, the response is very little affected by the *shape* of the F-t curve, but is mainly dependent upon the *area* under the F-t curve.

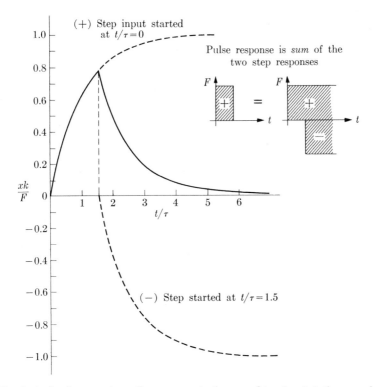

Fig. 3–4. For linear systems, the response to the sum of two inputs is the sum of the responses to the two individual inputs.

Under this condition ($\Delta t \ll \tau$), we can replace the actual input with an *impulse* $\mathcal{g}$, where

$$\mathcal{g} \equiv \int_0^{\Delta t} F\,dt, \qquad\qquad (3\text{--}7)$$
$$\underset{\substack{\Delta t \to 0 \\ F \to \infty}}{}$$

In a mechanical system, we recognize the impulse as equal to the momentum transfer during an impact. The response of a first-order system to an impulse is given by

$$\frac{xk\tau}{\mathcal{g}} = e^{-t/\tau}. \qquad\qquad (3\text{--}8)$$

This result can be obtained by simply considering a pulse (Fig. 3–4) of duration $\Delta t < 0.1\tau$, where the output is essentially proportional to time. In the initial part of the curve (Fig. 3–2), the slope is unity, hence

$$x = \frac{Ft}{k\tau} = \frac{F\Delta t}{k\tau} = \frac{\mathcal{I}}{k\tau},$$

and the maximum value of $xk\tau/\mathcal{I}$ is unity. At the end of Δt, x will simply decay exponentially as in Fig. 3–4. Hence $xk\tau/\mathcal{I} = e^{-t/\tau}$.

(b) *Periodic inputs.* As was mentioned previously, we are also interested in the response of instruments to input quantities which fluctuate periodically. We can develop an insight into the response to a general periodic input by analyzing the response to sinusoidal inputs at various frequencies. Then for response to a nonsinusoidal cyclic input, we can approximate the input by a Fourier series of sinusoidal inputs, and superpose the responses to these inputs. Simple Fourier analysis will be discussed later in this chapter.

For a sinusoidal input we can represent F_t as either

$$F_t = F_0 \cos \omega_f t \tag{3–9}$$

or

$$F_t = \text{(the real part of)}^* \ F_0 e^{j\omega_f t} \tag{3–10}$$
$$\equiv F_0 e^{j\omega_f t}$$

where ω_f is the forcing frequency in rad/sec, and F_0 is the maximum value of the input force.

Using Eq. (3–10), we have for the equation of motion

$$\tau \dot{x} + x = \frac{F_0 e^{j\omega_f t}}{k}. \tag{3–11}$$

We now assume that the response x varies in a sinusoidal fashion at the forcing frequency ω_f, and we expect that the response will lag somewhat behind the input by a phase angle ϕ, as shown in Fig. 3–5, on the complex plane.

Thus we assume

$$x = A e^{j\omega_f t},$$
$$\dot{x} = j\omega_f A e^{j\omega_f t}, \tag{3–12}$$
$$\ddot{x} = -\omega_f^2 A e^{j\omega_f t}.$$

---

* In this book we will always be concerned with the real part of various complex quantities. However, for simplicity we will not write "the real part of . . ." each time. It is left to the reader to bear this in mind.

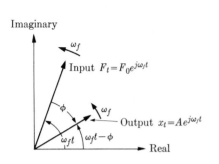

Fig. 3–5. Assumed response of first-order system to sinusoidal input.

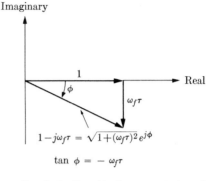

Fig. 3–6. Graphical representation of the numerator of Eq. (3–15).

Combining Eqs. (3–11) and (3–12), we obtain

$$j\tau\omega_f A e^{j\omega_f t} + A e^{j\omega_f t} = \frac{F_0}{k} e^{j\omega_f t} \tag{3-13}$$

or

$$\frac{A}{F_0/k} = \frac{1}{1 + j\omega_f\tau}. \tag{3-14}$$

We rationalize Eq. (3–14) by multiplying numerator and denominator by the conjugate of the denominator and thus

$$\frac{A}{F_0/k} = \frac{1}{1 + j\omega_f\tau} \times \frac{1 - j\omega_f\tau}{1 - j\omega_f\tau} = \frac{1 - j\omega_f\tau}{1 + (\omega_f\tau)^2}. \tag{3-15}$$

The numerator of Eq. (3–15) can be represented graphically as shown in Fig. 3–6. Hence

$$\frac{A}{F_0/k} = \frac{1}{\sqrt{1 + (\omega_f\tau)^2}} e^{j\phi}, \tag{3-16}$$

where $\phi = \tan^{-1}(-\omega_f\tau)$. Finally,

$$x = \frac{(F_0/k)e^{j(\omega_f t + \phi)}}{\sqrt{1 + (\omega_f\tau)^2}}. \tag{3-17}$$

Note that in Eq. (3–16) we have associated the fact that the output *lags* input with a negative phase angle ϕ. We could equally as well have recognized the lag by employing a $-j$ in the exponent of Eq. (3–16) and then allowing the phase angle to be positive.

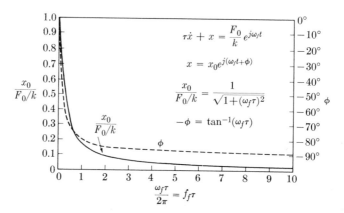

Fig. 3–7. Response of first-order system to a sinusoidal input F_0 at frequency ω_f rad/sec, or f_f, cps.

We should also note that Eq. (3–14) can be rewritten as

$$\frac{x_t}{F_t/k} = \frac{1}{1 + j\omega_f\tau}.$$
(3–14a)

This relates the instantaneous output x_t to the instantaneous input F_t. Later in this chapter, when we consider compensating networks, we shall find it convenient to use this latter representation of the system response.

The ratio of the maximum output amplitude x_0, to that expected under steady-state conditions from the maximum input F_0/k, is called the amplitude ratio, where

$$\frac{x_0}{F_0/k} = \frac{1}{\sqrt{1 + (\omega_f\tau)^2}}.$$
(3–18)

The amplitude ratio $x_0/(F_0/k)$ and phase angle ϕ are shown as functions of $\omega_f\tau/2\pi$ and $f_f\tau$ in Fig. 3–7.

The response curve of Fig. 3–7 is plotted on rectilinear coordinates and provides a clear picture of the rapidity with which the response falls off. For certain applications it is more convenient to represent the response on logarithmic coordinates. Figure 3–8 shows such a plot; the curve is asymptotic to a horizontal line and a $-45°$ line, which intersect at $\omega_f\tau = 1$ and $x_0/(F_0/k) = 1$.

Response characteristics are often discussed, and tabulated in lists of specifications, in terms of decibels and octaves; hence the reader should be familiar with these terms. The decibel was first defined in terms of

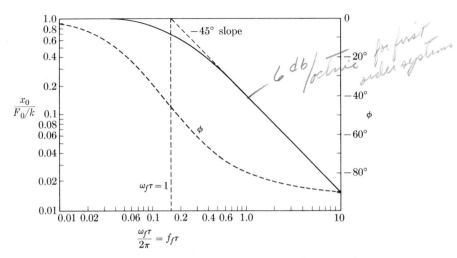

Fig. 3–8. First-order frequency response curve plotted on logarithmic coordinates.

the ratio of power output P_o to power input P_i for electrical systems:

$$\text{decibels} = 10 \log_{10}\left(\frac{P_o}{P_i}\right). \qquad (3\text{–}19)$$

Because power varies with the square of voltage (for constant impedance), decibels are also used to denote the ratio of output voltage V_o to input voltage V_i:

$$\text{decibels} = 20 \log_{10}\left(\frac{V_o}{V_i}\right). \qquad (3\text{–}20)$$

The use of the decibel system has been extended to describe the dimensionless amplitude ratio of any dynamic system. Hence

$$\text{decibels} = 20 \log_{10} (\text{amplitude ratio}). \qquad (3\text{–}21)$$

This is shown plotted in Fig. 3–9. We should note that in the vicinity of zero decibels, one decibel is equivalent to approximately 10% change in the amplitude ratio. Hence, a recorder which is specified as being "down 3 db at 200 cps" exhibits approximately 30% error at this frequency.

Frequency measure in octaves is simply a logarithmic frequency range; the frequency is doubled for each octave change. Hence, the −45° slope of Fig. 3–8 can be spoken of as "decreasing at the rate of 6 decibels/octave."

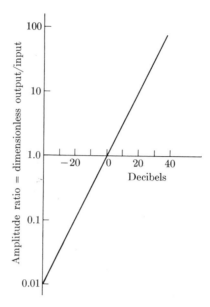

Fig. 3–9. The relationship between amplitude ratio and decibels.

The real advantage of logarithmic frequency plots is realized when various dynamic components are cascaded, or placed in series, the output of one being the input of the next. The system frequency response of a series system is obtained by *multiplying* the individual amplitude ratios, and *adding* the individual phase angles. Two logarithmic amplitude ratio curves can be multiplied by simply *adding* the logarithms at each frequency.

3–2. Second-order systems (where input is a force)

The second-order system that we shall consider is like the first-order system of Fig. 3–1 except that now the mass m is considered to be important. We let y indicate the motion of the support in Fig. 3–10. This motion can be zero, or, in the case of vibration studies, it is the quantity of interest. If we let a fictitious "inertia force" $(-m\ddot{x})$ act on the mass of Fig. 3–10, we can show all forces acting in Fig. 3–11. The equation of motion is then

$$m\ddot{x} + c(\dot{x} - \dot{y}) + k(x - y) = F_t. \tag{3–22}$$

Equation (3–22) can be put in more convenient form by dividing

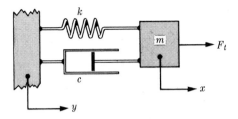

Fig. 3–10. Schematic drawing of general second-order mechanical system.

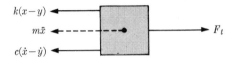

Fig. 3–11. Force balance in second-order system.

through by m and letting

$$\omega_n = \sqrt{k/m} \equiv \text{natural frequency (undamped), rad/sec,}$$

$$\zeta = \frac{c}{2\sqrt{km}} \equiv \text{damping ratio, dimensionless.}$$

The damping ratio ζ is the ratio of the actual damping c to that required for critical damping c_c:

$$c_c = 2m\omega_n = 2\sqrt{km}. \tag{3-23}$$

Then

$$\ddot{x} + 2\zeta\omega_n(\dot{x} - \dot{y}) + \omega_n^2(x - y) = F_t/m. \tag{3-24}$$

(a) *Transient inputs.* We shall first consider the case where y and its derivatives are zero, and we let F_t take on various forms.

When F_t is a step function of magnitude F, we have

$$\ddot{x} + 2\zeta\omega_n\dot{x} + \omega_n^2 x = F/m \qquad (t > 0). \tag{3-25}$$

It will be recalled that the solution of an equation of this type involves a "particular solution" and a "homogeneous solution." The particular solution is seen to be

$$x = \frac{F}{k},$$

because all derivatives of x are zero. The homogeneous solution is obtained by solving

$$\ddot{x} + 2\zeta\omega_n\dot{x} + \omega_n^2 x = 0. \tag{3-26}$$

The complete solution will be of the form

$$x = F/k + C_1 e^{r_1 t} + C_2 e^{r_2 t}, \tag{3-27}$$

where r_1 and r_2 are roots of the characteristic equation

$$r^2 + 2\zeta\omega_n r + \omega_n^2 = 0. \tag{3-28}$$

Thus

$$r_{1,2} = \frac{-2\zeta\omega_n \pm \sqrt{4\zeta^2\omega_n^2 - 4\omega_n^2}}{2}, \tag{3-29}$$

$$r_{1,2} = \omega_n(-\zeta \pm \sqrt{\zeta^2 - 1}). \tag{3-30}$$

Three cases thus develop:

$\zeta < 1$, the two roots are conjugate complex numbers;

$\zeta = 1$, the roots are equal and real (critically damped);

$\zeta > 1$, the roots are unequal and real.

The solutions of Eq. (3–25) corresponding to these three cases are as follows:

Second-order system, step input: $F_t = F$ $(t > 0)$.

$\underline{\zeta < 1}$:

$$\frac{x}{F/k} = 1 - \frac{1}{\sqrt{1 - \zeta^2}} e^{-\zeta\omega_n t} \sin(\sqrt{1 - \zeta^2}\,\omega_n t + \phi),$$

where

$$\phi = \tan^{-1} \frac{\sqrt{1 - \zeta^2}}{\zeta}. \tag{3-31}$$

$\underline{\zeta = 1}$:

$$\frac{x}{F/k} = 1 - (1 + \omega_n t)e^{-\omega_n t}.$$

$\underline{\zeta > 1}$:

$$\frac{x}{F/k} = 1 - \frac{\nu}{\nu - 1}\left(e^{-\omega_n t/\sqrt{\nu}} - \frac{1}{\nu} e^{-\sqrt{\nu}\omega_n t}\right),$$

where

$$\nu = \frac{\zeta + \sqrt{\zeta^2 - 1}}{\zeta - \sqrt{\zeta^2 - 1}}.$$

The solutions of Eq. (3–25), when F_t increases linearly with time (ramp input) are given by the following.

Second-order system, ramp input: $F = C_1 t$.

$\zeta < 1$:

$$\frac{x\omega_n k}{C_1} = \frac{1}{\sqrt{1 - \zeta^2}} e^{-\zeta\omega_n t} \sin(\sqrt{1 - \zeta^2}\, \omega_n t + \phi) - 2\zeta + \omega_n t,$$

$$\tan \phi = \frac{\zeta\sqrt{1 - \zeta^2}}{\zeta^2 - 1/2}.$$

$\zeta = 1$:

$$\frac{x\omega_n k}{C_1} = (2 + \omega_n t)e^{-\omega_n t} + \omega_n t - 2. \qquad (3\text{-}32)$$

$\zeta > 1$:

$$\frac{x\omega_n k}{C_1} = \frac{\nu\sqrt{\nu}}{\nu - 1}\left[e^{-\omega_n t/\sqrt{\nu}} - \frac{1}{\nu^2} e^{-\sqrt{\nu}\omega_n t} \right] - \frac{\nu + 1}{\sqrt{\nu}} + \omega_n t,$$

$$\nu = \frac{\zeta + \sqrt{\zeta^2 - 1}}{\zeta - \sqrt{\zeta^2 - 1}}.$$

Similar solutions for an impulse input g are as follows.

Second-order system, impulse input: $g = \int_0^{\Delta t}_{\Delta t \to 0} F\, dt$.

$\zeta < 1$:

$$\frac{x\sqrt{mk}}{g} = \frac{1}{\sqrt{1 - \zeta^2}} e^{-\zeta\omega_n t} \sin(\sqrt{1 - \zeta^2}\, \omega_n t).$$

$\zeta = 1$:

$$\frac{x\sqrt{mk}}{g} = \omega_n t e^{-\omega_n t}. \qquad (3\text{-}33)$$

$\zeta > 1$:

$$\frac{x\sqrt{mk}}{g} = \frac{\sqrt{\nu}}{\nu - 1} e^{-\omega_n t/\sqrt{\nu}} - e^{-\sqrt{\nu}\omega_n t}.$$

Equations (3-31), (3-32), and (3-33) are plotted in Figs. 3-12, 3-13, and 3-14, for reference.

We saw earlier that for a first-order system subject to a ramp input, the dynamic error η (for 5% error, $\eta = 0.05$) was equal to τ/t for relatively large values of t. If we examine the response of the second-order system to a ramp input [Eq. (3-32)] for relatively large values of t, we find that the error η is equal to $2\zeta/\omega_n t$. This quantity can be reduced to c/kt, which is precisely equal to τ/t for the first-order system ($\tau = c/k$).

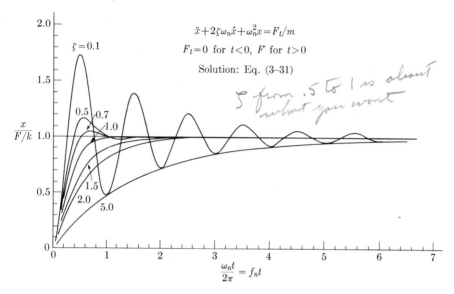

Fig. 3–12. Response of second-order system to "step" input.

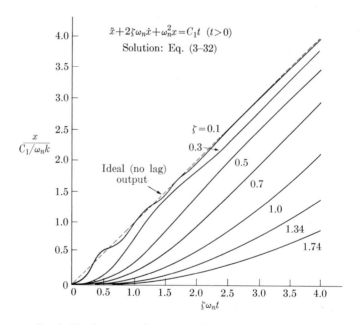

Fig. 3–13. Response of second-order system to "ramp" input.

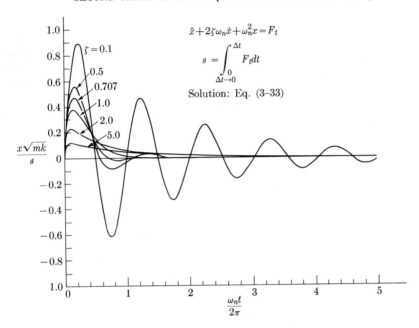

Fig. 3–14. Response of second-order system to "impulse" input.

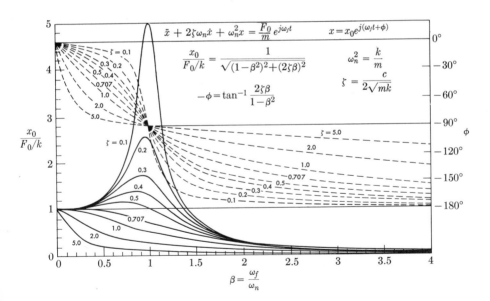

Fig. 3–15. Response of second-order system to a sinusoidal input, F_0 at frequency ω_f, rad/sec.

Hence, for a given damping ratio and natural frequency, we can calculate the time required to reach a certain accuracy. Conversely, if we know the time over which an input can be represented as a ramp, we can calculate the combination of natural frequency and damping ratio which will provide the desired accuracy.

(b) *Periodic inputs.* The response of a second-order system to a sinusoidal input can be calculated in the same manner as for the single-order system, except that we now combine Eqs. (3–10), (3–12), and (3–21) to give

$$\frac{x}{F_0/k} = \frac{e^{j(\omega_f t + \phi)}}{\sqrt{(1 - \beta^2)^2 + (2\zeta\beta)^2}}, \tag{3–34}$$

where

$$\beta = \frac{\omega_f}{\omega_n}, \quad \tan \phi = \frac{-2\zeta\beta}{1 - \beta^2}.$$

Equation (3–34) is represented in Fig. 3–15. We see here the occurrence of *resonance* in the vicinity of $\beta = 1$, that is, where the forcing frequency ω_f is nearly equal to the natural frequency ω_n. Extreme amplitudes will be reached unless either damping is introduced or the system operates at $\beta = 1$ for a very short time. In Eq. (3–34) it is assumed that the initial transients have died down.

3–3. Second-order systems (where input is a displacement)

If we now return to Fig. 3–10, and let $F_t = 0$, but let the "base" y be a movable member, we have the situation existing in most accelerometers and vibrometers. We shall look at the response of this system to sinusoidal variations of y at various frequencies ω_f. With these results in hand, we will be able to determine the suitability of a particular system for measuring vibrational effects.

First, we note that in this system we cannot measure x or y directly, but a displacement-measuring device placed between the mass and the base will measure $x - y$. Therefore we let

$$z = x - y. \tag{3–35}$$

Equation (3–22) can then be written as

$$m(\ddot{z} + \ddot{y}) + c(\dot{z}) + kz = 0, \tag{3–36}$$

or

$$\ddot{z} + 2\zeta\omega_n\dot{z} + \omega_n^2 z = -\ddot{y}. \tag{3–37}$$

The input y to the system varies sinusoidally:

$$y = y_0 e^{j\omega_f t}, \qquad \dot{y} = j\omega_f y_0 e^{j\omega_f t}, \qquad \ddot{y} = -\omega_f^2 y_0 e^{j\omega_f t}, \qquad (3\text{--}38)$$

and we assume the output to do likewise:

$$z = A e^{j\omega_f t}, \qquad \dot{z} = j\omega_f A e^{j\omega_f t}, \qquad \ddot{z} = -\omega_f^2 A e^{j\omega_f t}. \qquad (3\text{--}39)$$

Substituting (3–38) and (3–34) into (3–37) gives

$$-\omega_f^2 A + 2j\zeta\omega_n\omega_f A + \omega_n^2 A = \omega_f^2 y_0. \qquad (3\text{--}40)$$

If we let the frequency ratio $\omega_f/\omega_n = \beta$, then

$$\frac{A}{y_0} = \frac{\beta^2}{1 - \beta^2 + 2j\zeta\beta}. \qquad (3\text{--}41)$$

When Eq. (3–41) is rationalized by multiplying numerator and denominator by $(1 - \beta^2) - (2j\zeta\beta)$, we obtain

$$\frac{A}{y_0} = \frac{\beta^2(1 - \beta^2 - 2j\zeta\beta)}{(1 - \beta^2)^2 + (2\zeta\beta)^2}. \qquad (3\text{--}42)$$

The numerator of Eq. (3–42) can be transformed into

$$\beta^2\sqrt{(1 - \beta^2)^2 + (2\zeta\beta)^2}\ e^{j\phi},$$

thus giving

$$\frac{A}{y_0} = \frac{\beta^2 e^{j\phi}}{\sqrt{(1 - \beta^2)^2 + (2\zeta\beta)^2}} = \frac{z}{y}, \qquad (3\text{--}43)$$

$$\tan\phi = \frac{-2\zeta\beta}{1 - \beta^2}.$$

The amplitude ratio z_0/y_0 is plotted in Fig. 3–16, while the phase angle ϕ is the same as that shown in Fig. 3–15.

Vibrometer. If we want this system to have an output z proportional to input displacement y over a large range of input frequencies, we should pick a curve that is a horizontal line in Fig. 3–16. For very large β, all curves converge to $z_0/y_0 = 1$. Thus if we always operate above $\beta = 5$, the amplitude ratio will be within 5% of unity and the phase angle almost constant, even if we use very little damping ($\zeta < 0.1$). However, if there is a possibility that lower-frequency components may be present, a higher damping ratio is indicated. Unfortunately, this produces a noticeable phase shift with different frequencies. However, the useful frequency range (5% error) can be extended downward to $\beta = 1.2$ for $\zeta = 0.6$.

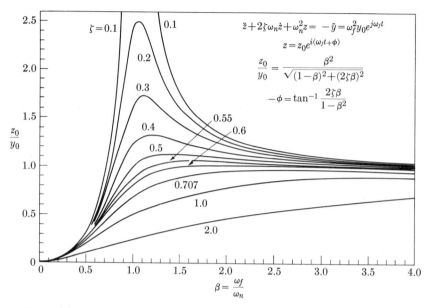

Fig. 3–16. Response of a second-order system to a sinusoidal motion of the supporting member. The input is y at frequency ω_f. The output z is the motion of the mass *relative* to the supporting member.

One of the great advantages in using a vibrometer for many vibration measurements is that it is *not limited* at the upper vibration frequency end: the higher the better. We will see that the reverse is true for accelerometers.

Velocity meter. In order that the output be proportional to velocity over a large frequency range, it is evident that the function $z/\dot{y}$ should be essentially constant, i.e.,

$$\frac{z}{\dot{y}} = \frac{z}{j\omega_f y} = -\frac{j}{\omega_f}\frac{\beta^2 e^{j\phi}}{\sqrt{(1-\beta^2)^2 + (2\zeta\beta)^2}}, \qquad (3\text{-}44)$$

$$\frac{z}{\dot{y}} = \frac{1}{\omega_n}\frac{\beta e^{j(\phi-\pi/2)}}{\sqrt{(1-\beta^2)^2 + (2\zeta\beta)^2}}.$$

From the above equation, we see that in order for $z/\dot{y}$ to be constant, z_0/y_0 must increase proportional to ω_f or to β. From Fig. 3–16, we see that in the vicinity of $\beta = 1$, the highly damped systems do have linear characteristics. At $\beta = 1$

$$\frac{z}{\dot{y}} = \frac{e^{-j\pi}}{2\zeta\omega_n} = -\frac{1}{2\zeta\omega_n}. \qquad (3\text{-}45)$$

The deviation of (3–44) from (3–45) is a measure of the accuracy of the device. For large damping ratios ($\zeta > 2$), it can be used as a velocity meter over a fairly large frequency range.

Accelerometers. In order that z be proportional to $\ddot{y}$, the following function must be held constant:

$$\frac{z}{\ddot{y}} = \frac{z}{-\omega_f^2 y} = \frac{1}{\omega_f^2} \frac{\beta^2 e^{-j\phi}}{\sqrt{(1 - \beta^2)^2 + (2\zeta\beta)^2}}, \tag{3–46}$$

$$\frac{z}{\ddot{y}} = -\frac{1}{\omega_n^2} \frac{e^{-j\phi}}{\sqrt{(1 - \beta^2)^2 + (2\zeta\beta)^2}}.$$

In Fig. 3–16, an ideal accelerometer would be represented by a parabola. For small values of β, all curves approximate parabolas. Again we have to compromise damping and frequency response to obtain the overall most useful device. In this instance, β will be less than unity, so that as we increase β, one term in the denominator of Eq. 3–46 will increase while the other will decrease and thus tend to compensate. If $\zeta = 0.6$, the error will be less than 2% for β up to 0.7.

We see then that a given mechanical transducer, often with an electrical output, will act differently in different frequency regions. At low frequencies relative to its natural frequency, it will act as an accelerometer; in the vicinity of resonance, it will provide an output proportional to velocity (if there is sufficient damping); while at high frequencies it will be a displacement meter or vibrometer. It is generally difficult to build devices that have either very high or very low natural frequencies. Hence, it is generally easier to measure acceleration at low frequencies and displacement at high frequencies than vice versa.

3–4. Compensating networks

We have seen that for rapidly varying input signals, the frequency response characteristics of a system limit its range of usefulness. In many mechanical measuring systems, the final frequency response limitation is that of the sensitivity of a displacement transducer; i.e., by increasing spring constants, higher frequency response could be obtained, but the deflection to be measured would decrease. However, there are other systems where the output signal is relatively large but where we cannot easily change the frequency response characteristics. This is often the case with temperature-measuring systems. If we have ample signal, or if we can amplify the signal substantially without introducing too much noise, it would seem possible to pass the signal through a "compensating network" which would effectively at-

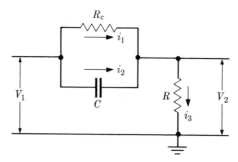

Fig. 3–17. Schematic drawing of a first-order compensating network.

tenuate, or filter out, lower frequencies more than high frequencies and thus render the system useful over a larger frequency range.

(a) *First-order system compensation.* We have seen that the dynamic characteristics of a first-order system, for example one with voltage output V_1, can be represented in the form [see Eq. (3–14a)]

$$\frac{V_1}{Sx} = \frac{1}{1 + j\omega_f\tau},\tag{3-47}$$

where $V_1 = Sx$ represents the steady-state voltage output of a system having any mechanical input x, ω_f is the frequency at which x varies, and τ is the mechanical system time constant $\tau = c/k$.

Figure 3–17 shows a "lead network" which will attenuate lower frequencies more than higher frequencies. We can readily analyze this system by noting that

$$V_2 = i_3R = (i_1 + i_2)R,$$
$$i_1 = (V_1 - V_2)/R_c,$$
$$i_2 = (V_1 - V_2)j\omega C.$$

Hence

$$V_2 = R(V_1 - V_2)\left(\frac{1}{R_c} + j\omega C\right), \qquad \frac{V_2}{V_1} = \frac{1 + j\omega\tau_c}{(R_c/R) + 1 + j\omega\tau_c},$$

where $\tau_c = R_cC$. If we let $\alpha = R/(R + R_c)$, then

$$\frac{V_2}{V_1} = \alpha\,\frac{1 + j\omega\tau_c}{1 + j\omega\alpha\tau_c}.\tag{3-48}$$

The result of feeding the transducer output V_1 through the compensating network is obtained by multiplying Eqs. (3–47) and (3–48), giving

$$\frac{V_2}{Sx} = \frac{\alpha(1 + j\omega\tau_c)}{(1 + j\omega\alpha\tau_c)(1 + j\omega\tau)}.\tag{3-49}$$

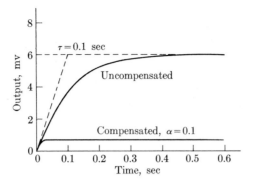

Fig. 3–18. Thermocouple output due to step input (32°F to 212°F).

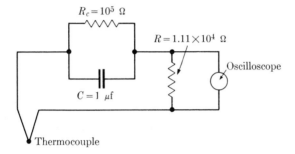

Fig. 3–19. A thermocouple with compensating network.

If we make $\tau = \tau_c$, two terms of Eq. (3–49) cancel, leaving

$$\frac{V_2}{Sx} = \frac{\alpha}{1 + j\omega(\alpha\tau)} . \qquad (3\text{–}50)$$

Thus, we still have a first-order system response, but if $\alpha < 1$, both the sensitivity and time constant have been reduced. If sufficient gain and signal to noise ratio are available, α can approach 10^{-2}.

EXAMPLE. Let us consider a thermocouple which responds to a step change in temperature, as shown in Fig. 3–18. The response is essentially first order with a time constant $\tau = 0.1$ sec.

If we are to use an oscilloscope having high sensitivity (0.1 mv/cm), we can attenuate the output of Fig. 3–18 by a factor of 10 and retain a readable output. Figure 3–19 shows the compensated system, designed to give $\alpha = 0.1$:

$$\alpha = \frac{R}{R + R_c} = 0.1, \qquad \tau = R_c C = 0.1.$$

Let $R_c = 10^5$ ohms. Then $R = 1.11 \times 10^4$ ohms, and $C = 10^{-6} = 1\ \mu\text{f}$.

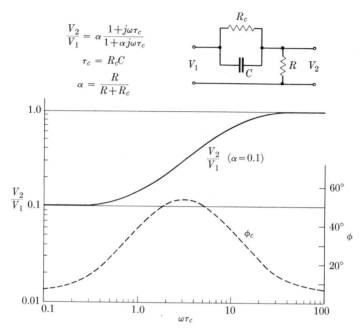

Fig. 3–20. Amplitude and phase characteristics of the compensating network shown in Fig. 3–17 ($\alpha = 0.1$).

The lower curve of Fig. 3–18 shows the compensated output. It is clear that we have gained frequency response at the expense of sensitivity.

The effect of a compensating network can be obtained by graphically superposing the logarithmic characteristics of the transducer and the network. Figure 3–20 shows the network frequency response curves for the single case $\alpha = 0.1$. When this curve is graphically added to that of Fig. 3–8, the curves of Fig. 3–21 are obtained. It is of particular interest to note that when $\tau_c > \tau$, the system will "overshoot," and have certain characteristics of a second-order system. For $\tau_c/\tau = 1.1$, the overshoot is about 5%, and the frequency response (for 5% maximum error) is extended, from $\omega\tau = 3.5$ when $\tau = \tau_c$, to $\omega\tau = 5.5$. Thus, judicious adjustment of τ_c can result in response characteristics even more favorable than those predicted from Eq. (3–50). For instance, by varying C (and thus τ_c) we can make the response of a thermocouple to a step input overshoot. The dynamic response is optimized when this overshoot is of the order of 5%.

Networks can also be devised which vary the frequency characteristics in such a way as to substantially change the output to some other

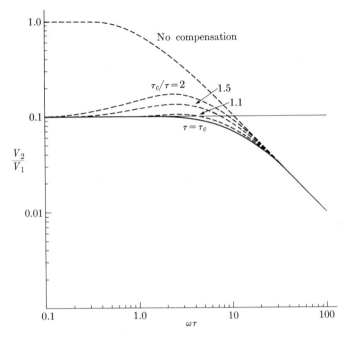

Fig. 3–21. System characteristics vary when the compensating time constant τ_c varies.

output. For instance, we saw that for very high-frequency vibrations, it is relatively easy to produce a vibrometer, or displacement meter, which will give output proportional to the displacement of the base, i.e., $V_1 = C_1 y$. If the output signal V_1 is differentiated with respect to time, we would have an output proportional to velocity. There are a number of ways to carry out differentiation or integration; we shall consider only methods involving passive networks.

The circuit shown in Fig. 3–22 can be considered a differentiating network if the read-out device draws negligible current, i.e., does not "load" the circuit.

We can see from the voltage diagram that

$$\frac{V_2}{V_1} = \sin \phi_1 e^{j(\pi/2 - \phi_1)}, \qquad \tan \phi_1 = RC\omega_f = \omega_f \tau. \qquad (3\text{–}51)$$

For $\omega_f \tau < 0.1$, $\sin \phi_1 \sim \tan \phi_1 \sim \phi_1$; thus

$$\frac{V_2}{V_1} = \omega_f \tau e^{j(\pi/2 - \omega_f \tau)}. \qquad (3\text{–}52)$$

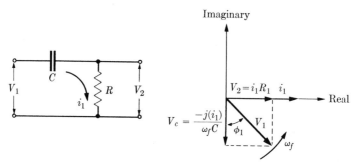

Fig. 3–22. A passive differentiating network.

If we combine this information with Eq. (3–43), then

$$\frac{V_2}{C_1 y} = \frac{\beta^2 \omega_f \tau e^{j(\pi/2 - \phi_1 - \phi)}}{\sqrt{(1 - \beta^2)^2 + (2\zeta\beta)^2}}. \tag{3-53}$$

Since $\dot{y} = j\omega_f y$,

$$\frac{V_2}{C_1 \dot{y}} = \frac{-j\beta^2 \tau e^{j(\pi/2 - \phi_1 - \phi)}}{\sqrt{(1 - \beta^2)^2 + (2\zeta\beta)^2}}; \tag{3-54}$$

but $-j = e^{-j\pi/2}$ and

$$\frac{V_2}{C_1 \dot{y}} = \frac{\beta^2 \tau e^{-j(\phi + \phi_1)}}{\sqrt{(1 - \beta^2)^2 + (2\zeta\beta)^2}}. \tag{3-55}$$

For large values of β, Eq. (3–55) can be approximated by

$$\frac{V_2}{C_1 \dot{y}} = \tau e^{-j(\pi + \omega_f \tau)} \tag{3-56}$$

and the output V_2 is essentially proportional to input velocity $\dot{y}$. Using similar reasoning, if the output $V_1 = C_1 z$ from an accelerometer [Eq. (3–46)] is fed (cascaded) through a simple integrating network, which is similar to Fig. 3–22 except that the capacitor C is replaced with an inductance L, we again obtain an output proportional to velocity,

$$\frac{V_2}{C_1 \dot{y}} = \frac{R}{L} \frac{1}{\omega_n^2} \frac{e^{j(\phi - \phi_2)}}{\sqrt{(1 - \beta^2)^2 + (2\zeta\beta)^2}}, \tag{3-57}$$

where $\tan \phi_2 = R/\omega_f L$ and must be less than 0.1.

(b) *Second-order system compensation.* There are a number of ways in which the output from second-order systems can be compensated to extend or improve the frequency response. In any real situation it is impossible to perfectly match an electrical network to a mechanical system. Hence, the results will not be as good as theory will predict. Compensating networks, particularly second-order networks, should only be employed when it is either impossible or impracticable to obtain an uncompensated system having the desired characteristics. A poorly matched second-order compensating network can easily produce poorer response characteristics than a noncompensated system.

Networks can be used to increase or decrease the apparent damping in a system, or can be used to provide an input, to a galvanometer, which is greater at higher frequencies, thus extending the apparent galvanometer response.

Many transducers are built with damping insufficient for optimum performance. The network shown in Fig. 3–23 can be used to increase the apparent damping. In essence, the series RCL shunt is tuned to be conducting at frequencies near $\beta = 1$ for the mechanical system. The analyses of this "notch filter" (so named from the shape of its frequency response curve) is quite simple if negligible current flows through the output circuit. The circuit current i is given by

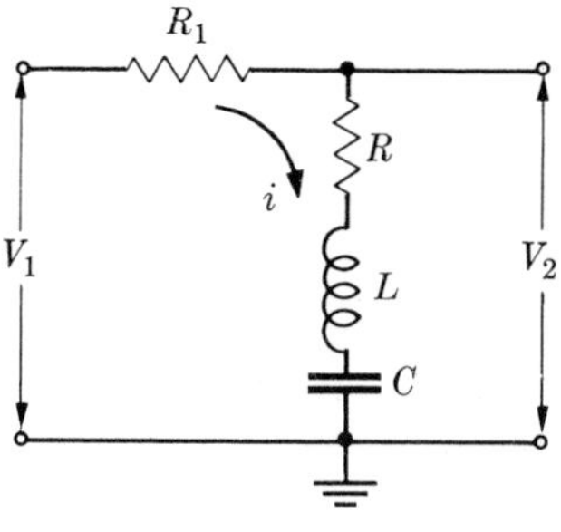

Fig. 3–23. A passive "notch filter" for increasing the apparent damping in a second-order system.

$$i = \frac{V_1}{R_1 + R + j\omega L - j/\omega C}, \quad (3\text{–}58)$$

$$V_2 = V_1 - iR_1. \quad (3\text{–}59)$$

Hence

$$\frac{V_2}{V_1} = \frac{R + j\omega L - j/\omega C}{R_1 + R + j\omega L - j/\omega C}. \quad (3\text{–}60)$$

If we let

$$\omega_{n_1} = \sqrt{\frac{1}{LC}},$$

then

$$\beta_1 = \frac{\omega}{\omega_{n_1}}, \quad \zeta_1 = \frac{R}{2\sqrt{L/C}}, \quad \zeta_2 = \frac{R + R_1}{2\sqrt{L/C}},$$

$$\frac{V_2}{V_1} = \frac{1 - \beta_1^2 + 2j\zeta_1\beta_1}{1 - \beta_1^2 + 2j\zeta_2\beta_1}. \quad (3\text{–}61)$$

The numerator of Eq. (3–61) can be adjusted to cancel the characteristic of a mechanical second-order system, leaving a new second-order system having higher damping ($\zeta_2 > \zeta_1$).

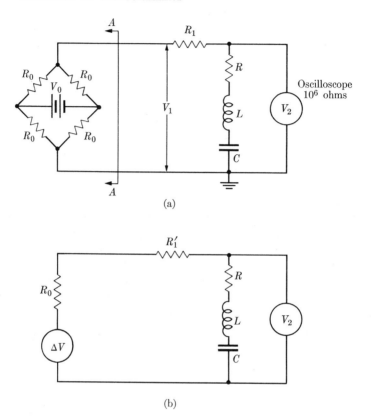

Fig. 3–24. Bridge network with compensation: (a) actual network; (b) bridge replaced by its equivalent as seen from AA.

EXAMPLE. Let us consider a strain-gage force transducer having the following characteristics:

(1) Four-active-arm, 120-ohm bridge excited by a d-c voltage of 5 volts.

(2) Sensitivity of 10^{-6} volt/volt/lb; maximum load 1000 lb; natural frequency, 1000 cps; damping ratio $= 0.1$.

(3) Output to be recorded on an oscilloscope having maximum sensitivity of 0.2 mv/cm and input impedance of 10^6 ohms.

Our problem is to design a compensating network that will improve the dynamic response characteristics of the system. Because of the extremely low damping, vibrations of the transducer at its natural frequency will greatly obscure events taking place during times of the order of the natural period of the transducer. Our first step will, therefore, be to increase the "apparent" transducer damping. The circuit shown in Fig. 3–24(a) can accomplish this. In order to simplify our calculations, we can replace the bridge circuit by its equivalent as shown in Fig. 3–24(b). When we look to the left

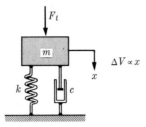

Fig. 3–25. Schematic view of a force transducer.

at AA, we see a net resistance R_0 in series with a voltage source ΔV, the bridge output voltage, which is proportional to the dynamometer displacement x. Under steady-state conditions, the output ΔV is related to the input F by the sensitivity $\Delta V/V_0 = SF$. For the dynamic system shown in Fig. 3–25, we can write:

$$m\ddot{x} + c\dot{x} + kx = F_t,$$

or

$$\ddot{x} + 2\zeta\omega_n\dot{x} + \omega_n^2 x = F_t/m.$$

Using the procedure previously developed, we assume that

$$F_t = F_0 e^{j\omega_f t}, \qquad x_t = Ae^{j\omega_f t},$$

and through manipulation we obtain

$$\frac{x_t}{F_t/k} = \frac{1}{1 - \beta^2 + 2j\zeta\beta} \equiv \frac{\Delta V/V_0}{SF_t},$$

where

$$\beta = \frac{\omega_f}{\omega_n} = \frac{\omega_f}{\sqrt{k/m}}, \qquad \zeta = \frac{c}{2\sqrt{km}}.$$

We can now find the output V_2 from the compensating network:

$$\frac{V_2}{\Delta V} \times \frac{\Delta V/V_0}{SF_t} = \frac{V_2/V_0}{SF_t} = \frac{1 - \beta_1^2 + 2j\zeta_1\beta_1}{1 - \beta^2 + 2j\zeta_2\beta_1} \times \frac{1}{1 - \beta^2 + 2j\zeta\beta}.$$

It is clear that if we match the electrical and mechanical systems so that $\beta = \beta_1$, that is, $k/m = 1/LC$ and $\zeta = \zeta_1$, that is,

$$c/2\sqrt{km} = R/2\sqrt{L/C}$$

or

$$\frac{c}{R} = \frac{m}{L},$$

two of the terms in the above equation will cancel, leaving another second-

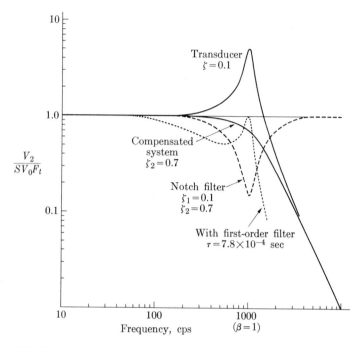

Fig. 3–26. Showing how the apparent damping of a transducer can be increased.

order system having greater damping than the original. For the problem at hand

$$\omega_n = 6280, \qquad \zeta = 0.1.$$

If we let $L = 0.1$ henries, then $C = 0.0253 \ \mu f$ and $R = 125$ ohms. For $\zeta_2 = 0.7$, $R_1 = 750$ [Eq. (3–61)]. For this example, we should note (Figs. 3–23 and 3–24) that $R_1 = R_1' + R_0$; hence

$$R_1' = 630 \text{ ohms}.$$

In a real device, the spring k, the dashpot c, the resistor R, and the inductor L will not be "pure" linear devices. Hence, the cancellation of effects will never be perfect. However, large linear effects can be removed.

In order to show graphically what has been accomplished, Fig. 3–26 shows the system frequency response before and after compensation. The dashed curve is that for the "notch" filter alone.

When a low-impedance galvanometer is employed, the analysis for compensation is somewhat more complex. Here we must provide the circuit resistance required for proper galvanometer damping, and must also take into account current flow through the galvanometer (as this is what drives the galvanometer). However, a notch filter is still applicable.

When we simply wish to reduce the apparent system response in the vicinity of $\beta = 1$, without concern for the maximum frequency response, we can introduce a very simple first-order compensating or damping circuit. Consider the circuit of Fig. 3–24 with $R_1' = R = L = 0$, so that only R_0 and C remain in the circuit. It is easily shown that for this case,

$$\frac{V_2}{\Delta V} = \frac{1}{\sqrt{1 + (\omega\tau)^2}},$$

where $\tau = R_0 C$. For our example, at $\beta = 1$, the transducer output is too great by a factor of 5. Let us then set

$$\frac{V_2}{\Delta V} = \tfrac{1}{5} \quad \text{at } \beta = 1 \quad (1000 \text{ cps}),$$

$$\omega\tau = 4.9, \quad \tau = 7.8 \times 10^{-4} \text{ sec}, \quad C = 6.5 \ \mu\text{f}.$$

The dotted curve in Fig. 3–26 represents the system with this first-order filter. It is clear that while we can reduce the resonance condition, we reduce the useful frequency range to below about 60 cps.

3–5. Harmonic analysis

Any cyclicly varying quantity can be considered to be the sum of a number of simple sinusoidal components at different frequencies and amplitudes. In our various dynamic analyses, we consider the response of systems to sinusoidal inputs of various frequencies. Hence, if we obtain a cyclic output from a system, and if we could analyze that output to determine the amplitude, frequency, and phase relations of the components making up the output, we would understand the input better, and we would know if our system had sufficient response to faithfully reproduce the input. Even if the system had insufficient response, we could theoretically work "backward" to determine the input. This latter step may be impractical, partially because of the work involved, but mostly because of the necessity of knowing the *exact* dynamic characteristics of the system.

The steps involved in making a harmonic analysis are quite simple. Although the entire operation may appear to be quite tedious, study of the example given below will show that a relatively small amount of computation can yield significant results.

Any cyclic quantity f_t can be written as

$$f_t = A_0 + \sum_{n=1}^{\infty} (A_n \cos n\omega t + B_n \sin n\omega t), \qquad (3\text{–}62)$$

where A_0, A_n, B_n are the Fourier, or harmonic, coefficients, and ω is the fundamental, or lowest, frequency present. Thus one complete cycle occurs during the time period $T = 2\pi/\omega$.

It is easy to determine ω by observing the time required for a given number of cycles.

The average A_0 of f_t is given by

$$A_0 = \frac{1}{2\pi} \int_0^T f_t \, dt. \tag{3-63}$$

It is convenient to let $\omega t = \theta$, where $\theta = 2\pi$ represents one cycle. Then $f_t = f_\theta$ and

$$A_0 = \frac{1}{2\pi} \int_0^{2\pi} f_\theta \, d\theta. \tag{3-64}$$

The coefficients A_n and B_n are given by

$$A_n = \frac{1}{\pi} \int_0^{2\pi} f_\theta \cos (n\theta) \, d\theta, \tag{3-65}$$

$$B_n = \frac{1}{\pi} \int_0^{2\pi} f_\theta \sin (n\theta) \, d\theta. \tag{3-66}$$

While it is possible to evaluate A_0, A_n, B_n graphically, it is generally easier to use numerical methods where $d\theta$ is replaced by $\Delta\theta$; the smaller $\Delta\theta$, the more precise the results. A value of $\Delta\theta = 10°$ will generally be found to be convenient. For this condition, f_θ is determined from the curve at $k = 36$ equally spaced values of θ. Then

$$A_0 = \frac{\Delta\theta}{360} [f_{\theta=0} + f_{\theta=\Delta\theta} + f_{\theta=2\Delta\theta} + \cdots],$$

$$A_0 = \frac{\Delta\theta}{360} \sum_{k=0}^{k=360/\Delta\theta} f_{\theta=k\Delta\theta}, \tag{3-67}$$

$$A_n = \frac{\Delta\theta}{180} \sum_{k=0}^{k=360/\Delta\theta} f_\theta \cos (n\theta)_{\theta=k\Delta\theta}, \tag{3-68}$$

$$B_n = \frac{\Delta\theta}{180} \sum_{k=0}^{k=360/\Delta\theta} f_\theta \sin (n\theta)_{\theta=k\Delta\theta}. \tag{3-69}$$

If an array of columns is set up headed by θ, f_θ, $\cos\theta$, $\sin\theta$, $f_\theta \cos\theta$, $f_\theta \sin\theta$, $\cos 2\theta$, $f_\theta \cos 2\theta$, etc., the actual arithmetic will be quite simple, albeit tedious.

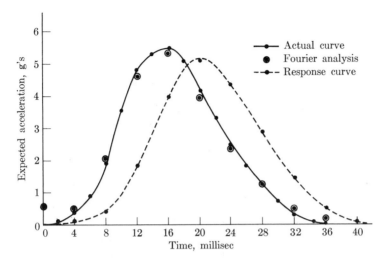

Fig. 3–27. Fourier analysis of pulse response.

Having determined A_0, A_n, B_n, we can simplify Eq. (3–62) by writing f_t as a cosine series, where

$$f_t = A_0 + \sum_{n=1}^{\infty} C_n \cos (n\omega t - \phi_n), \qquad (3\text{–}70)$$

where

$$C_n = \sqrt{A_n^2 + B_n^2}, \quad \text{and} \quad \phi_n = \tan^{-1}\left(\frac{B_n}{A_n}\right).$$

EXAMPLE 1. In order to demonstrate a number of points brought forth in this chapter, we consider a relatively complex problem. Let us assume that we are considering purchase of an accelerometer whose specifications are $f_n = 50$ cps ($\omega_n = 314$ rad/sec), $\zeta = 0.7$, and range $= \pm 10$ g.

With this accelerometer we expect to measure an acceleration pulse of 0.036 sec duration having an expected shape approximately as shown in Fig. 3–27. We ask: How well should this particular accelerometer respond to this input?

While there are various ways of looking at this problem, let us start by making a harmonic analysis of the curve of Fig. 3–27. We can do this by considering the pulse to be a single cycle of a continuing wave. While this method will *not* be exact, it can provide a good approximation. For simplicity here, we let $\Delta\theta = 20°$ (the pulse duration of 36 millisec makes the numbers easier!).

Table 3–1 shows the numerical quantities necessary for computing the first four Fourier terms. There is apt to be ambiguity as to the phase angle ϕ_n because a positive tangent can be in either the first or third quadrant, while a negative tangent can be in either the second or fourth quadrant. A 180° error

TABLE 3–1

Fourier Analysis–Example Data

$$\Delta\theta = 20°, \quad k = 0 \rightarrow 18, \quad \frac{\Delta\theta}{360} = \frac{1}{18}, \quad \frac{\Delta\theta}{180} = \frac{1}{9}$$

0°	$f(\theta)$ (accel, g)	$\cos\theta$	$\sin\theta$	$f(\theta)\cos\theta$	$f(\theta)\sin\theta$	$\cos 2\theta$	$f(\theta)\cos 2\theta$
0	0	1	0	0	0	1.0	0
20	0.1	0.940	0.342	0.09	0.03	0.761	0.08
40	0.4	0.761	0.633	0.31	0.25	0.174	0.07
60	0.9	0.50	0.866	0.45	0.78	−0.50	−0.45
80	1.9	0.174	0.985	0.33	1.87	−0.940	−1.79
100	3.6	−0.174	0.985	−0.63	3.54	−0.94	−3.39
120	4.8	−0.50	0.866	−2.40	4.16	−0.50	−2.40
140	5.3	−0.761	0.633	−4.03	3.36	0.174	0.92
160	5.5	−0.940	0.342	−5.17	1.88	0.761	4.18
180	5.1	−1	0	−5.10	0	1.00	5.10
200	4.2	−0.940	−0.342	−3.95	−1.44	0.761	3.20
220	3.3	−0.761	−0.633	−2.51	−2.09	0.174	0.57
240	2.5	−0.50	−0.866	−1.25	−2.17	−0.50	−1.25
260	1.9	−0.174	−0.985	−0.33	−1.87	−0.94	−1.79
280	1.3	0.174	−0.985	0.23	−1.28	−0.94	−1.22
300	0.8	0.50	−0.860	0.40	−0.69	−0.50	−0.40
320	0.3	0.761	−0.633	2.28	−0.19	0.174	−0.05
340	0.1	0.940	−0.342	0.09	−0.03	0.761	0.08
	$\sum f(\theta) = 42.0$			$\sum f(\theta)\cos\theta$ $= -21.19$	$\sum f(\theta)\sin\theta$ $= +6.11$		$\sum f(\theta)\cos 2\theta$ $= +1.50$

$$A_0 = \frac{42.0}{18} \qquad\qquad A_1 = \frac{-21.19}{9}, \quad B_1 = \frac{+6.11}{9} \qquad\qquad A_2 = \frac{+1.50}{9}$$

$$A_0 = 2.33 \qquad\qquad A_1 = -2.35, \quad B_1 = +0.68 \qquad\qquad A_2 = +0.167$$

$$C_1 = \sqrt{A_1^2 + B_1^2} = 2.45$$

TABLE 3-1

(*Continued*)

sin 2θ	$f(\theta)$ sin 2θ	cos 3θ	$f(\theta)$ cos 3θ	sin 3θ	$f(\theta)$ sin 3θ
0	0	1.0	0	0	0
0.633	0.06	0.50	0.05	0.866	0.09
0.985	0.39	−0.50	−0.20	0.866	0.37
0.866	0.78	−1.0	−0.90	0	0
0.342	0.65	−0.5	−0.95	−0.866	−1.65
−0.342	−1.23	0.5	1.80	−0.866	−3.12
−0.866	−4.15	1.0	4.80	0	0
−0.985	−5.22	0.5	2.65	0.866	4.60
−0.633	−3.65	−0.5	−2.25	0.866	4.77
0	0	−1.0	−5.10	0	0
0.633	2.68	−0.5	−2.20	−0.866	−3.64
0.985	3.25	0.5	1.65	−0.866	−2.86
0.866	2.17	1.0	2.50	0	0
0.342	0.65	0.5	0.95	0.866	1.65
−0.342	−0.44	−0.5	−0.65	0.866	1.13
−0.866	−0.69	−1.0	−0.80	0	0
−0.985	−0.30	−0.5	−0.15	−0.866	−0.26
−0.633	−0.06	0.5	0.05	−0.866	−0.09
	$\sum f(\theta)$ sin 2θ $= -5.11$		$\sum f(\theta)$ cos 3θ $= +0.75$		$\sum f(\theta)$ sin 3θ $= +1.00$

$$B_2 = \frac{-5.11}{9} \qquad A_3 = \frac{+0.75}{9} \qquad B_3 = \frac{+1.00}{9}$$

$$B_2 = -0.568 \qquad A_3 = +0.0833 \qquad B_3 = +0.111$$

$$C_2 = \sqrt{A_2^2 + B_2^2} = 0.592 \qquad\qquad C_3 = \sqrt{A_3^2 + B_3^2} = 0.139$$

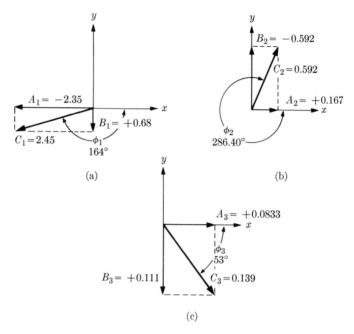

Fig. 3–28. Phase relationships within Fourier terms.

in phase angle will change the sign of the cosine Fourier term. One of the simplest methods to avoid this ambiguity is to recall that

$$\cos \theta = (\text{Real part of}) \ (e^{j\theta}),$$
$$\sin \theta = (\text{Real part of}) \ (-je^{j\theta}).$$

Hence if we plot $+A_n$ in the $+x$ direction, and $+B_n$ in the $-y$ direction, the proper phase angle will be seen. Figure 3–28 shows the terms for this example. Equation (3–70) is given in terms of a *lagging* phase angle $-\phi_n$; hence we must determine how far C_n lags behind the cosine term $+A_n$ which is the $+x$-axis. Thus

$$\phi_1 = 164°,$$
$$\phi_2 = 286.4° \text{ or } -73.6°,$$
$$\phi_3 = 53°.$$

The Fourier equation then becomes

$$f_\theta = a = 2.33 + 2.45 \cos (\theta - 164) + 0.592 \cos (2\theta + 73.6)$$
$$+ 0.139 \cos (3\theta - 53°).$$

Because $\cos (\alpha + 180) = -\cos \alpha$, we can change the sign of C_1 by adding

TABLE 3–2

n	ω_f	β	$\omega_n^2 z/y$	ϕ
0	0	0	1	0°
1	175	0.577	0.96	49°
2	350	1.114	0.63	99°
3	525	1.671	0.34	127°

180° to the phase angle, giving

$$f_\theta = 2.33 - 2.45 \cos (\theta + 16) + 0.592 \cos (2\theta + 73.6)$$
$$+ 0.139 \cos (3\theta - 53°).$$

It should be clear that additional terms ($n = 4, 5, 6, \ldots$) would provide a more accurate representation of the actual curve. Points from this equation are represented by the hollow circles in Fig. 3–27. It is evident that the above equation represents the pulse curve quite well.

We now must establish the frequency response (amplitude and phase) of the accelerometer to the Fourier input components. The basic frequency of the input is 27.8 cps or 175 rad/sec $= \omega_1$.

Table 3–2 shows the response of the accelerometer as calculated from Eq. (3–46). When the Fourier input equation is altered according to these values, we have

$$a_{\text{out}} = 2.33 - 2.45 \times 0.96 \cos (\theta + 16 - 49) + 0.592 \times 0.63$$
$$\times \cos (2\theta + 74 - 99) + 0.139 \times 0.34 \cos (3\theta - 53 - 127).$$

This can be reduced to

$$a_{\text{out}} = 2.33 - 2.35 \cos (\theta - 33) + 0.37 \cos (2\theta - 25) - 0.047 \cos (3\theta).$$

The solid points in Fig. 3–27 are from this equation. We see that the maximum indicated response is low by about 10%, and the shape of the curve is quite distorted; the highest slope portion being greatly misrepresented. We can also see that this method is fundamentally not exactly correct because we are assuming that the pulse is one cycle of a continuous wave. This assumption gives rise to the indicated response at zero time.

If we are primarily interested in having the output correspond closely in maximum amplitude, doubling the natural frequency of the accelerometer will give a satisfactory system. However, if we want the shape of the curve to be reproduced at the proper times within perhaps 5% of the actual value, we will have to use an accelerometer having a much higher natural frequency.

A simple method for determining just what characteristics are necessary in order to obtain the desired accuracy is briefly mentioned in Chapter 5, and will be considered here.

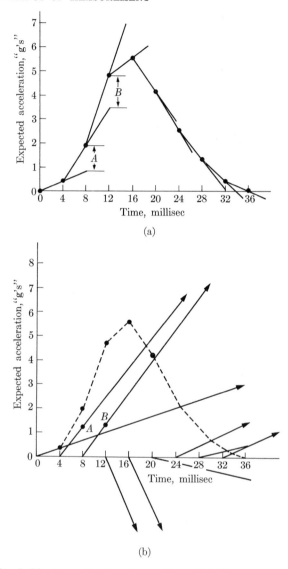

Fig. 3–29. Approximation of curve by straight line segments.

From the assumed curve of Fig. 3–27, we determine the least number of points that we feel would be necessary to draw a response curve to our satisfaction. These points are to be equally spaced in time. For Fig. 3–27 we have taken 10 points spaced every 4 millisec as shown in Fig. 3–29(a). If the curve is approximated by a series of straight lines, we can say that it is composed of the sum of a series of linearly increasing accelerations. In Fig. 3–29(b)

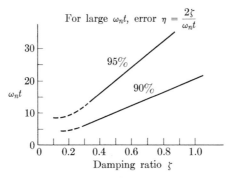

Fig. 3–30. Time required for a second-order output to reach a given portion of the input.

we see one linearly increasing acceleration starting at time zero, and others every 4 millisec. It is evident that the sum of the various components in Fig. 3–29(b) is equal to the curve of Fig. 3–29(a). If we assume that the physical system is represented by a linear differential equation of the type we have considered, then the response to the curve of Fig. 3–29(a) will be the same as the sum of the responses to the series of linear accelerations in Fig. 3–29(b). We know that the response of a second-order system to a linearly increasing input is as given in Eq. (3–32). Hence by analogy, when the input y to Eq. (3–37) is also a linearly increasing quantity, we know that the solution must be as in Eq. (3–32) with the following *substitutions:*

$$z \text{ substituted for } x, \quad \ddot{y} = C_2 t \text{ substituted for } \frac{F}{m} = \frac{C_1 t}{m}.$$

Therefore,

$$\frac{z \omega_n k}{C_2 m} = \frac{z \omega_n^3}{C_2} \text{ substituted for } \frac{x \omega_n k}{C_1}.$$

Thus for $\zeta < 1$, Eq. (3–32) can be written as

$$\frac{z \omega_n^3}{C_2} = \frac{1}{\sqrt{1 - \zeta^2}} e^{-\zeta \omega_n t} \sin \left(\sqrt{1 - \zeta^2}\, \omega_n t + \phi \right) - 2\zeta + \omega_n t,$$

$$\tan \phi = \frac{\zeta \sqrt{1 - \zeta^2}}{(\zeta^2)\, -1/2}. \tag{3–71}$$

If both sides of Eq. (3–71) are divided by $\omega_n t$, we obtain a dimensionless output/input ratio:

$$\frac{\omega_n^2 z}{\ddot{y}} = 1 - \frac{2\zeta}{\omega_n t} + \frac{1}{\omega_n t \sqrt{1 - \zeta^2}} e^{-\zeta \omega_n t} \sin \left(\sqrt{1 - \zeta^2}\, \omega_n t + \phi \right). \tag{3–72}$$

Figure 3–30 shows $\omega_n t$ as a function of ζ for the condition that $\omega_n^2 z / \ddot{y}$ is 90%

or 95%. (The data in Chapter 5 are the same.) We see that for 5% error when $\zeta = 0.7$, $\omega_n t \approx 28$. Therefore for each of the time increments in Fig. 3–16, we must have $\omega_n t \geq 28$). As we have picked an interval of 4×10^{-3} sec,

$$\omega_n t = 28, \qquad t = 0.004,$$

$$\omega_n = \frac{28}{0.004} = 7000 \text{ rad/sec,}$$

$$f_n \approx 1000 \text{ cps.}$$

All things taken into account, we should not purchase the accelerometer!

3–6. Dynamic data analysis

It is certainly not possible here to list all of the methods that researchers might use to analyze dynamical data. Often we find that very costly data are given only a casual perusal. Other times, peak values are extracted from the data, or the data are averaged, or perhaps two records are simply compared visually. The reason behind such simple-minded use of expensive data is that we often do not know how to analyze the data, and perhaps might not know what to do with the analyzed data. As we have previously pointed out, we *should* have *beforehand* a plan of how the data will be used, and what it will mean.

Any dynamic data (recordings, oscillographic traces, etc.) will be composed of the transducer output signal (which may or may not truly represent the input) plus various extraneous, or noise, signals. "Noise" arises from a variety of sources, and varies greatly from setup to setup. It can arise from such sources as: moving leads, electric fields, magnetic fields, radiation, mechanical vibration including sound waves, thermal noise produced in resistors and inductors, a-c filament voltages, etc.

There are many instances where the noise is produced by the occurrence to be measured. For instance, measurement of current flow and voltages or mechanical pressures caused by a spark discharge can give rise to serious problems. The occurrence (spark) produces noise (electromagnetic and sound waves) which does not exist prior to the occurrence. Hence, it is easy to fall into the trap of assuming that because the noise level is insignificant before and after the measured occurrence, it is also insignificant during the occurrence. In order to check for the existence of this type of noise, it is necessary to replace the transducer with a mockup device that is similar in all respects to the actual transducer (electrically, magnetically, etc.) except that it will have *no* output from the input signal that one desires to measure. If this system gives negligible output when the occurrence takes place, we can be reasonably sure that the noise level is acceptably low. It can be very difficult to perform the above test in some instances, and it may be necessary to employ several different transducers and analyze their relative outputs in order to establish the noise level.

If the noise level is acceptably low, we are still always faced with the question of whether or not the recorded output signal is a faithful dynamic record of the input signal. Previously in this chapter, we have seen what can be done beforehand to estimate the dynamic capabilities of the system. If the noise level is sufficiently low, and if we know the dynamic characteristics of the transducer, we can "work backward" to determine what the actual input must have been in order to give us the recorded output. The accuracy of this method depends on the accuracy to which we know the transducer dynamic characteristics. The method is really quite simple, and is perhaps best demonstrated by an example. Let us consider the same acceleration pulse problem that was analyzed previously in this chapter. We shall assume that we are using the accelerometer having as dynamic characteristics

$$f_n = 50 \text{ cps}, \quad \text{(i.e., } \omega_n = 314 \text{ rad/sec)}, \quad \zeta = 0.7.$$

The dashed curve of Fig. 3–27 is the output that would be obtained from the transducer. We shall take this curve and "work backward" to approximate the actual input. We have shown that the accelerometer response is represented by Eq. (3–37):

$$\ddot{z} + 2\zeta\omega_n\dot{z} + \omega_n^2 z = -\ddot{y}.$$

The recorded output curve is actually a plot of $\omega_n^2 z$. This is equal (in magnitude) to $\ddot{y}$ only when $\ddot{z} = \dot{z} = 0$. Thus in order to obtain the true value of $\ddot{y}$, we must *add* to $\omega_n^2 z$ the sum $\ddot{z} + 2\zeta\omega_n\dot{z}$. Because the output is proportional to z, we can graphically differentiate the $\omega_n^2 z$ curve to obtain $\omega_n^2\dot{z}$ and $\omega_n^2\ddot{z}$. Thus, we find the magnitude of $\ddot{y}$ to be

$$-\ddot{y} = (\omega_n^2 z) + \frac{2\zeta}{\omega_n}(\omega_n^2\dot{z}) + \frac{1}{\omega_n^2}(\omega_n^2\ddot{z}).$$

In Fig. 3–31 we have graphically shown the three terms in the above equation and their sum. The sum is represented by the solid data points, while the solid line is the actual input as taken from Fig. 3–27. It is clear that for this rather idealized case, the improvement is tremendous. We must remember, however, that the correction process here involves differentiation of a signal. Relatively small signal variations due to noise will greatly affect the derivative of the signal, and will

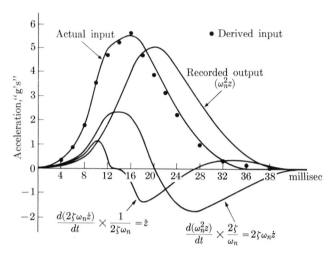

Fig. 3–31. Graphical determination of actual input from recorded output.

tremendously affect the second derivative. Hence, an operation of this type can be realistically conducted only on a "smooth" noiseless curve. For these purposes, it is perfectly realistic to visually "smooth" a noisy output curve, so long as we are sure that in doing so we are removing noise and not signal variation. It is frequently possible to filter a large portion of the noise from the signal by employing the simple RC network discussed in the latter part of "compensating networks." We must ensure, however, that the filter attenuates only frequencies above those to which the transducer will readily respond. If the filter is permitted to attenuate within the useful range of the transducer, the combined transducer-filter frequency response must be employed when "working backward."

Analytic methods, such as these, cannot be employed to extend the response characteristics of a transducer indefinitely. They must be used only when the corrective terms are small compared with the primary output. We generally cannot determine the slope of a recorded curve to a precision greater than 10% to 20%. If we want the final result to deviate from true by less than 5%, we can establish the rough limitation that

$$\pm 20\%(\ddot{z}, 2\zeta\omega_n\dot{z}) < 5\%(\omega_n^2 z), \qquad \ddot{z}_{\max}, 2\zeta\omega_n\dot{z}_{\max} < \frac{\omega_n^2 z}{4}.$$

For the example shown (Fig. 3–31), there is one zone where $|2\zeta\omega_n\dot{z}| \approx \omega_n^2 z$. Hence, we should probably not expect the result to be correct to within 5%.

Output data recordings can also be analyzed through use of Fourier analysis in a method exactly the reverse of that previously described. Namely, the output can be obtained from the record as Fourier series; then the input required to produce each output term is calculated; these input terms are then summed up paying careful attention to phase. This method is particularly useful when the response characteristics have been empirically determined in the form of amplitude ratio and phase angle versus frequency curves. If the response curves indicate a classic first- or second-order system having substantial damping, the graphical method will involve less work than the Fourier method. If the system has little damping, no method will give good results when there are significant Fourier terms near $\beta = 1$.

PROBLEMS

1. A thermocouple, having first-order response characteristics, is to be used to measure a single temperature pulse, having a sinusoidal shape (half-wave). The duration of the pulse T is equal to four time constants τ of the thermocouple ($T = 4\tau$). Determine the response of the thermocouple to the pulse using graphical techniques. Compare a plot of the actual response to that which would be obtained assuming the pulse to be part of a continuous sinusoidal input.

2. Plot the amplitude ratio V_2/V_1 and the phase between V_2 and V_1 as functions of frequency for the two simple filters shown in Fig. 3–32. Assume that the impedance of the source (at V_1) is small, while the impedance of the output device (at V_2) is large. [*Ans.* (a) $V_2/V_1 = e^{j\phi}/\sqrt{1 + (RC\omega)^2}$; $\tan \phi = -RC\omega$. (b) $V_2/V_1 = e^{j\phi}/\sqrt{1 + (1/RC\omega)^2}$; $\tan \phi = 1/RC\omega$.]

3. A first-order thermocouple (τ) is subject to an input of maximum value T_0 and of duration 7τ as shown in Fig. 3–33. Plot the output as a function of time.

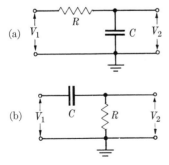

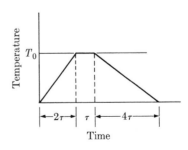

Fig. 3–32. $V_1 = V_{1_0}e^{j\omega_f t}$.   Figure 3–33

4. The damping ratio of lowly damped second-order systems is often determined experimentally by subjecting the system to an impulsive type input and noting the decay curve. Determine the damping ratio ζ as a function of amplitude reduction per cycle. [*Ans.* $\zeta/\sqrt{1 - \zeta^2} = (1/2\pi) \ln (x_n/x_{n+1})$.]

5. Devise three practical methods for experimentally determining the natural frequency and damping ratio of an accelerometer.

6. It is often considered desirable to have the phase lag in a device vary linearly with input frequency. Why is this advantageous? [*Hint:* Phase distortion causes errors in wave form or *shape*. Fourier analysis will show advantage.]

7. Design a linear accelerometer, having $\zeta = 0.6$, utilizing wire-resistance strain gages, and having as high a natural frequency as you can obtain. (a) 10^{-6} in./in. strain corresponding to 1 g acceleration; (b) 10^{-6} in./in. strain corresponding to 10^{-3} g acceleration.

8. Design a seismic vibrometer, to fit within a 4-in. cubic space, having as low a natural frequency as you can obtain. The maximum amplitude to be measured is 0.1 in.

9. For an accelerometer, plot the maximum input frequency ratio β_{max} as a function of damping ratio ζ for maximum error in the range $0 < \beta < \beta_{max}$ of (a) 5%, (b) 1%, (c) 0.1%.

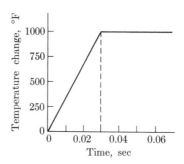

Figure 3–34

10. A first-order thermocouple, having a time constant $\tau = 0.01$ sec, is to be used to measure a temperature change approximately as shown in Fig. 3–34. (a) Plot the "indicated temperature" (from thermocouple output) together with the actual temperature (as shown). (b) The temperature change is observed on an oscilloscope having an input impedance of 10^6 ohms, and having three times the sensitivity required to give full-scale output with the 1000° temperature change. Design a first-order compensating network which will reduce sensitivity (and τ) by a factor of 3. Plot the response of this compensated system on the same graph as in part (a).

11. For the circuit shown in Fig. 3–35, find the amplitude ratio V_2/V_1 and phase angle ϕ as functions of input frequency ω_f. Plot the frequency

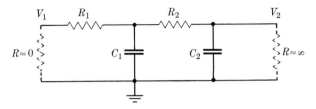

Figure 3–35

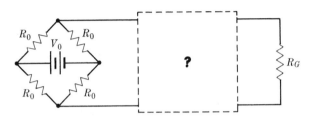

Figure 3–36

response curve for $R_1 = R_2$; $C_1 = C_2$. Does this correspond to a second-order system? Explain.

12. It is desired to use a strain-gage force transducer in conjunction with an oscillographic recorder without employing additional amplification, as shown in Fig. 3–36. There are three oscillograph galvanometers available with the characteristics listed below. The dynamometer characteristics are also listed. Determine the best galvanometer to use and design any necessary impedance-matching and/or compensating networks required to give the "best" frequency response characteristics. (*Dynamometer:* $f_n = 500$ cps, $\zeta = 0.1$, $S = 1$ volt/volt/lb, $V_0 = 10$ volts, $R_0 = 120$ ohms, four active arms, maximum load expected is 500 lb.) (*Galvanometers:* See table below.)

External damping resistance required, ohms	f_n, cps	R_G, ohms	S_G, in./μ amp
(a) 350	50	30	0.217
(b) 350	100	40	0.033
(c) 120	210	25	0.017

13. An air blast pressure pulse is *expected* to be approximately as shown in Fig. 3–37. A wire-resistance strain-gage pressure transducer is available that employs a flush mounted diaphragm as the sensing device. The transducer characteristics are: $f_n = 1500$ cps, $\zeta < 0.1$, 0 to 100 psi, 120-ohm gages, 25 mv output/100 psi input. The pulse is to be observed on an oscilloscope having a maximum sensitivity of 2 mv full scale, and an input impedance of 10^6 ohms. Determine and plot the system response that you would expect.

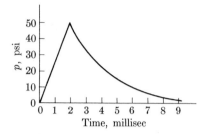

Figure 3-37

Would any compensating or filter networks improve the response? If so, design same and plot the resultant output pressure-time curve. (Use Fourier analysis.)

14. A thermocouple, to be used in measuring transient gas temperatures, has unknown dynamic characteristics. Devise a method for determining the system characteristics.

15. Repeat Problem 14 for a thermocouple to be used to measure transient liquid temperatures.

REFERENCES

BECKWITH, T. G., and N. L. BUCK, *Mechanical Measurements*, Addison-Wesley Publishing Co., Reading, Mass., 1961. Good examples of waveforms comprised of two sinusoidal components.

CARSLAW, H. S., and J. C. JAEGER, *Conduction of Heat in Solids*, Clarendon Press, Oxford, 1947. Thermal analyses which permit estimation of thermal dynamics of systems, i.e., "time constants."

DRAPER, C. S., W. McKAY, and S. LEES, *Instrument Engineering*, Vol. II, McGraw-Hill Book Co., New York, 1952. Comprehensive plots of solutions to linear differential equations of first and second order.

JACOBSEN, L. S., and R. S. AYRE, *Engineering Vibrations*, McGraw-Hill Book Co., New York, 1958. Graphical methods (phase plane), nonlinear vibrations, Coulomb friction, multidegree of freedom systems.

Instrument Notes, Statham Instruments, Los Angeles. Numerous brief articles on transducer performance characteristics.

CHAPTER FOUR

Displacement Measurement

Many measuring systems depend ultimately on measuring a displacement that is analogous to the quantity being measured. Thus, we frequently measure force via the displacement of a spring, pressure via the displacement of a diaphragm, acceleration via the displacement of a spring-supported mass, etc. If we are interested in measuring transient quantities, the natural frequency of the measuring system must be high. This generally means fairly rigid mechanical parts and hence the measurement of extremely small displacements. In many instances, the measuring system must be rigid in order not to influence the quantity being measured. A machine-tool dynamometer, with which we measure the forces acting on a cutting tool, is an ideal example of this situation. Obviously, if the measuring system that supports the tool is not sufficiently rigid, the cutting action will be altered, if not completely stopped.

We find, then, that more stringent measuring conditions require systems capable of measuring extremely small displacements, of the order of one-millionth of an inch (one microinch $= 1 \mu$ in.) or less. It is because of these requirements, so often encountered in the design of experimental apparatus, that we shall give substantial coverage to the problem of measuring small displacements. We must bear in mind that although we are discussing displacements, the actual measurement to be performed using these techniques may well be acceleration, force, temperature, etc.

The basic methods that we shall consider for measurement of small displacements are:

1. Mechanical methods
2. Optical methods
3. Fluid gages
4. Electrical methods
   a. Variable resistance
   b. Variable capacitance
   c. Variable inductance
   d. Miscellaneous

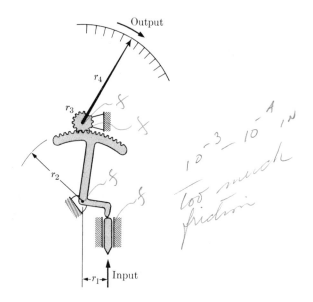

Fig. 4–1. Schematic view of dial gage element.

4–1. Displacement measuring by mechanical means

Of the many methods for mechanically measuring small displacements, we shall consider only two. One of the most-used pieces of commercial measuring equipment, and one that is capable of measuring relatively small displacements, is the mechanical *dial gage*. This device is made in many forms and is familiar to most experimenters. The units consist of mechanical levers, and gears which suitably amplify the motion. Figure 4–1 shows schematically the working parts of a simple dial gage. It is apparent that the magnification of the unit shown is

$$\text{Magnification} = \frac{r_2}{r_1} \times \frac{r_4}{r_3}.$$

By suitable gearing, magnification of the order of 1000 can be obtained, i.e., an input of 10^{-4} inch produces a readable output of 10^{-1} inch. These units are subject to Coulomb friction hysteresis and their use for measurements of motions of less than 10^{-4} inch is questionable. A small-amplitude high-frequency vibration or "dither" applied to the system can generally reduce the static errors due to friction by effectively separating the rubbing parts many times per second. It is clear that these instruments, by their very nature, will not generally respond to inputs that vary at more than a few cycles per second.

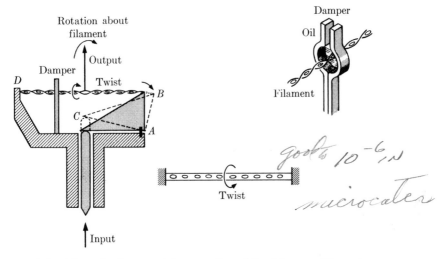

Fig. 4–2. Schematic diagram of the operation of the Johansson Microcator.

A mechanical dial gage which is quite different in operating principle from the lever-gear gages discussed above is the Microcator, made by the Johansson Company. These gages are capable of measurement to 10^{-6} inch or less, and operate in a manner shown schematically in Fig. 4–2. Vertical motion of the spindle causes the triangle ABC to rotate about A, causing a horizontal displacement of B. The thin twisted filament between B and D is initially made as shown, with the ends held stationary while the center is rotated, causing plastic deformation of the filament, which then remains in the shape shown. At the center of the twisted filament is fastened a needle which moves past a scale. Whenever the filament is stretched, the center "unwinds" elastically, causing rotation of the needle. We should note that, except for friction between the spindle and housing, the system is purely elastic and has no hysteresis except that due to internal friction in the stressed members. Under these conditions the needle can vibrate violently with the slightest disturbance; hence a viscous damper is used. This damper is simply a drop of oil which surrounds the filament, and which is held by a member attached to the frame as shown.

We have described these two mechanical measuring methods in order to indicate what can conveniently be done mechanically with readily available commercial items, and also to point out that hysteresis is minimized when using elastic mechanisms rather than sliding mechanisms.

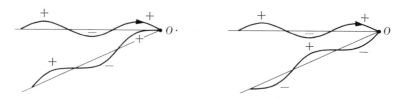

Fig. 4–3. Two light waves from the same source arrive at point 0: (a) light waves in phase and *add;* (b) light waves 180° out of phase *cancel.*

4–2. Optical measuring methods

The use of light as a medium for making measurements is very attractive from many points of view. The speed of light is so great that, for most mechanical measurements, we can completely ignore the fact that it takes time for light to travel from one part of a system to another. Also, the mass of light is essentially zero, and hence produces negligible load on the part being observed. For measuring purposes, light travels in a straight line and can be used as a very long "lever" of zero inertia. We are all familiar with the manner in which a spot of light moves when it is reflected from a rotating mirror and projected on a distant screen. Perhaps less familiar, and hence requiring more discussion in a text of this scope, is the manner in which the wavelike properties of light can be employed for making extremely precise and accurate measurements of very small distances and motions.

Interference. For purposes of discussion, we can here ignore the "true nature of light" (which is really not yet understood) and consider light to be composed of transverse electromagnetic waves of high frequency (and low amplitude) which can be characterized by a sine wave. When two such waves of light emanating from a single source arrive at a given point, they can have various phase relationships. Figure 4–3 shows how two waves that are in phase tend to add or reinforce each other, producing light more intense than either wave, and how waves that are 180° out of phase will effectively cancel, reducing the intensity to zero. This effect is termed *interference*, which is actually a misnomer, as the two waves do *not* interfere; rather they superpose, each acting as if the other were not there. If, then, we have two waves from the same source arriving at a point, and we are able to vary the phase of one wave relative to the other, we will observe areas that are alternately light and dark, depending on whether the waves are additive or subtractive.

One convenient method for making waves arrive with varying phase relationships is to vary the length of path taken by the two waves. If the wavelength of light is λ, and the distance from the source to the

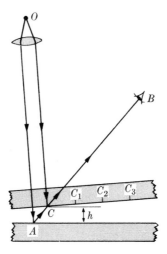

Fig. 4–4. The difference in path length is equal to 2h.

point in question is l_1 via path 1 and l_2 via path 2, then the number n of wavelengths between source and observation point is

$$n_1 = \frac{l_1}{\lambda}, \qquad n_2 = \frac{l_2}{\lambda}.$$

The difference in number of wavelengths is

$$n_1 - n_2 = \frac{1}{\lambda}(l_1 - l_2). \tag{4-1}$$

Now when $n_1 - n_2$ is a whole number $(1, 2, 3, \ldots)$, the two waves will be in phase, while if $n_1 - n_2$ is a whole number plus $\frac{1}{2}$ (i.e., $\frac{1}{2}, \frac{3}{2}, \frac{5}{2}, \ldots$), the waves will be out of phase. Thus, when $l_1 - l_2$ is an *even* multiple of $\lambda/2$, $(2\lambda/2, 4\lambda/2, 6\lambda/2 \ldots)$, the waves will reinforce, and when $l_1 - l_2$ is an *odd* multiple of $\lambda/2$, $(\lambda/2, 3\lambda/2, 5\lambda/2 \ldots)$, the waves will cancel.

This effect can be seen very clearly when two glass surfaces are brought close together, particularly in monochromatic light. Figure 4–4 shows that the difference in path length of the two beams is essentially equal to twice the spacing between the surfaces. Thus, the eye at B will see bright light at A-C when $2h = l_1 - l_2 = \lambda, 2\lambda, 3\lambda, \ldots$, or it will see darkness when $2h = \lambda/2, 3\lambda/2, 5\lambda/2, \ldots$. As the eye looks from C to C_1 to C_2, etc. (Fig. 4–4), the distance h increases and the eye sees alternate light and dark areas. The horizontal spacing between any two light or dark areas will thus correspond to a variation of $\lambda/2$

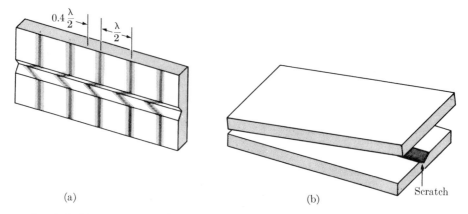

(a)   (b)   Scratch

Fig. 4–5. The appearance of a surface scratch when using interferometry techniques.

in the distance h. A common monochromatic light source, green mercury, has a wavelength $\lambda = 5460\,\text{A}$ $(1\,\text{A} = \text{one angstrom unit} = 10^{-8}\,\text{cm}$, or $21.5\,\mu\,\text{in.})$. Thus the change in h corresponding to the horizontal distance between two dark fringes is $\lambda/2 = 10.8\,\mu\,\text{in.}$

Figure 4–5 shows how a surface scratch will appear when viewed by interferometry techniques. The fringes shown are deflected to the left about $\frac{4}{10}$ of the distance between fringes; hence the depth of the scratch is $\frac{4}{10} \times \lambda/2 \approx 4.3\,\mu\,\text{in.}$ The fringes are not really as sharp as they are shown in Fig. 4–5, the variation in intensity being a $\cos^2$ function, and it is difficult to estimate the position of the center of a fringe much closer than $\lambda/10$ or $\lambda/20$. We can immediately appreciate the usefulness of interferometry for measuring surface irregularities or the motion between two surfaces. If in Fig. 4–5 we raise the upper plate, the fringes will move to the left. The number of fringes passing any point indicates the number of half-wavelengths that the surfaces have been moved apart.

One of the most useful and well-known devices employing the interference effect is the *Michelson interferometer*, shown schematically in Fig. 4–6. Light originating at O hits the 45° mirror at A. This mirror is half-reflecting, i.e., half of the incident light is reflected and the other half is transmitted. The reflected half goes to C, back through A and down to the eye at D. The transmitted portion goes through A, is reflected back from B to A, and reflected down to D. The light arriving at D via B must pass through $3\sqrt{2}$ thicknesses of glass. In order that the light arriving at D via C may pass through an equal thickness of glass, a 45° piece of unsilvered glass is placed at E. Now if the distances AB and AC are identical, the length of path $OABAD$ is equal to

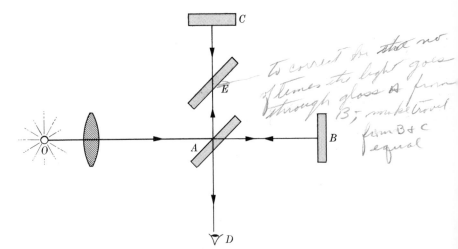

Fig. 4–6. Principle of operation of the Michelson interferometer.

$OACAD$, and light will arrive at D via the two paths *in phase*. If AC or AB is increased by $\lambda/4$, the two waves will be out of phase and the eye at D will see darkness; another $\lambda/4$ and the eye will see light again, etc. Thus the workings of the Michelson interferometer are similar to those shown for the two plates in Fig. 4–5, except that the two surfaces C and B need not be close together or touching. The Michelson interferometer and its many commercial ramifications are very useful for evaluating surface defects when it is inconvenient or impossible to put a reflecting surface very close to the surface to be observed. The principal use of the Michelson interferometer is to make very precise *absolute* measurements of master gage blocks and the like.

The General Conference on Weights and Measures has defined the standard of absolute measurement based on the wavelength of the orange-red light of a krypton-86 lamp. The definition is

$$1 \text{ meter } = 1{,}650{,}763.73 \text{ wavelengths (1960).}$$

The standard definition of an inch is

$$1 \text{ inch } = 2.54 \text{ centimeters (exactly).}$$

The combination of these definitions, together with the various commercially available interferometers, give us our standard of absolute length.

The standard of absolute length is currently in a position of flux as there have been several proposed standards (light sources) that are

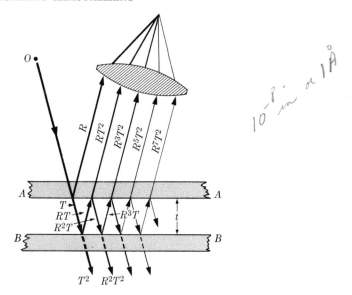

10^{-1} in. or $1\overset{\circ}{A}$

Fig. 4–7. The principles of multiple-beam interferometry.

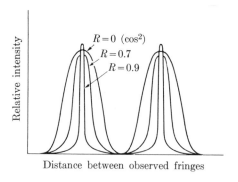

Fig. 4–8. Increasing R improves the fringe definition in multiple-beam interferometry.

either more precise, or less effected by external effects of pressure, temperature, etc.

Multiple-beam interferometry. When the two reflecting surfaces can be brought close together (a few λ apart), the fringe definition can be greatly improved by a method known as multiple-beam interferometry. Figure 4–7 shows the effect of a light beam originating at O being reflected and transmitted by the partially reflecting surfaces AA and BB, each of which reflects $R\%$ and transmits $T\%$ of the incident light. Due to the multiple reflection, many beams arrive at the eye from a single source. For surfaces that have varying spacing, the effect is to sharpen the fringes greatly. Figure 4–8 shows qualitatively the effect of varying R on the distribution of light intensity within a fringe. It is present practice to use a silver deposition which produces $R = 94\%$, $T = 1\%$, and absorption $= 5\%$. Under these conditions, the width of the fringe is about $\frac{1}{50}$ of the distance between fringes, and it is possible to estimate the position *within* a fringe to $\frac{1}{10}$ or $\frac{1}{20}$ of the fringe width. Since the distance between fringes corresponds to $\lambda/2$, we can estimate to a precision of

$$\frac{1}{20} \times \frac{1}{50} \times \frac{\lambda}{2} \approx \frac{\lambda}{2000},$$

which is approximately

$$3 \text{ A} \quad \text{or} \quad 10^{-8} \text{ inch.}$$

In order to employ this technique, we must have surfaces which are very close together; otherwise poor definition will result due to phase shifting with nonparallel reflecting surfaces.

It is possible to use any polished metallic part for the reflector BB in Fig. 4–7, and thus to examine its surface directly. However, if the surface is made up of crystals of varying orientation, errors may be introduced due to the fact that the light must penetrate several layers of atoms (or ions) before being reflected. The mean depth at which reflection occurs can vary with crystal orientation.

4–3. Fluid gages

It is often convenient to measure displacement of a part by having it change the position of a valve in a fluid (liquid or gaseous) system. This causes a variation of pressure, flow, or both, in the system, and one of these changes is measured to indicate the valve motion. The elements of such a fluid gage are shown in Fig. 4–9. Fluid, entering at pressure P_0, goes through an orifice of diameter d_1, and then out the gap between the flapper valve and a sharp-edged tube of diameter d_2.

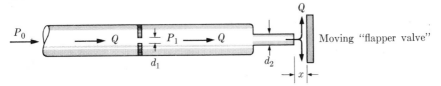

Fig. 4–9. The elements of a simple fluid-type displacement gage.

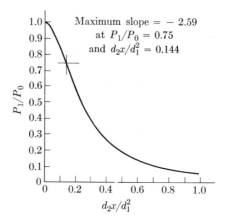

Fig. 4–10. Characteristics of a fluid gage.

We can estimate the performance of such a system quite readily. *Incompressible* fluid flow through an orifice is given by

$$Q = CA\sqrt{\Delta P}, \qquad (4\text{-}2)$$

where $\quad Q$ is the flow, in^3/sec,

A is the orifice area, in^2,

ΔP is the pressure drop across orifice, psi,

C is a constant depending on fluid, etc.

Thus, for the first orifice,

$$Q = C\,\frac{\pi\,d_1^2}{4}\,\sqrt{P_0 - P_1}, \qquad (4\text{-}3)$$

and for the exit orifice,

$$Q = C\pi\,d_2x\sqrt{P_1}. \qquad (4\text{-}4)$$

Eliminating Q, we obtain

$$\frac{P_1}{P_0} = \frac{1}{1 + 16\,(d_2x/d_1^2)^2}. \qquad (4\text{-}5)$$

Equation (4–5) represents the steady-state characteristics of such a system, and is shown plotted in Fig. 4–10. If we set

$$\frac{d^2(P_1/P_0)}{d(d_2x/d_1^2)^2} = 0,$$

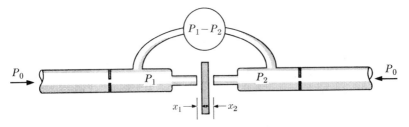

Fig. 4–11. Two fluid gages in opposition.

we can solve for the point of maximum slope and for the value of that slope. These are shown in Fig. 4–10. In order to obtain best linearity and sensitivity from the system, we should operate at this point of maximum slope (inflection point).

The system can be made considerably more sensitive by having two systems in opposition, as shown in Fig. 4–11, and by using the difference between the two back pressures as a measure of displacement. If when $x_1 = x_2$, we operate at the value $x d_2/d_1^2 = 0.144$, we will have maximum sensitivity. The characteristics of this system are given by

$$\frac{P_1 - P_2}{P_0} = \frac{1}{1 + 16(d_2 x_1/d_1^2)^2} - \frac{1}{1 + 16(d_2 x_2/d_1^2)^2}. \quad (4\text{–}6)$$

As an example, consider the case shown in Fig. 4–11, with $d_1 = d_2 = 0.020$. Then the initial value of $x(x_0)$ should be $x_0 = 0.0028$ in order that $x_0 d_2/d_1^2 = 0.144$. If we use the approximate relationship from Fig. 4–10, that is,

$$\frac{\Delta P_1}{P_0} = -2.59 \,\Delta x \,\frac{d_2}{d_1^2}, \quad (4\text{–}7)$$

then

$$\frac{P_1 - P_2}{P_0} = 5.18 \,\Delta x \,\frac{d_2}{d_1^2} = 5.18 \,\Delta x \left(\frac{0.144}{x_0}\right),$$

or

$$\frac{P_1 - P_2}{P_0} = 0.745 \,\frac{\Delta x}{x_0}. \quad (4\text{–}8)$$

If we use a supply pressure of 100 in. H_2O, and assume that we can very easily read a change of 0.1 in. H_2O on a simple differential manometer, we can read

$$\frac{P_1 - P_2}{P_0} = \frac{0.1}{100} = 10^{-3}.$$

Therefore, we can measure $\Delta x = 0.0028 \times 10^{-3}/0.745 = 3.7\,\mu$ in. If water is used, the flow Q will be of the order of 1 gallon per hour. We can appreciate the simplicity of such a system.

It must be noted that the simple analyses used are based on steady-state behavior. When the flapper valve is moved, fluid must flow into or out of the manometer or other pressure-sensing device. Because the flow is through small orifices, the time required to attain the equilibrium condition may be quite large.

This same basic system is sold commercially using air rather than a liquid as the operating medium. As long as we use a pressure drop across the orifices which is low enough, the effect of compressibility is small and the equations developed above will apply. However, as the ratio of outlet to inlet pressure approaches 0.5, the flow becomes critical (i.e., sonic) in the throat, and the equations for compressible flow must be used.

4–4. Displacement measurement through electrical means

There is a tremendous number of displacement measuring methods which employ electrical means. However, such devices can be grouped into four categories: resistive, inductive, capacitive, and miscellaneous. In this section we shall discuss a number of the more commonly used displacement transducers, and the circuitry normally used.

4–4.1. Variable-resistance displacement-measuring transducers

(a) *Moving-contact elements.* The reader is familiar with many moving-contact devices that can be used to transform a change in position into a change in resistance. These include carbon and wire-wound potentiometers, either linear or rotary, and straight, slide-wire resistances. Units employing a conducting fluid with moving electrodes would probably also be classed as moving-contact transducers.

Wire-wound potentiometers are limited in resolution due to the discrete resistance change from winding to winding. However, present potentiometers can be made with wire spacing as small as 10^{-3} inch; and linearity as good as 0.01% full scale. The force required to move wire-wound potentiometers is high enough to preclude their use in very low force or torque systems.

It would appear at first glance that a single straight resistance wire with a sliding contact would have very good resolution. However, when we have a movable contact, the "contact resistance" is not perfectly uniform, due to the presence of oxide films and adsorbed layers. Thus for the presently used resistance wire materials, effective resolution is limited to that length of wire which has a resistance equal to the variation in contact resistance. Contact resistance can be reduced to a minimum (10 to 100 milliohms) by plating the contacts with noble metals and employing heavy contact pressures. If uniform high-resistance wires become available, this type of unit will gain in usefulness.

It would also appear that an electrolytic variable-displacement gage would be simple, have high resolution, and if properly designed, have ideal damping characteristics. When used in a d-c circuit, any such device develops polarized layers in the electrolyte near each electrode, and hence the resistive characteristics change. However, when used in a relatively high-frequency a-c circuit (> 1000 cps), the polarized layers do not have time to form. The frequency required for negligible polarization depends on the electrolyte used. All standard electrolytes have resistances which depend rather strongly on temperature, and hence are quite temperature sensitive. When electrolytes are used in a bridge circuit, variations in steady-state temperature can be made to cancel; however, thermal gradients will still cause variations. When an electrolytic gage is used for small displacements, any gas evolution, electrode corrosion or coating, or electrolyte breakdown will render the transducer useless. By enumerating the above factors, we do not mean to imply that electrolytic units should not be considered, but only that they must be designed and used with caution.

In general, moving-contact resistance units are useful for measuring relatively large motions where resolution of 10^{-3} inch or larger is satisfactory. The power level can often be high enough to obviate the use of amplifiers.

(b) *Fixed-contact resistance elements.* The use of elastic resistance elements has grown from almost nil in 1940 until the present time, when they are used in most fields of mechanical measurement. This type of element works on the principle that the resistance of a wire or sheet will change when it is elastically or plastically deformed. When a wire is stretched, its length increases and its diameter decreases due to the Poisson effect. As a result of these and other physical changes, its resistance increases. The amount that a resistance R changes when its length l is changed by an amount Δl is given by the "gage factor" G.F., where

$$\frac{\Delta R}{R} = (\text{G.F.})\frac{\Delta l}{l} = (\text{G.F.})\epsilon, \qquad (4\text{--}9)$$

and

$$\epsilon = \frac{\Delta l}{l} = \text{strain.}$$

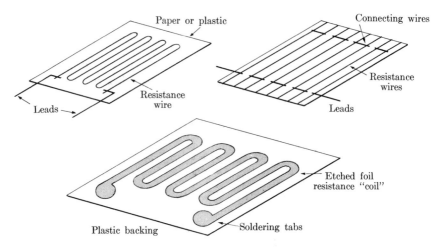

Fig. 4–12. Schematic drawings of typical wire- and foil-bonded resistance strain gages.

The gage factor is truly a measure of the strain sensitivity of the wire. Throughout this book we shall let S represent the sensitivity, or steady-state input-output characteristic, of the element. Hence for a wire-resistance strain gage,

$$S = \frac{\Delta R/R}{\epsilon}, \qquad (4\text{–}10)$$

where ϵ is elastic strain. For commonly used resistance wire materials, where the wire diameter is of the order of 10^{-3} inch, the G.F. ranges from 2 to 5. Semiconductor materials can exhibit G.F.'s of the order of 100 or more. In the future we should expect that semiconductor developments will provide very sensitive, stable strain-measuring materials.

Wire-resistance strain gages take many forms today. A number of these, shown schematically in Fig. 4–12, are called "bonded" gages because the resistance wire is bonded to a paper or plastic backing which can then be cemented to the part to be measured. As the diameter of a wire becomes smaller, the ratio of surface area to cross-sectional area increases. Hence with the very small wires and foils used (cross-sectional area $\sim 10^{-6}$ in^2), a relatively weak cement is able to furnish the force required to extend or compress the wire.

With common strain gages, strains as small as 10^{-7} are readily detected, and strains greater than 10^{-3} can be measured. The temperature range over which strain gages can be used is constantly being increased.

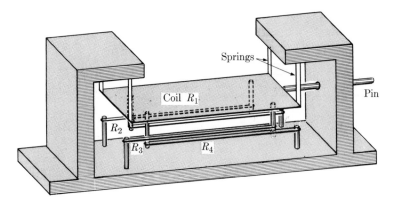

Fig. 4–13. A typical "four arm" unbonded wire-resistance strain gage.

Strain gage wires are by nature temperature sensitive. However, it is possible through the use of two types of wire to make a gage which has very little dependency on temperature. A system using two or four gages in a bridge circuit can be made insensitive to steady-state temperature variations even though the individual gages are uncompensated.

Unbonded strain gages are made by winding coils of wire about movable pins. When the pins are moved apart, the coils stretch. The unbonded gage shown schematically in Fig. 4–13 is typical in that it employs four coils wound under initial tension. Thus when the pins are moved, two coils undergo additional tension, and two coils have part of the initial tension removed. This is equivalent, from a resistance point of view, to stretching two coils and compressing two.

The bonded gages must be cemented to a member which is strained by the forces in the system. Because this member must be large relative to the wire used, the forces are relatively high. On the other hand, the use of the unbonded gages may require very little force, since in extreme cases only the wires themselves are deformed.

The output of a strain gage is limited by I^2R heating in the wire itself, the maximum current generally being of the order of 25×10^{-3} amp.

Bonded gages can be obtained in a variety of sizes down to $\frac{1}{16} \times \frac{1}{16}$ inch for the smallest foil gage.

(c) *Circuitry employed with resistance units.* Low-resolution units such as potentiometers, and slide-wire resistors, can be successfully used with simple series circuits. Figure 4–14 shows three such circuits. The method shown in 4–14(a) has poor characteristics, while the methods shown in 4–14(b) and (c) are quite satisfactory when the meter resistance R_m is two orders of magnitude greater than R_0.

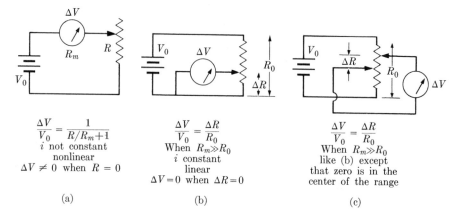

$$\frac{\Delta V}{V_0} = \frac{1}{R/R_m + 1}$$
i not constant
nonlinear
$\Delta V \neq 0$ when $R = 0$

(a)

$$\frac{\Delta V}{V_0} = \frac{\Delta R}{R_0}$$
When $R_m \gg R_0$
i constant
linear
$\Delta V = 0$ when $\Delta R = 0$

(b)

$$\frac{\Delta V}{V_0} = \frac{\Delta R}{R_0}$$
When $R_m \gg R_0$
like (b) except
that zero is in the
center of the range

(c)

Fig. 4–14. Examples of series resistance circuits.

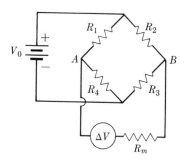

Fig. 4–15. The Wheatstone bridge.

For measuring the small resistance changes in wire-resistance strain gages, the series circuits are not sufficiently sensitive. The Wheatstone bridge circuit is ideal for measuring small resistance changes. We shall also use bridge circuits with other measuring systems; hence we shall consider them in some detail. Bridge circuits are generally most suitable for any measurement made by electrical means.

Figure 4–15 shows a Wheatstone bridge, with an applied d-c voltage V_0, and a meter having resistance R_m, to read output voltage ΔV. The output ΔV will be zero whenever the bridge is "balanced." This occurs whenever

$$\frac{R_1}{R_2} = \frac{R_4}{R_3},$$

the simplest case being that where $R_1 = R_2 = R_3 = R_4$. This is the case that we shall consider; initially all resistances equal R_0, and $R_m \ggg R_0$.

We can obtain a qualitative picture of what happens when any of the four resistances R_0 changes by a small amount ΔR. Initially, due to the equality of all resistors, the current is equal through all resistors, being simply $I = V_0/2R_0$. If now R_1 is increased by ΔR ($\Delta R \ll R_0$), the currents will not change appreciably, and the voltage drop (IR_1) will increase by $I\,\Delta R/2$ or $V_0\Delta R/4R_0$. Thus the voltage at A will become lower than that at B and we will read a negative ΔV; that is, $\Delta V/V_0 = \Delta R/4R_0$. If we now *increase* the resistance of R_2 by the same ΔR, the voltage at B will decrease by the same $V_0\,\Delta R/4R_0$, and we will read $\Delta V = 0$. If, however, the resistance R_2 is decreased by ΔR, the voltage at B will increase and we will read $\Delta V/V_0 = \Delta R/2R_0$. Hence, we find that *equal* changes in adjacent arms of the bridge produce *zero* output, while *opposite* changes in adjacent arms produce *doubled* output. Thus for maximum output two *opposite* arms (i.e., R_1 and R_3) should undergo one change ΔR while the other two *opposite* arms (i.e., R_2 and R_4) should undergo a negative ΔR. Under these conditions, we find that

$$\frac{\Delta V}{V_0} = \frac{\Delta R}{R_0}. \tag{4-11}$$

This is the condition for four active arms.

If we now include the meter impedance R_m in our calculations, and allow for large values of $\Delta R/R$, we can obtain a generalized expression for a bridge with all arms of equal initial value R_0 and four active arms:

$$\frac{\Delta V}{V_0} = \frac{\Delta R/R_0}{1 + (R_0/R_m)[1 - (\Delta R/R_0)^2]}. \tag{4-12}$$

As long as $R_0/R_m \lll 1$, the four-active-arm bridge is completely linear, even for large values of $\Delta R/R_0$. For wire-resistance strain gages, $\Delta R/R_0$ is generally less than 0.01, so that the main effect of a lowered meter resistance is to reduce sensitivity, while not affecting linearity. However, with a wire-wound potentiometer, or with an electrolytic resistance gage, $\Delta R/R_0$ can approach one and the nonlinearities can become large.

When two active arms are used, the deviation from linearity depends on *which* two arms are used. When two *adjacent* arms of initially equal R_0 undergo *opposite* ΔR, then

$$\frac{\Delta V}{V_0} = \frac{\Delta R/R_0}{2 + (R_0/R_m)[2 - (\Delta R/R_0)^2]}, \tag{4-13}$$

which is very similar to the case for four active arms. However, when two *opposite* arms undergo *equal* changes, then

$$\frac{\Delta V}{V_0} = \frac{\Delta R/R_0}{2 + \Delta R/R_0 + 2(R_0/R_m)(1 + \Delta R/R_0)}. \quad (4\text{–}14)$$

Here we see a first-order nonlinearity in $\Delta R/R_0$ which occurs even when $R_0/R_m \approx 0$. A similar result is obtained when only one arm is active. Then

$$\frac{\Delta V}{V_0} = \frac{\Delta R/R_0}{4 + 2\,\Delta R/R_0 + (R_0/R_m)(4 + 3\,\Delta R/R_0)}. \quad (4\text{–}15)$$

Thus, when $R_0/R_m \approx 0$ and we can obtain both $+\Delta R/R_0$ and $-\Delta R/R_0$, the system is linear. However, when we have only $+\Delta R/R_0$ or $-\Delta R/R_0$ in one or two active arms, the system deviates from ideal linearity. The deviation is:

$$\text{Deviation from ideal linearity} = \frac{1}{2}\frac{\Delta R}{R_0}. \quad (4\text{–}16)$$

Thus for $\Delta R/R_0 = 0.02$, the deviation would be 1%. This is negligible for most wire-resistance strain gage uses.

Generally $\Delta R/R_0$ is small (i.e., less than 10^{-2}); therefore we can write the bridge sensitivity, when n active arms are used, as

$$S = \frac{\Delta V/V_0}{\Delta R/R_0} \approx \frac{n/4}{1 + R/R_m}. \quad (4\text{–}17)$$

If the resistance of one arm changes due to temperature variation, we will read a fictitious output. However, if an identical resistance in an adjacent arm undergoes the identical temperature variation, there will be zero net output. Thus if two adjacent arms, or all four arms, undergo the same temperature variations, the system will be temperature compensated. This is often accomplished by attaching two adjacent arm gages, or all four gages, to a single mechanical element. It must be borne in mind that *thermal gradients* in any of the parts will cause misleading readings.

Gages can be obtained or fabricated which are "temperature compensated" for a given base material to which they will be attached. This means that the net effect of steady-state thermal expansion and resistance change with temperature is nil. We must not forget, however, that nonlinear thermal gradients across a member will introduce thermal strains which are indistinguishable from elastic strains.

When a strain gage bridge is assembled it will never be in perfect balance, and provision must be made for bringing the bridge into balance so that there is zero output for zero input. For a bridge using d-c excita-

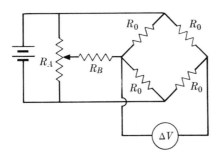

Fig. 4–16. Balancing circuit for d-c bridge.

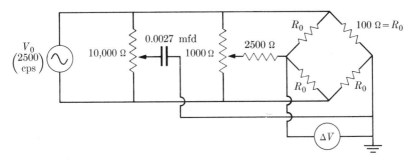

Fig. 4–17. Balancing circuit for a-c bridge.

tion (V_0), this simply involves a system to change slightly the initial resistance of one or more arms. Figure 4–16 shows a very satisfactory circuit. The potentiometer R_A is of the order of $10R_0$, while the maximum possible adjustment is governed by R_B. For strain gage work, $R_B = 25R_0$ will be satisfactory.

When a-c excitation is used, the balancing problem is somewhat greater, since there will be reactive imbalance as well as resistive imbalance. Thus, in addition to the resistive balance control discussed above, a reactive (often called capacitive) balance control must be provided. Figure 4–17 shows a typical a-c balancing system.

In order to resolve strains of the order of $\epsilon = 10^{-6}$, it is necessary to read outputs of the order of $\Delta V = 10^{-5}$ volt. Hence, amplification is necessary. Because it is relatively easier to build stable high-gain a-c amplifiers than it is to build similar d-c amplifiers, many strain-gage systems employ an audio-frequency (2500 cps) carrier wave excitation which is amplitude-modulated by the strain gages. With an a-c input and output, the only way to distinguish a minus output from a plus output is to compare the *phase* of the output signal with that of the input. For a resistive transducer, the signals will either be in phase or

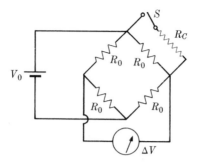

Fig. 4–18. Operation of a calibrating resistor R_c.

180° out of phase. A *phase-sensitive demodulator* demodulates or rectifies the output ΔV to give a d-c signal, and compares the phase of ΔV with that of V_0 to determine the sign of the d-c signal. Normally, such demodulators are insensitive or only partially sensitive to signals $\pm 90°$ out of phase. Hence, it is important that ΔV be completely in phase or out of phase with V_0 in order to appear at full value.

With any transducer that is associated with electronic equipment, it is necessary to provide some means for determining the output of the entire system due to a given input. For resistance strain gages, this can be readily accomplished by providing a fixed calibrating resistance R_c which can be shunted across one arm of the bridge, as shown in Fig. 4–18. When the calibrating resistance is shunted across R_0, the total resistance of that arm is reduced by an amount ΔR_{cal}. The resulting change is

$$\left(\frac{\Delta R}{R_0}\right)_{\text{cal}} = \frac{R_0}{R_c + R_0}. \tag{4–18}$$

The value of R_c is generally much greater than R_0, so that

$$\left(\frac{\Delta R}{R_0}\right)_{\text{cal}} \approx \frac{R_0}{R_c}. \tag{4–19}$$

Because this operates on only one arm of the bridge,

$$\left(\frac{\Delta V}{V_0}\right)_{\text{cal}} = \frac{1}{4}\frac{R_0}{R_c}. \tag{4–20}$$

We have already seen that with an n-active-arm strain bridge,

$$\frac{\Delta V}{V_0} = \frac{n}{4}\,(\text{G.F.})\,\epsilon. \tag{4–21}$$

If we equate Eqs. (4–20) and (4–21), we obtain

$$\epsilon_{cal} = \frac{1}{n(\text{G.F.})} \frac{R_0}{R_c}. \tag{4–22}$$

This says that regardless of V_0, when we shunt R_c we obtain an output voltage, (pen motion) equivalent to that obtained by straining the gages an amount ϵ_{cal}.

EXAMPLE. If $R_0 = 100\,\Omega$, $R_c = 10^6\,\Omega$, $n = 4$, G.F. $= 2.5$, $\epsilon_{cal} = 10^{-5}$ in./in. Thus the pen motion due to shunting R_c is equivalent to a strain of 10^{-5} in./in.

Natural limitations. Strain gages, like all other measuring devices, have certain natural limitations which cannot be overcome regardless of the development of better cements, amplifiers, etc. The first limitation is due to the *thermal noise* that is present in every resistive element. This noise or voltage is due to the random thermal motion of the conduction electrons within the resistor which tend to "pile up" at one end or the other of the resistor, causing an apparent voltage to appear across the resistor. The root-mean-square voltage V_{rms} is readily shown to be

$$V_{rms} = (4kTR\,\Delta f)^{1/2}, \tag{4–23}$$

where

k is Boltzmann's constant,

T is the absolute temperature,

R is the resistance, and

Δf is the frequency range of measuring instrument sensitivity, cps.

For usual strain gage work, at room temperature, the thermal noise *from the gage* will be equivalent to a strain of 10^{-9} and is negligible. However, noise within other resistances in the circuitry will become bothersome at much larger values of strain and will generally limit the useful system resolution.

The second fundamental limitation is associated with the speed at which an elastic wave can pass through a strain gage. The system can only "see" the average strain in a gage; hence time or spatial strain variations along the length of a gage cannot be observed with any fidelity. The time t_l required for a wave to travel the length of a gage is

$$t_l = \frac{l}{c}, \tag{4–24}$$

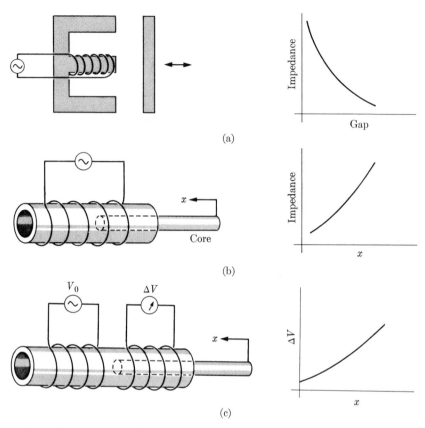

Fig. 4–19. Example of three types of variable-inductance transducers. In (a) and (b) variation of impedance is measured; in (c) variation of induced voltage is measured.

where l is the gage length, and c is the speed of sound in the base material. For typical situations, t_l is of the order of 1 to 10 microsec. When rapidly varying transients are to be measured, t_l may introduce a severe limitation. Often, however, the time required for an event to produce a wave, and for that wave to travel to the gage, is the dominant factor.

A practical limitation in many cases is set by slight plastic yielding of the cement which bonds the gage to the supporting member. This often limits the strain resolution to about 10^{-7}.

4–4.2. Variable-inductance displacement-measuring transducers.

There is a wide variety of devices that employ a permeable member which moves to vary the inductance of an electrical system. The most

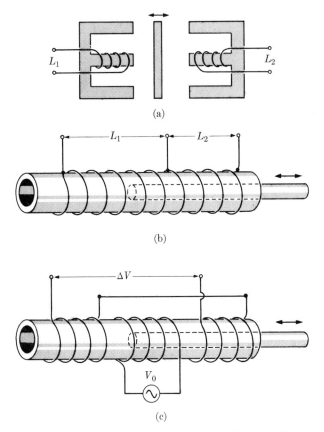

Fig. 4–20. The elements of Fig. 4–19 arranged to produce more linear characteristics: (a) and (b) variable-inductance transducers; (c) a differential transformer.

widely used systems involve only three general types, as shown in Fig.
4–19. In two of these, motion causes a variation of impedance, while in
the third, motion causes a variation of an induced voltage. These
systems, as shown, have nonlinear characteristics, which can be improved by shaping the moving member. However, the greatest improvement is obtained when a pair of such devices is used in a push-pull
system such that we sum two nonlinear characteristics and obtain a
nominally linear system. The same units so arranged are shown schematically in Fig. 4–20. In Fig. 4–20(a) and (b), the system is arranged
so that when the core moves, the impedance of one inductor increases
while the other decreases. In Fig. 4–20(c), as the core moves, the induced voltage in one secondary winding increases while that in the other

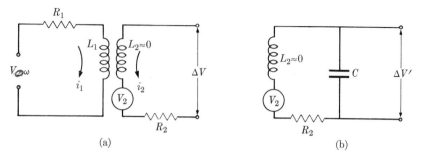

Fig. 4–21. Schematic representation of L.V.D.T.: primary coil (i_1, R_1, L_1); secondary coil (i_2, R_2, L_2, V_2).

decreases. If these coils are wired so that the induced voltages oppose each other, the net output ΔV is nearly proportional to the motion of the core away from the electrical center of the system.

The sensitivity of variable-inductance transducers and linear variable differential transformers (L.V.D.T.) varies with the geometry and the electrical characteristics of the materials used. However, for an L.V.D.T. the sensitivity is generally of the order of 1 to 5 (volts/volt)/inch; i.e., for a 1-volt input, the output will be 1 to 5 millivolts for a core motion of 0.001 in.

Because of imperfect manufacture and impure sinusoidal input, there is always some output at the null position. While this can be reduced to a minimum by circuit alterations, it generally corresponds to the voltage output due to a 10 to 50×10^{-6} inch motion of the core.

Also, due to the nature of the transducer, there is a phase shift between input and output voltages. An idealized schematic drawing of an L.V.D.T. is shown in Fig. 4–21. The primary coil has resistance R_1, inductance L_1, and is excited by a voltage V_0 at ω rad/sec. The coupled secondaries exhibit negligible inductance, and a resistance R_2. They can be considered to be excited by the induced voltage V_2. Figure 4–22 shows the pertinent voltage and phase relationships on the complex plane.

In Fig. 4–22(a) we see that the current lags the voltage V_0 by ϕ_1, where

$$\phi_1 = \tan^{-1} \frac{\omega L_1}{R_1}. \tag{4-25}$$

The induced voltage V_2 depends on the rate of change of the magnetic flux produced by i_1; thus V_2 leads i_1 by 90°, as shown. Or we can say

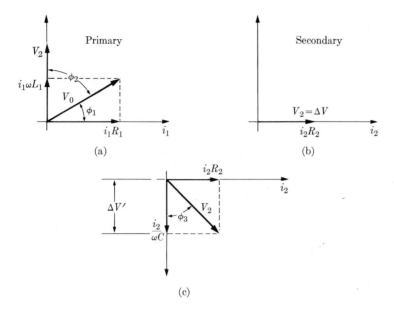

Fig. 4–22. Representation of phase relationships in an L.V.D.T. circuit.

that V_2 leads V_0 by ϕ_2, where

$$\phi_2 = \tan^{-1} \frac{R_1}{\omega L_1}. \qquad (4\text{–}26)$$

Referring to Fig. 4–22(b), we see that the output voltage $\Delta V = V_2$, and thus leads V_0 by ϕ_2.

In order to use an L.V.D.T. with an electronic system involving phase-sensitive demodulation, it is necessary that the output ΔV be in phase with the input V_0, or severe nonlinearity will result. This in-phase status can be accomplished by using a phase-shifting capacitor such as C in Fig. 4–21(b). The phase plot is shown in Fig. 4–22(c). The new output $\Delta V'$ is the voltage appearing across C. It is apparent that $\Delta V'$ lags V_2 by ϕ_3, where

$$\phi_3 = \tan^{-1} \omega R_2 C. \qquad (4\text{–}27)$$

Thus $\Delta V'$ and V_0 will be in phase when $\phi_2 = \phi_3$, or

$$\frac{R_1}{\omega L_1} = \omega R_2 C; \qquad (4\text{–}28)$$

thus,

$$C = \frac{R_1}{\omega^2 R_2 L_1}. \qquad (4\text{–}29)$$

It is also apparent that $\Delta V'$ is smaller than V_2, so that the sensitivity is reduced by a factor r, where

$$r = \frac{\Delta V'}{V_2} = \cos \phi_3 = \frac{1}{\sqrt{1 + (\omega R_2 C)^2}}. \tag{4-30}$$

EXAMPLE. Consider a small L.V.D.T. made by the Schaevitz Engineering Company. The pertinent characteristics are:

$R_1 = 55\ \Omega$,   Sensitivity at 2000 cps

                                   $= 1.6$ volts/volt/inch,

$L_1 = 1.5 \times 10^{-3}$ henries,

$L_2 \approx 0$, $V_0 = 5$ volts, 2000 cps,

$R_2 = 85\ \Omega$,   2000 cps $= 12{,}570$ rad/sec.

The required capacitance C for phasing is

$$C = \frac{55}{1.59 \times 10^8 \times 85 \times 1.5 \times 10^{-3}} = 2.7 \times 10^{-6} \text{ farad.}$$

The new sensitivity will be

$$S = \frac{1.6}{\sqrt{1 + (12{,}570 \times 85 \times 2.7 \times 10^{-6})^2}} = \frac{1.6}{1.35} = 1.19 \frac{\text{volt/volt}}{\text{in.}}\ ;$$

$\phi_2 = 71°$.

If phase sensitivity is not required (i.e., if the device is always operated on one side of null), and phase-sensitive demodulation will not be used, there is no need for phase correction.

With variable-inductance devices of the type shown in Fig. 4–20(a) and (b), there are a number of bridge circuits that we can use. Because any inductor has ohmic resistance as well as reactance, both resistive and reactive balancing must be provided. The outputs of such bridges are generally out of phase with the input and a correction must be made. Let us consider an example involving two variable-inductance arms with two resistive arms, as shown in Fig. 4–23(a). Figure 4–23(b) shows the phase relationships. Initially i_1 and i_2 are equal and in phase. When L_2 decreases, the i_2 vector rotates counterclockwise, giving rise to a ΔV between $i_1 R_3$ and $i_2 R_4$. For very small variations of L_1 or L_2, ΔV is vertical and hence leads V_0 by ϕ_1, where

$$\tan \phi_1 = \frac{R_1 + R_3}{\omega L}. \tag{4-31}$$

In this situation, ΔV can be brought back into phase with V_0 by an

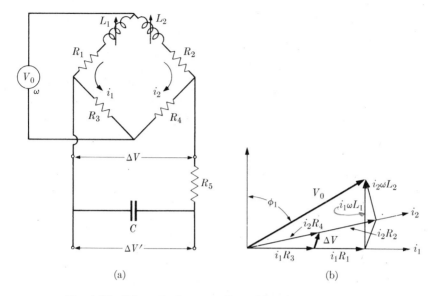

Fig. 4–23. Schematic diagram of variable-inductance bridge.

RC network, as shown. The phase-shift diagram will be similar to that shown in Fig. 4–22(c), and perfect phasing (for small variations of L) will be accomplished when $\phi_1 = \phi_3$. Therefore,

$$\frac{R_1 + R_3}{\omega L} = \omega R_5 C, \tag{4–32}$$

or

$$C = \frac{R_1 + R_3}{\omega^2 R_5 L}. \tag{4–33}$$

EXAMPLE. Consider a gage such as that shown in Fig. 4–23(a). The following are the pertinent characteristics:

$$L_1 = L_2 = 100 \times 10^{-3} \text{ henries,}$$
$$R_1 = R_2 = 60 \ \Omega, \qquad\qquad \omega = 377 \text{ rad/sec;}$$
$$R_3 = R_4 = 100 \ \Omega, \qquad\qquad \text{that is, } f = 60 \text{ cps;}$$

$$\phi_1 = \tan^{-1} \frac{60 + 100}{377 \times 10^{-1}} = 77°.$$

Let $R_5 = 10{,}000 \ \Omega$, then

$$C = \frac{60 + 100}{377^2 \times 10^4 \times 10^{-1}} = 1.1 \times 10^{-6} \text{ farad.}$$

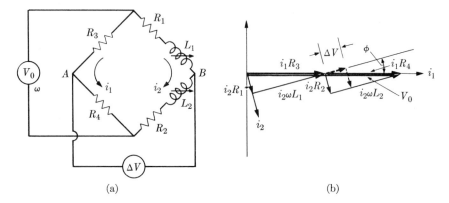

Fig. 4–24. The second type of variable-inductance bridge.

In the case of a resistance bridge, it makes no difference which pair of leads we use as input, and which pair as output. However, with asymmetrical bridges, such as the inductance-resistance bridge of Fig. 4–23, there can be very important differences. Most texts on bridge networks consider only the null condition; here there is no difference. Consider the bridge of Fig. 4–23 rotated 90° to appear as in Fig. 4–24. Point A is always in phase with V_0. Figure 4–24(b) shows the phase plot for the initial case of equal inductance (solid lines) and the case of unequal inductances (dashed lines); ΔV is not in phase with V_0 but leads by ϕ, where

$$\tan \phi = \frac{R_1}{\omega L_1}. \qquad (4\text{--}34)$$

In this case, if $R_1/\omega L_1$ is made sufficiently small (high Q), ΔV will be nearly in phase with V_0 and the phase will not shift significantly during operation. There are instances in which the circuit of Fig. 4–24 will provide significantly better performance than that of Fig. 4–23.

With either L.V.D.T.'s or with variable-inductance gages utilizing a small variable air gap, it is quite easy to obtain resolution of the order of 10^{-6} inch.

It should be noted that the force required to actuate these devices is very small, equal to the magnetomotive force. For a differential or push-pull unit, the force will be such as to pull the core into the electrical null position. This force is typically of the order of 0.1 gm for full-scale deflection of the device.

The practical resolution limitation in variable-inductance gaging is generally the thermal noise developed within the amplifier.

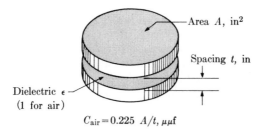

$C_{\text{air}} = 0.225 \ A/t, \ \mu\mu\text{f}$

Fig. 4–25. Two-plate capacitance gage.

4–4.3. Variable-capacitance displacement-measuring transducers

Of the three types of basic electrical displacement-measuring devices (R, L, C), the capacitance gage is probably least used. It does offer some instrumentation difficulties; but for sensitivity, ease of incorporation into an experimental apparatus, and low force level, it is unsurpassed.

A capacitance gage simply involves two or more movable capacitance plates, insulated from each other. Figure 4–25 shows such a capacitor. The value of the capacitance C is

$$C = 0.225\epsilon \frac{A}{t} \ \mu\mu\text{f}, \tag{4–35}$$

where
        C is in 10^{-12} farad, $\mu\mu\text{f}$,

        ϵ is the dielectric constant, unity for air,

        A is the plate area, in^2, and

        t is the gap thickness, in.

Thus a parallel-plate capacitor in air having an area of $1 \ \text{in}^2$ and separated by 0.0225 in. would have a capacitance of 10×10^{-12} farad. This is indeed a small quantity, a factor which is the primary drawback to using capacitance gages. The impedance Z of a capacitor is

$$Z = -\frac{j}{\omega C}. \tag{4–36}$$

At a frequency of 2500 cps, the impedance of a 10-$\mu\mu\text{f}$ capacitor is 6.4×10^6 ohms (6.4 megohms). This represents a high impedance; but to obtain good sensitivity and linearity, any meter system must have considerably higher impedance. Also, due to the low initial capacitance, the capacitance changes to be measured will be extremely small.

Thus variable capacitances due to nearby equipment, leads, etc., can be large enough to cause errors.

In using variable capacitance, either ϵ, A, or t, Eq. (4–35), may be varied. Variation of ϵ has been used successfully to measure the thickness of rubber, the moisture content of paper, textiles, etc. Variation of A is convenient for measuring large motions. The common variable-tuning capacitor used in radios has a variable A. A rod entering a tube will give variable A. In these instances, capacitance will vary linearly with position. For measuring small displacements, t is usually varied. Here, however, the capacitance-displacement characteristic is not linear but hyperbolic.

We can readily investigate the deviations from linearity of either a single capacitor, or a pair of capacitors so arranged that when one increases the other decreases.

A capacitance of initial value $C_0 = 0.225\epsilon A/t_0$ actually varies when t changes by Δt according to

$$\left(\frac{\Delta C}{C_0}\right)_{\text{act}} = -\frac{\Delta t}{t_0 + \Delta t}. \tag{4–37}$$

If we take the slope of the C-t curve at t_0 as an idealized linear condition, then

$$\left(\frac{\Delta C}{C_0}\right)_{\text{ideal}} = -\frac{\Delta t}{t_0}. \tag{4–38}$$

The deviation of ideal from actual is

$$\frac{(\Delta C)_{\text{ideal}} - (\Delta C)_{\text{act}}}{(\Delta C)_{\text{act}}} = \frac{\Delta t}{t_0}. \tag{4–39}$$

Thus for the capacitance-displacement characteristic to deviate from linearity by 1%, $(\Delta t/t_0)_{\text{max}} = 0.01$.

If now we consider a pair of capacitors arranged as shown in Fig. 4–26, we find that they can be placed in adjacent arms of a bridge circuit so that the changes of capacitance add. In this case the actual change of capacitance is

$$\left(\frac{\Delta C}{C_0}\right)_{\text{act}} = \frac{2\,\Delta t/t_0}{1 - (\Delta t/t_0)^2}. \tag{4–40}$$

The idealized linear variation is

$$\left(\frac{\Delta C}{C_0}\right)_{\text{ideal}} = 2\,\frac{\Delta t}{t_0}, \tag{4–41}$$

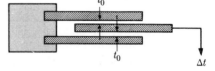

Fig. 4–26. A pair of push-pull capacitors.

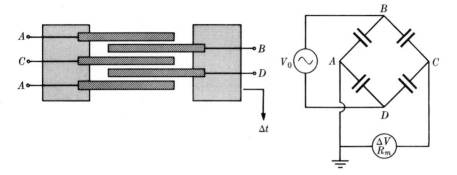

Fig. 4–27. Four-active-arm capacitance gage and the associated bridge network.

and the deviation is

$$\text{Deviation} = \left(\frac{\Delta t}{t_0}\right)^2. \tag{4–42}$$

Hence, for a pair of capacitors arranged in push-pull, the capacitance change-displacement characteristic is linear to $(\Delta t/t_0)^2$. For 1% deviation from linearity, $\Delta t/t_0$ can be as large as $\frac{1}{10}$. The improvement over a single capacitor is obvious.

Capacitance gages, as the other electrical gages we have considered, are best used in bridge circuits. Resonant circuits can also be used, but they generally give lower stability.

The first type of bridge we shall consider is a four-active-arm capacitance bridge, as shown in Fig. 4–27. Due to the high impedance of the individual arms, we must carefully consider the effect of meter impedance R_m. This system is identical with that considered for a four-active-arm resistance bridge except that the resistance impedance $Z = R$ must be replaced by the capacitive impedance $Z = -j/\omega C$. Carrying out this change gives

$$\frac{\Delta V}{V_0} = \frac{\Delta t/t_0}{\sqrt{1 + \{[1/\omega R_m C_0][1 - (\Delta t/t_0)^2]\}^2}} e^{j\phi}, \tag{4–43}$$

where

$$\tan \phi = \frac{1 - (\Delta t/t_0)^2}{\omega R_m C_0}.$$

As one would expect, the quantity $1/\omega R_m C_0$ has significance similar to the term R_0/R_m.

It is not possible to build an inductor that has only inductance without resistance; however, it is possible to build a capacitor having completely

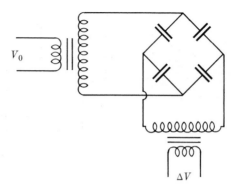

Fig. 4–28. The use of impedance-matching transformers with a capacitance gage.

negligible resistance. Hence, with the four-arm capacitance bridge, all voltages lag the current by 90°, and the output ΔV will be in phase with the input V_0.

With a capacitance bridge such as that shown in Fig. 4–27, the input voltage limitation is determined by the breakdown voltage of the dielectric. For air, the dielectric strength is of the order of 50,000 volts/inch. Hence, a capacitor with $t_0 = 0.010$ in. can be excited with up to 500 volts.

It would often be convenient if capacitance gages could be used with conventional wire-resistance strain gage instrumentation. However, such instrumentation employs a low (3 to 5 volt) excitation voltage, and has relatively low input and output impedances because it is designed to work with transducers having impedances of the order of 100 to 500 ohms rather than 1 to 10 megohms. It is possible to improve the situation considerably through use of an input transformer to raise the input voltage, and an output transformer or a cathode-follower preamplifier to match more closely the capacitance gage output impedance. In a transformer, the input-output voltage ratio equals the turns ratio, while the impedance ratio is equal to the square of the turns ratio. Thus a transformer having a 100:1 turns ratio, and a 100-ohm input impedance would have an output impedance of 10^6 ohms.

Figure 4–28 shows a circuit employing two impedance-matching transformers. The transformer impedance should be greater than the capacitor impedance if full sensitivity is to be achieved. The output is generally not in phase with the input, and the magnitude of the difference depends on the transformer characteristics. A simple output shunt capacitor can again be used to shift phase.

Cathode-follower preamplifiers are ideally suited for output impedance matching with capacitance gages. A cathode-follower preamplifier is

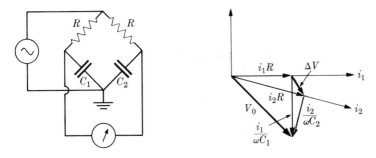

Fig. 4–29. De Sauty's bridge.

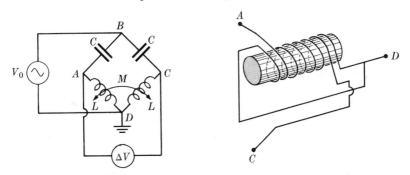

Fig. 4–30. Capacitance bridge with mutually coupled inductive arms.

actually an impedance-changing device rather than an amplifier. It always has a gain of slightly less than unity, and can have input impedances of over 1000 megohms, and output impedances of less than 500 ohms.

De Sauty's bridge, having two resistive ratio arms, is shown in Fig. 4–29. A phase plot for the condition that $R = 1/\omega C_0$ is shown. It is clear that the output ΔV for this case is in phase with V_0. The read-out instrument must have a high input impedance. The input and output can be exchanged if desirable.

Probably the most satisfactory capacitance-measuring circuit employs two closely coupled mutual inductances for ratio arms, as shown in Fig. 4–30. The two inductances are wound with two wires side by side, as shown, in order to have the inductances identical and very closely coupled. The inductances are wound on a toroidal coil of highly permeable material so that the ratio of inductance to resistance is very high. When the bridge is balanced, equal currents flow through both arms and the magnetic fields due to the two inductances cancel, reducing the inductance of each arm to zero. Thus only a very small IR voltage

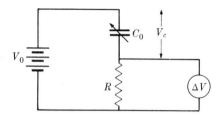

Fig. 4–31. Dynamic capacitance-measuring device utilizing d-c excitation.

exists between AD and DC. Hence A and B are almost at ground potential, and stray capacitive voltages to ground will have no effect on the output. When the bridge is unbalanced, not only is the effect of capacitance change noted, but the inductance of the two arms is no longer zero, and a large potential will develop across the meter AC. Using devices of this general type, we can observe motions of the order of 10^{-9} inch!

We have discussed simple means for measuring displacement with capacitors which are sensitive to either static or dynamic motions. When only dynamic motions are of interest, as in vibration studies, a very simple d-c capacitor system can be used. The circuit shown in Fig. 4–31 is essentially that used in capacitive microphones. When the d-c potential V_0 is applied, it appears across the variable capacitor C_0 and produces a charge $Q = C_0 V_0$ on the capacitor plates. The time constant τ for charging or discharging the capacitor will be $\tau = RC_0$. Now if changes in C_0 are made during times which are small compared with τ, the charge Q on the capacitor will not change; hence the voltage V_c across it will change; $V_c = Q/C$. We know that the sum of the voltages across C and R must equal V_0. Hence

$$\frac{\Delta V}{V_0} = 1 - \frac{C_0}{C}. \tag{4-44}$$

For small variations in the initial capacitor spacing t_0,

$$\frac{\Delta V}{V_0} = \frac{\Delta t}{t_0}. \tag{4-45}$$

We saw in Chapter 3 that if the spacing t varies in a sinusoidal manner at frequency f cps, the output ΔV will follow within 5% if $f\tau \geq 5$. Hence, for low-frequency response, τ must be made as large as possible. It is clear that the read-out meter impedance must be larger than R. If the meter impedance is constant, it can replace R.

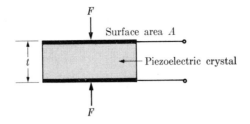

Fig. 4–32. Cross section of piezoelectric pickup.

The force exerted between capacitance plates is small enough to be completely negligible in most instances. It is easily calculated however:

$$F \approx 10^{-12} \frac{V^2 A}{t^2}, \tag{4–46}$$

where
F is in pounds,

V is in volts, and

A and t^2 are in the same units.

4–4.4. Miscellaneous electrical-displacement transducers

While there are literally dozens of items that could be included here, we shall discuss only two.

(a) *Piezoelectric transducers* operate on the principle that when an asymmetrical crystal lattice is distorted, there will be a charge reorientation resulting in a net charge on two surfaces. Consider such a crystal having conducting charge collectors attached to each side, as shown in Fig. 4–32.

The total charge, Q coulombs, is proportional to the applied force F:

$$Q = kF, \tag{4–47}$$

where k is the piezoelectric constant.

The collector plates, separated by thickness t of the piezoelectric crystal, act as a capacitor. The voltage across a capacitor due to a charge Q is

$$V = \frac{Q}{C}, \tag{4–48}$$

where
V is in volts,

Q is in coulombs, and

C is in farads.

TABLE 4-1

Material	Piezoelectric constant $k,\ \dfrac{\text{coulomb}}{\text{lb}}$	Voltage sensitivity $g,\ \dfrac{\text{volts/in.}}{\text{lb/in}^2}$
Quartz	10^{-11}	9.7
Barium titanate ceramics	6×10^{-11}	2.0

We have already seen that

$$C = 0.225\,\frac{\epsilon A}{t}\,;\qquad(4\text{--}49)$$

hence

$$V = \frac{kF}{0.225\epsilon A/t} = \frac{ktP}{0.225\epsilon}\,,\qquad(4\text{--}50)$$

where P is the pressure F/A. The quantity $k/0.225\epsilon$ is called the piezoelectric voltage sensitivity g, and

$$V = gtP.\qquad(4\text{--}51)$$

In order to obtain an idea of the numbers involved, let us consider Table 4-1, which gives the piezoelectric characteristics for two commonly used materials. We see that a barium titanate piezoelectric pickup, $0.2 \times 0.2 \times 0.05$ in., subject to a force of 1 lb, would develop a voltage of

$$V = 2.0 \times 0.05 \times \frac{1}{0.04} = 2.5\ \text{volts.}$$

With proper construction, piezoelectric crystals can be made sensitive to compression, shear, bending, or twisting. The piezoelectric action is reversible in that if a voltage is applied across the crystal, it will deform.

It must be noted that a piezoelectric device actually produces a *charge* as the result of physical *deformation*. The voltages arrived at above exist only as long as the charge does not leak off. As there is invariably finite leakage, such devices are not satisfactory for steady-state operation. Their operation is actually very similar to the d-c capacitive device previously discussed.

(b) *An interesting electronic displacement transducer* is in the form of a triode with a movable plate, as shown in Fig. 4–33. The plate is attached to a rod passing through a metallic diaphragm in the top of the tube. The pin can be rotated (using the diaphragm as a pivot) about $\frac{1}{2}°$ either way. A force of about $\frac{1}{2}$ oz is required to rotate the pin the full $\frac{1}{2}°$. This unit differs from most other sensitive displacement units in that the output is at a relatively high level. With a plate voltage of 300 volts, and a load resistance of 75,000 ohms, the output at full $\frac{1}{2}°$ deformation is 20 volts. The tube can be used to measure high-frequency variations, since its natural frequency is of the order of 12,000 cps.

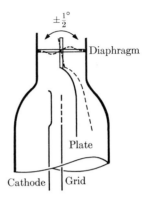

Fig. 4–33. Schematic view of RCA 5734 transducer tube.

PROBLEMS

1. Bi-filar spring suspensions are often used to produce relatively linear, low-hysteresis, small-amplitude motion. A similar mechanism can be used in "shear" instead of "bending" to change a linear motion into a rotation. Both systems are employed in a Sheffield Corporation gage, as shown schematically in Fig. 4–34. Estimate the magnification (in. output/in. input), and also the input force required per unit of input motion. List assumptions. All spring elements are steel, 0.020 in. thick by 0.2 in. wide. [*Ans.* $y/x \approx 20$; $F/x \approx 500$ lb/in]

2. For the resistance-measuring circuit of Fig. 4–14(b), plot $\Delta V/V_0$ versus $\Delta R/R_0$ for $R_m/R_0 = 0.1, 1.0, 10.0$.

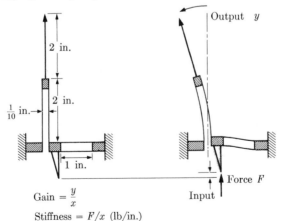

Figure 4–34

3. When driving a high-frequency galvanometer from an amplifier, or directly from a strain gage bridge, it is generally necessary to satisfy two requirements in order to obtain optimum performance. (a) The input impedance of the galvanometer system, as seen by the bridge or amplifier, must be matched to the amplifier or bridge output impedance R_B for maximum power transmittal. (b) The impedance of the amplifier system, as seen by the galvanometer, must be a specified value R_D in order to obtain proper damping of the unit.

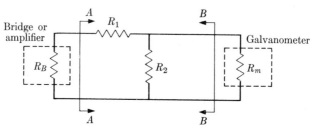

Figure 4–35

It is clear that these two requirements will generally be contradictory. It is possible, however, to insert an impedance-matching "L-pad," as shown in Fig. 4–35, which will allow each component to "see" the required impedance. For $R_B = 500 \, \Omega$, R_{BB} desired $= 50 \, \Omega$, $R_m = 1 \, \Omega$, and R_{AA} desired $= 500 \, \Omega$, find R_1 and R_2. [Ans. $R_1 = 499 \, \Omega$; $R_2 = 52.7 \, \Omega$]

4. For the one-active-arm strain gage bridge shown in Fig. 4–36, the resistances R_0 and R_A need not be equal. Assuming that $R_m \gg R_A$, R_0, and that the maximum $\Delta R/R_0 = 0.01$, determine the ratio of R_A/R_0 which will give greatest sensitivity within the limits of 1% linearity. [Ans. $R_0 = R_A$]

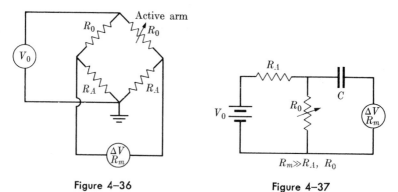

Figure 4–36   **Figure 4–37**

5. For *dynamic* measurements, the simple series circuit shown in Fig. 4–37 can be used. What are the characteristics of such a circuit? Is there any advantage over a Wheatstone bridge?

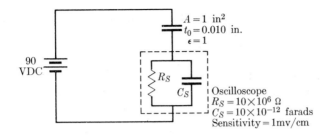

Figure 4-38

6. For vibration measurement, a battery, a two-plate variable capacitor, and an oscilloscope are arranged as shown in Fig. 4–38. Determine the displacement sensitivity and 95% frequency response. [*Ans.* 9×10^6 cm/in.; $f_{95\%} > 22{,}000$ cps]

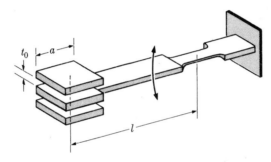

Figure 4-39

7. In certain variable-capacitance devices, it is desirable to have the center plate move by rotating about a distant point, as shown in Fig. 4–39. Does this reduce or extend the linear range of the device? For square plates, $a \times a$, with an initial spacing t_0, and an effective axis of rotation l from the center of the plate, plot the *total* (for the two capacitors) $\Delta C/C_0$ versus $\Delta t/t_0$, where Δt is measured at the center of the plate; use $t_0/a = 0.01$, $l/a = 3$. [*Partial Ans.* $\Delta C/C_0 = -(3/\Delta t/t_0) \ln \{[1 - (\Delta t/t_0)^2]/[1 - \frac{4}{9}(\Delta t/t_0)^2]\}$]

REFERENCES

BECKWITH, T. G., and N. L. BUCK, *Mechanical Measurements*, Addison-Wesley Publishing Co., Reading, Mass., 1961. Good description of numerous input transducers, with extensive references.

HARRIS, F. K., *Electrical Measurements*, John Wiley and Sons, New York, 1952. Discussion of measurement of *electrical* quantities.

LION, K. S., *Instrumentation in Scientific Research*, McGraw-Hill Book Co., New York, 1959. Description of wide variety of mechano-electrical input transducers, including extensive references.

MILLIS, DEAN, 3rd, and RICHARD D. DOUGLAS, eds., *Semiconductor and Conventional Strain Gages*, Academic Press, New York, 1962.

PARTRIDGE, G. R., *Principles of Electronic Instruments*, Prentice-Hall, Englewood Cliffs, New Jersey, 1958. Good discussion of voltage-measuring devices.

ROBERTS, H. C., *Mechanical Measurements by Electrical Methods*, The Instruments Publishing Co., Pittsburgh, 1951. Description of numerous mechano-electrical input transducers, some circuitry considerations.

A. B. DuMont Laboratories, *Transducers*, Clifton, N. J., 1953. A comprehensive compilation of mechano-electric and other transducers, their characteristics and their manufacturers. Out of date, but still very useful.

CHAPTER FIVE

Force and Torque Measurement

5-1. Preliminary requirements

When we make force and torque measurements, we can employ a wide variety of possible methods, but there are many requirements that have to be met in any application. Before we make any attempt to design a force-measuring system, we should study the mechanics of the unknown forces in order to establish reasonable design criteria. The following list of questions must be answered; the answers to them will help establish many of the design criteria.

1. Are we sure that measurement of the forces acting on the system will provide the desired information? Occasionally, measurement of the *result*, or action, of the force application (such as acceleration or velocity) will be more meaningful.
2. Will the force (or torque) always be applied at the same spatial point on the system, or will its point of application move?
3. Will it be necessary to determine the point of force application?
4. Can the system be altered so that the force *will* always act at the same point?
5. Is the direction of the resultant force (or torque) vector known, or must this be ascertained?
6. If it is necessary to measure more than one force component, what set of mutually perpendicular components will most facilitate analysis after measurement?
7. Often a force interaction within a system is to be measured. In this case, should we measure the force or its reaction force? Often one measurement is easier to accomplish than the other. For instance, in order to measure the force in wire-drawing, we measure either the force on the wire or the force on the die. Because the wire moves, it may be easier to measure the force on the die.
8. What is the greatest force expected? What is the average force expected? What is the least force expected?
9. What degree of resolution is necessary and reasonable for the least load and for the average load?

10. What absolute accuracy is required?

11. Invariably there is some deflection of the system associated with a force measurement. What magnitude of deflection can be tolerated without unduly influencing the process under investigation?

12. Is time an important variable, or can steady-state measurements be made after transients have died away? How rapid must the measurement be?

13. If transient forces are important, what force-time characteristics will be expected? What must the dynamic characteristics of the force-measuring system be in order to "follow" the force variations?

14. What type of measuring equipment is available?

15. Are there any particular space-weight requirements?

16. Is the system of a type that is prone to self-excited vibration?

17. What are the cost and time limitations?

For someone not experienced in force measurements, the answers to the above questions will provide a very quick and helpful guide toward a satisfactory method of measurement, and will point out the important problem areas.

5-2. Systems for measuring force

Figure 5–1 shows a generalized system for measuring a force F. Any system involves components having inertial qualities, spring qualities, and damping qualities, although we may not readily identify such components without some study. In the general system, the applied force F tends to displace the mass m a distance y.

In most force-measuring devices, particularly those used to measure rapidly varying forces, the displacement y is measured (using the techniques of Chapter 4) as an indication of the force. Under steady-state conditions,

$$F = ky. \tag{5-1}$$

In other systems, such as balance systems, an opposing force F' is applied and adjusted to make $y = 0$, and therefore $F = F'$. The force F' can be applied by gravity, by electrical means, by pneumatic or hydraulic means, etc. This type of system requires some type of servo-loop in order to adjust F' to give $y = 0$. Generally such a system is slower in response than one using the spring system, but it does produce the final measurement under zero deflection conditions. Also, because it is a comparison technique, the accuracy can be determined by the accuracy of F' while the sensitivity depends on the effective k and the minimum detectable value of y.

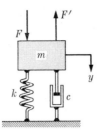

Fig. 5-1. Generalized single-component force-measuring system.

The equation of motion for the idealized system of Fig. 5-1 is

$$m\ddot{y} + c\dot{y} + ky = (F - F')_t \qquad (5\text{-}2)$$

or

$$\ddot{y} + 2\zeta\omega_n\dot{y} + \omega_n^2 y = \frac{(F - F')_t}{m}, \qquad (5\text{-}3)$$

where

$$\omega_n = \sqrt{k/m} \quad \text{natural frequency (undamped, rad/sec)},$$

$$\zeta = \frac{c}{2\sqrt{km}} \qquad \text{damping ratio.}$$

In Chapter 3, where the dynamics of measurement are discussed in some detail, the response characteristics of Eq. (5-3) with $F' = 0$ are also discussed in detail. There it is shown that if we are concerned with a step-type input (Fig. 3-8), optimum conditions are obtained with a damping ratio $\zeta \sim 0.7$. Under this condition there will be about a 5% overshoot, but the output will be within 5% of its steady-state value in a time corresponding to about $\frac{1}{2}$ of a natural period ($\omega_n t/2\pi = \frac{1}{2}$) of the system.

When the input force varies cyclically with time, as with a sinusoidal input at frequency ω_f, a damping ratio of $\zeta = 0.7$ will again give very good amplitude results (as shown in Fig. 3-10) in that the indicated amplitude will deviate from the desired amplitude by less than 5% for input frequencies up to $\frac{1}{2}$ of the system natural frequency ($\omega_f/\omega_n < \frac{1}{2}$). However, we can also see from this figure that there is a considerable phase lag between input and output.

When it becomes necessary to closely follow rapid force variation the problem is quite difficult. For instance, if we consider the case where the input force F varies linearly with time,

$$F = C_1 t, \qquad (5\text{-}4)$$

TABLE 5–1

RESPONSE TO LINEARLY INCREASING FORCE

ζ	Time for $ky/F = 0.95$
0.1	$\omega_n t \approx 10$
0.3	≈ 11
0.5	≈ 20
0.7	≈ 26

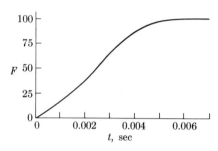

Fig. 5–2. Assumed force curve.

it can be shown that in order for ky to reach 95% of F the times listed in Table 5–1 are required. The data in Table 5–1 imply that when forces are fluctuating, and we are interested in a change of force occurring during a time element Δt, then Δt must be at least twice the natural period of vibration $(2\pi/\omega_n)$ for $\zeta = 0.1$, and at least four times the period for $\zeta = 0.7$ (for 5% error).

EXAMPLE. Assume that we expect a force-time curve as shown in Fig. 5–2, and that we are interested in the transient conditions during the first 0.005 sec. If we think that the curve could be approximated by 10 points, 0.0005 sec = Δt apart, then the minimum system natural frequency would be as given in Table 5–2. Thus it is the minimum time increment Δt that governs the required frequency, rather than the entire force duration. It is evident that for certain types of loading $\zeta = 0.7$ is desirable, while for others it may be preferable to

TABLE 5–2

ζ	ω_n, rad/sec	f_n, cps
0.1	2×10^4	3200
0.7	5×10^4	8000

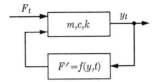

Fig. 5-3. Block diagram of balancing-type system.

use $\zeta = 0.1$ to 0.3. If $\zeta < 0.1$, there will generally be rather large oscillations which will obscure the true readings.

Balancing-type systems require a servo-loop of some kind in order to produce the balancing force. Hence we must analyze their response, taking into account the characteristics of the servo component. Figure 5-3 shows the block diagram of such a system. One of the simplest servo systems that will work here is one in which the feedback unit provides a force F' proportional to the integral of y:

$$F' = k_1 \int y \, dt. \tag{5-5}$$

Equation (5-2) then becomes:

$$m\ddot{y} + c\dot{y} + ky = \dot{F} - k_1 y \tag{5-6}$$

or

$$m\ddot{y} + c\dot{y} + ky + k_1 y = \dot{F}. \tag{5-7}$$

Under steady-state conditions, $y = 0$ and $F' = F$. For detailed analysis of the performance and stability of this type of system, the reader is referred to books on automatic control systems.

The foregoing part of this chapter should enable the reader to determine the desired characteristics of a proposed force-measuring system. The remainder of the chapter will be devoted to enumerating a number of useful methods for measuring force or torque. The methods discussed will certainly not be exhaustive, since any spring mechanism together with any deflection-measuring system will enable the reader to carry out force measurement.

Spring elements can either be used with a displacement transducer, or the elastic strains of the spring can be measured through the use of strain gages. Thus we are interested not only in the load-deflection characteristics of various springs, but also in their load-strain characteristics. We shall restrict ourselves to systems capable of high natural frequencies.

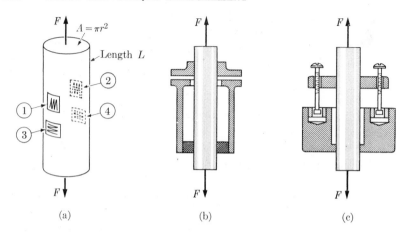

Fig. 5–4. Methods for using an axial rod to measure force.

5–3. Axially loaded members

Probably the simplest method for measuring unidirectional forces of greater than about 50 lb is to use a bar in tension or compression. Figure 5–4(a) shows a simple rod with strain gages attached. Gages 1 and 2 are on opposite sides of the bar and are aligned to measure axial strain. Gages 3 and 4 are on opposite sides and measure circumferential strain.

The strain in the gages will be

$$\epsilon_1, \epsilon_2 = \frac{F}{AE}, \qquad \epsilon_3, \epsilon_4 = -\frac{\mu F}{AE}, \qquad (5\text{--}8)$$

where

F is the axial force,

A is the cross-sectional area,

E is Young's modulus, and

μ is Poisson's ratio.

The axial spring constant k is

$$k = \frac{AE}{L}, \qquad (5\text{--}9)$$

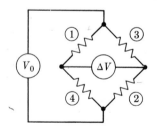

Fig. 5–5. The proper wiring for Fig. 5–4(a).

where L is the length of the rod.

Figure 5–5 shows the proper wiring of this unit. If the gages are symmetrically placed, the unit will be completely insensitive to any loading other than F. Thus a bending load might cause additional strain in gage 1. However, there would be equal and opposite additional strain in gage 2. Since these gages are in opposite arms of the bridge, these two changes cancel. The degree to which these effects actually cancel depends on just how symmetrical the gage placement is and how uniform the gage characteristics are.

EXAMPLE. A 1-in. diameter steel rod has 4 gages (G.F. = 2.3) placed as shown in Fig. 5–4(a). If the bridge is excited with a d-c voltage of 6 volts (6 VDC), what will the output ΔV be for a 100-lb load?

Two arms have $\epsilon = F/AE$, while the other two have $\epsilon = -\mu F/AE$. Letting $E = 30 \times 10^6$ psi and $\mu = 0.3$, we have

$$\frac{\Delta V}{V_0} = (\text{G.F.}) \left(\frac{F}{AE}\right) \left(\frac{2 + 2\mu}{4}\right) = \frac{2.3 \times 100}{(\pi/4) \times 30 \times 10^6} \left(\frac{2.6}{4}\right) = 6.35 \times 10^{-6}.$$

Therefore

$$\Delta V = 38 \times 10^{-6} \text{ volts.}$$

If the 1-in. diameter section is 2 in. long, the spring constant is

$$k = \frac{\pi}{4} \times \frac{1}{2} \times 30 \times 10^6 = 11.8 \times 10^6 \text{ lb/in.}$$

Figure 5–4(b) and (c) shows capacitance and inductance gages arranged to measure F. If the inductance gages are linear, they will not be affected by bending of the rod. However, the capacitance gage is nonlinear and will be affected, although there is some degree of compensation.

5–4. Cantilever beams

Cantilevers are ideally suited for the measurement of bending moments about two axes mutually perpendicular to the beam axis. If the point of load application along the beam is known, the bending moment can be directly translated into force. Figure 5–6 shows a cantilever

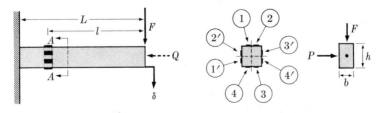

Fig. 5–6. Cantilever beam for measuring force.

gaged to measure F (gages 1, 2, 3, 4) and a force P perpendicular to F (gages 1', 2', 3', 4'). If the gages are symmetrically located with respect to the neutral axes of the beam, and are wired as shown in Fig. 5–5, the two perpendicular force components can be independently measured. It should be noted that an axial force component Q will not affect the readings if it acts at the center of the cross section. The pertinent equations for such a cantilever are:

$$\epsilon_{1,2,3,4} = \frac{6Fl}{Ebh^2}, \qquad \delta = \frac{4FL^3}{Ebh^3} \qquad \text{or} \qquad k = \frac{Ebh^3}{4L^3}. \qquad (5\text{--}10)$$

We should note that the portion of the bar between the gages and F can be made much stiffer, thus reducing δ while not affecting ϵ.

5–5. Rings

Rings, as shown in Fig. 5–7, have been used as springs in various load-measuring devices for years. However, the full potential of a ring as a load cell was not realized until their development by Cook in 1951. Because of the extreme usefulness of this device, we shall go into the details of its analysis.

Consider one-half of a ring (Fig. 5–8) with the loads shown. We shall consider the case where the top and bottom of the ring are restrained from rotation; M_0 is the moment required to satisfy this condition.

The bending moment M_θ at any point in the ring is

$$M_\theta = M_0 + \frac{Fr}{2}\sin\theta + \frac{Pr}{2}(1 - \cos\theta). \qquad (5\text{--}11)$$

The total elastic energy in the ring is

$$U = \frac{1}{2EI}\int_0^\pi M_\theta^2\, r\, d\theta. \qquad (5\text{--}12)$$

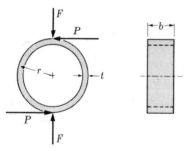

Fig. 5–7. A thin ring used to measure force.

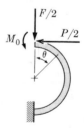

Fig. 5–8. Ring element for elastic analysis.

The angular rotation ϕ of the ring at $\theta = 0$ is 0; thus

$$\left(\frac{\partial U}{\partial M_0}\right)_{\theta=0} = 0 = \frac{1}{EI}\int_0^\pi M_\theta \frac{\partial M_\theta}{\partial M_0} r\, d\theta, \tag{5-13}$$

or

$$0 = \int_0^\pi \left[M_0 + \frac{Fr\sin\theta}{2} + \frac{Pr}{2}(1 - \cos\theta)\right] d\theta. \tag{5-14}$$

When integrated this gives

$$M_0\pi + Fr + \frac{Pr\pi}{2} = 0, \tag{5-15}$$

$$M_0 = -\frac{Fr}{\pi} - \frac{Pr}{2}. \tag{5-16}$$

We can now rewrite Eq. (5–11) as

$$M_\theta = \frac{Fr}{2}\left(\sin\theta - \frac{2}{\pi}\right) - \frac{Pr}{2}\cos\theta. \tag{5-17}$$

We note that the moment due to $F/2$ is zero when

$$\sin\theta = \frac{2}{\pi}, \qquad \theta = 39.6°, \tag{5-18}$$

and the moment due to $P/2$ is zero when

$$\cos\theta = 0, \qquad \theta = 90°. \tag{5-19}$$

The two positions $\theta = 39.6°$ and $\theta = 90°$ are each a strain node for one force. Hence we can write

$$M_{39.6°} = -\frac{Pr}{2}\cos 39.6° = -0.385\, Pr, \tag{5-20}$$

$$M_{90°} = \frac{Fr}{2}\left(\sin 90° - \frac{2}{\pi}\right) = +0.181\, Fr. \tag{5-21}$$

The strain ϵ in a thin ring is

$$\epsilon = \frac{6M}{Ebt^2}. \tag{5-22}$$

Therefore

$$\epsilon_{39.6°} = 2.31\frac{Pr}{Ebt^2}, \tag{5-23}$$

$$\epsilon_{90°} = 1.09\frac{Fr}{Ebt^2}. \tag{5-24}$$

It can be shown from symmetry that Eqs. (5–15) and (5–16) hold equally well for the whole ring of Fig. 5–7, provided that the top and bottom are restrained from rotation. We have then a unit capable of independently measuring two force components F and P.

We can compute the horizontal (δ_p) and vertical (δ_f) deflections of the ring:

$$\delta_p = \frac{\partial U}{\partial (P/2)} = \frac{1}{EI} \int_0^\pi M_\theta \frac{\partial M_\theta}{\partial (P/2)} r \, d\theta, \qquad (5\text{–}25)$$

$$\delta_p = \frac{1}{EI} \int_0^\pi \left[\frac{Fr}{2} \left(\sin \theta - \frac{2}{\pi} \right) - \frac{Pr}{2} \cos \theta \right] (-r \cos \theta) r \, d\theta. \qquad (5\text{–}26)$$

Hence

$$\delta_p = 9.42 \frac{Pr^3}{Ebt^3}. \qquad (5\text{–}27)$$

In a similar fashion

$$\delta_f = 1.79 \frac{Fr^3}{Ebt^3}. \qquad (5\text{–}28)$$

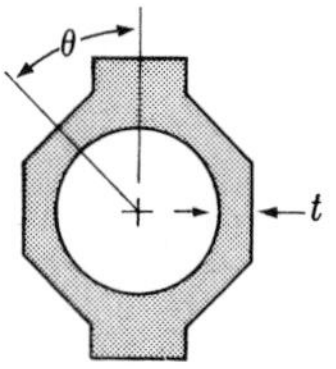

Fig. 5–9. Octagonal ring.

When maximum horizontal (P direction) stiffness is not required, round rings attached to the system frame by screws through small holes at $\theta = 0°$ and $\theta = 180°$ are perfectly satisfactory. However, there will be a tendency for the ring to roll due to P. This can be avoided by fabricating an octagonal ring as shown in Fig. 5–9. The upper and lower faces of the octagon are extended to form "bosses" for mounting to the frame. In this instance, there is no complete elasticity solution. However, empirical photoelastic determinations have shown that the strain nodes now occur at about $\theta = 50°$ and $\theta = 90°$. The strain and deflection equations are approximated by:

$$\epsilon_{50°} \approx 1.4 \frac{Pr}{Ebt^2}, \qquad (5\text{–}29)$$

$$\epsilon_{90°} \approx 0.7 \frac{Fr}{Ebt^2}, \qquad (5\text{–}30)$$

$$\delta_p \approx 3.7 \frac{Pr^3}{Ebt^3}, \qquad (5\text{–}31)$$

$$\delta_f \approx 1.0 \frac{Fr^3}{Ebt^3}. \qquad (5\text{–}32)$$

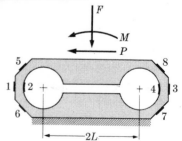

Fig. 5–10. Diagram showing how an octagonal ring can be extended for stability.

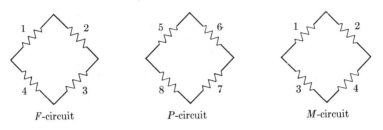

F-circuit   P-circuit   M-circuit

Fig. 5-11. Wiring diagram for the elements in Fig. 5-10.

Circular or octagonal rings can be used in a wide variety of ways for force measurement. We shall discuss just a few of these.

Figure 5-10 shows an octagonal ring extended by $2L$ in order to gain stability and approximately meet the requirement of zero rotation of the top surface. The wiring diagrams of Fig. 5-11 indicate gage connections for measuring F, P, or M. When using an extended ring to measure M, there will be rotation ϕ of the top member. The results of an analysis for strain and deflection of a circular extended ring are shown in Fig. 5-12. When used to measure F and P, an extended unit will give the same results independent of the load location (subject, of course, to

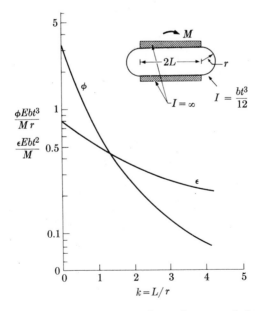

Fig. 5-12. Moment sensitivity and stiffness of an extended round ring.

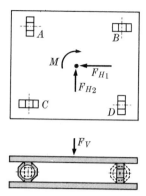

Fig. 5–13. A multicomponent dynamometer capable of measuring three force components independent of location, and three moment components.

errors due to nonsymmetrical gage placement, etc.). This can be seen from Figs. 5–10 and 5–11. If the vertical load F is displaced sideways, the total vertical load carried by the right and left half-rings is the same, even though the portion carried by either part changes. In the Wheatstone bridge circuit, the output is proportional to the *sum* of all strains, and hence proportional to the total load.

The same type of thinking is employed on the multicomponent dynamometer shown in Fig. 5–13. Here, all four rings are wired in a single bridge to measure F_V. Rings A and D measure F_{H_2} while B and C measure F_{H_1}. By simply interchanging two arms of the F_{H_1} or F_{H_2} bridge, M will be measured. The gages used to measure F_V can also be rewired to measure moments about horizontal axes.

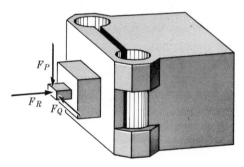

Fig. 5–14. Three-component lathe tool dynamometer.

Figure 5–14 shows a very satisfactory three-component lathe dynamomenter. It is left to the reader to determine gage location and wiring.

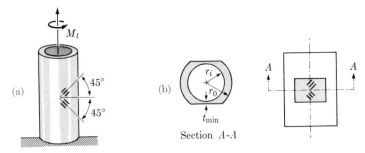

Fig. 5–15. Strain gages at 45° to axis measure torque M_t.

5–6. Torque tubes

A convenient method for measuring torque is by means of solid or hollow tubes twisted by the applied torque. Under torque loading there will be tensile and compressive strains at the tube surface at 45° to the tube axis as shown in Fig. 5–15(a). Elasticity gives

$$\epsilon_{45°} = \pm \frac{M_t r_0}{\pi G(r_0^4 - r_1^4)}, \tag{5–33}$$

$$\phi = \frac{2M_t l}{\pi G(r_0^4 - r_1^4)},$$

where
G is the shear modulus,

ϕ is the rotation, radians, and

l is the length of the tube.

If the sensitivity obtained from a simple tube is insufficient, it can be increased by thinning the tube wall at the gaging sections as shown in Fig. 5–15(b). The strain will be raised by the ratio of the initial thickness $r_0 - r_1$ to the minimum thickness t_{min}.

5–7. General considerations

When attempting to make force measurements from very slight deflections, particularly when multicomponent dynamometers are designed, we must bear in mind that because of the small size of the measuring deformations, other elastic deformations in the system can significantly alter the performance. Particularly troublesome are *mating* surfaces. It is impossible to produce truly mating surfaces that will remain in perfect contact during load. Thus it is often advisable to

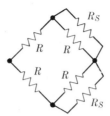

Fig. 5–16. The use of shunt resistors to alter effective gage factors.

reduce the contact area between mating parts to a few well-chosen, highly loaded pads. Then, even if the entire structure does warp somewhat under load, the contact points will remain fixed and deformations within the structure will vary linearly with load. If possible, it is preferable to avoid mating surfaces by machining from a solid member, or through brazing, welding, etc.

When multicomponent units are tested, it may be found that there is cross-interference; i.e., there may be a fictitious force reading in the x direction due to a force in the y or z direction. Many faults of this type can be corrected by simply varying the effective gage factor of one or more gages in the x bridge. Although this is a trial-and-error procedure, it is simple and fast. Most often, we can obtain the desired results by reducing the effective gage factor of two adjacent arms by simply shunting both arms with equal shunt resistors R_s, as shown in Fig. 5–16. This generally involves values of R_s larger than R, and a high-quality resistor will give satisfactory stability.

Equivalent gage factors can also be altered by a combination of shunt and series resistors, as shown in Fig. 5–17. Here, R_{s_2} is a small series resistor used to bring the total resistance up to the initial value R (to facilitate balancing of the bridge). In this instance, R_{s_2} must be extremely stable if it is not to give rise to drift.

Calibration of load cells or dynamometers is best accomplished by means of precision dead weights. While the use of lever systems and small weights to obtain large forces is often attractive, force magnifications greater than five tend generally to produce errors. For very large loads, a calibrated testing machine should be used.

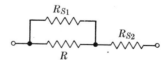

Fig. 5–17. The use of shunt and series resistors to reduce effective gage factors.

PROBLEMS

1. A load cell using capacitance plate displacement measurement is made as shown in Fig. 5–18. Estimate (compute) the error caused by a slightly eccentric loading. (Estimate error based on square plates.) [*Ans.* Approximately 1% error for ϵ = 0.0006 in.]

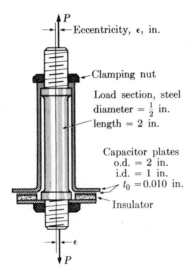

Figure 5–18

2. Is a single ring, firmly mounted at its base, capable of measuring the two force components shown in Fig. 5–19?

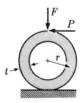

Figure 5–19

3. Is a torque tube, with four strain gages at 45° to the axis, subject to interference from an axial load? [*Ans.* No.]

4. For a given strain or load sensitivity, does a hollow cylindrical cantilever bar have a higher natural frequency than a solid one? [*Ans.* Yes.]

5. For a given strain or torque sensitivity, does a hollow torque tube have a higher natural frequency than a solid one? [*Ans.* For given strain, same

natural frequency; for given torsional spring constant, hollow tube has higher natural frequency.]

6. Design a strain gage load cell, axial or cantilever, capable of satisfactorily measuring the force transient of Fig. 5–2. Assume that G.F. = 2.0; V_0 = 5 volts; E = 30 × 10^6 psi; density γ = 0.28 lbs/in^3; read-out resolution = 10^{-5} volts.

7. Using the assumptions of Problem 6, design a torque-tube axial-load-cell combination having resolution of: torque, 1 in.-lb; load, 5 lb.

8. Design a load cell having an electrical output, and a resolution of 0.1 gm when used with a read-out device sensitive to 10^{-5} volt. Estimate the natural frequency of the cell.

9. It is generally desirable, in a strain-gage load cell, to have both high stiffness and high sensitivity. Consider three load cells: an axial rod, a cantilever, and a strain ring. For a sensitivity of 1 μ in./in. strain per 1-lb load, using $\frac{1}{4}$ in. × $\frac{1}{4}$ in. gages, what is the maximum stiffness practically obtainable for the three different types of cells?

10. We have seen that a shunt calibrating resistance has the same effect on bridge output as the application of a load input. Shunt resistors can also be used to give "zero suppression," i.e., to put the zero off scale such that the meter or recorder can be used at high sensitivity to observe or record inputs that would give greater than full-scale motion. Design an axial load cell, using strain gages of 120-ohm resistance, and G.F. = 2.0. The system is to resolve to 1 lb with a full range of 1000 lb. Input voltage is 5 volts, instrument resolution 10^{-5} volt. Design calibration and zero suppression circuits that will (a) produce a calibration signal (output) equivalent to 100 lb input, and (b) provide zero suppression of 100, 200, 300, 400, 500, 600, 700, 800, and 900 lb.

REFERENCES

AHRENDT, W. R., and J. F. TAPLIN, *Automatic Feedback Control*, McGraw-Hill Book Co., New York, 1951. Stability analyses suitable for servo-controlled balancing systems.

COOK, N. H., E. G. LOEWEN, and M. C. SHAW, "Machine-Tool Dynamometers," *American Machinist*, May 10, 1954.

LOEWEN, E. G., and N. H. COOK, "Metal Cutting Measurements and Their Interpretation," *S.E.S.A. Proceedings*, Vol. XIII, No. 2, 1955. Photoelastic analysis of "octagonal rings."

ROBERTS, H. C., *Mechanical Measurements by Electrical Methods*, The Instruments Publishing Co., Pittsburgh, 1951.

TIMOSHENKO, S., *Theory of Elasticity*, McGraw-Hill Book Co., New York, 1934. Thick-walled ring theories.

CHAPTER SIX

Temperature Measurement

Temperature can best be visualized as a measure of the thermal motion of the molecules or atoms making up a material. Higher temperatures imply motions of greater amplitudes. Because temperature is such a fundamental concept, it is not easy to define. A thermodynamic temperature scale can be defined in terms of efficiencies of Carnot cycles, but this definition is of little use for practical measurement. As a result, all temperature-measuring devices record some physical manifestation of the increased energy of the molecules or atoms. The most used changes are:

(1) change in physical state,

(2) change in chemical state,

(3) change in dimensions,

(4) change in electrical properties,

(5) change in radiation properties.

None of these changes gives an absolute measure of temperature but rather must be calibrated to some arbitrarily chosen standard. The standards chosen for the International Temperature Scale of 1948 are as follows:

Boiling point of oxygen	$-297.346°F$	$-182.970°C$
Melting point of ice	32 °F	0 °C
Boiling point of water	212 °F	100 °C
Boiling point of sulfur	832.28 °F	444.600°C
Melting point of silver	1761.4 °F	960.8 °C
Melting point of gold	1945.4 °F	1063.0 °C

All these definitions are at one standard atmosphere (14.6959 psia) and at an equilibrium of the two phases. The gap between these standard points is divided by using either a platinum resistance thermometer or a platinum versus platinum-10%-rhodium thermocouple. Outside this range there is not yet a universally accepted manner to define temperature.

For local standards, a precision mercury in glass thermometer is often used in conjunction with an ice bath to check one point on the scale.

6–1. Temperature-measuring devices

(a) *Bimaterials.* The commonest bimaterial is the liquid in glass thermometer. Both the glass and liquid expand upon heating and the differential expansion is used to indicate the temperature. The lower-temperature limit is $-38.78°F$ for mercury and down to $-321°F$ for pentane. The high-temperature limit is $1100°F$ for mercury. The initial precision of the thermometer depends upon the care used in calibration. Typical instruments will be checked and marked at from two to five reference temperatures. Intermediate points are then obtained by interpolation. Once calibrated, glass thermometers for use below $300°F$ will maintain their calibration to $0.2°F$ over long periods. For greater accuracy the thermometer should be occasionally checked against the ice point. Above $300°F$ the glass tends to creep or flow with time in an unpredictable manner. Calibration of a thermometer may be for partial or total immersion and for horizontal or vertical orientation. A correction should be applied if maximum accuracy is desired and other than calibration conditions are used. Failure to observe these conditions will result in errors of about $1°F$ for a typical total-immersion mercury thermometer used as a partial-immersion thermometer at the boiling point of water.

The time required for equilibrium readings varies from about 15 or 30 sec for a $\frac{1}{4}$-in. diameter bulb in stirred water to about 10 min for the same bulb in still air.

A second common bimaterial is the bimetal strip. Two metals brazed together along their length will bend into a uniform radius when the temperature changes. The radius will be

$$\rho = \frac{t[3(1 + m)^2 + (1 + mn)(m^2 - 1/mn)]}{6(\alpha_2 + \alpha_1)(T - T_0)(1 + m)^2},$$

where ρ is the radius of curvature at temperature T,

T_0 is the initial temperature for straight strip,

T is the temperature,

t is the total thickness of strip,

m is the ratio of thickness of low-expansion to high-expansion material,

n is the ratio of elastic modulus of low-expansion to high-expansion material,

α_1 is the lower coefficient of thermal expansion, and

α_2 is the higher coefficient of thermal expansion.

The useful range of bimetals is $-100°F$ to $1000°F$.

(b) *Pressure thermometers.* There are a wide variety of pressure thermometers, all based on the same mechanism. A relatively large bulb is filled with a liquid, gas, or liquid-vapor mixture. The bulb is connected to a Bourdon tube or other direct-reading pressure gage. The gages are calibrated on the basis of pressure change corresponding to temperature change.

The liquid and gas filled types are subject to error if the connecting tubing from bulb to gage is long and at a different temperature than that used at calibration. The liquid-vapor system does not have this error so long as a free liquid surface exists in the sensing bulb. These liquid-vapor systems follow Dalton's law, which states that if both liquid and vapor are present, there is only one pressure corresponding to a given temperature.

Pressure thermometers are often used with long connecting tubes, up to 200 ft, and since the tubes may be liquid filled, errors of considerable magnitude can occur in reading if the meter is at a different elevation than the bulb. The effects of gravity heads can be corrected for when they are known to exist.

The useful range of pressure thermometers is −400°F to +1000°F, with a range of about 400°F in a given instrument depending upon the sensing fluid or gas.

(c) *Resistance thermometers.* Resistance thermometers are divided into two classes depending on whether the active material is a "conductor" or a "semiconductor." In general, the resistance of highly conducting materials (metals) increases with increased temperature, and coils of these materials are termed "resistance thermometers." The resistance of semiconductors generally (not always) decreases with increased temperature. Thermosensitive resistors, having such negative resistance-temperature characteristics, are termed "thermistors." The temperature sensitivity of thermistors is much greater than that of resistance thermometers. However, they are far from linear, and not overly stable. Hence, we usually find the less sensitive, relatively linear resistance thermometers used for precise measurement, while thermistors are used for applications not requiring the highest accuracy. Table 6–1 shows the inherent sensitivities α of a number of thermoresistive materials, the approximate (linear) relation between temperature and resistance being

$$R/R_0 = 1 + \alpha \, \Delta\theta, \tag{6–1}$$

where R_0 is the initial resistance, ohms,

R is the final resistance, ohms,

$\Delta\theta$ is the temperature change (°F, °C), and

α is the resistance-temperature coefficient.

TABLE 6–1

RESISTANCE-TEMPERATURE COEFFICIENTS* FOR COMMON
MATERIALS (NEAR ROOM TEMPERATURE, °F^{-1})

Material	Coefficient
Aluminum	0.0025
Copper	0.0024
Gold	0.0022
Iron alloy	0.001 to 0.003
Lead	0.0023
Mercury	0.00055
Nickel	0.0037
Platinum	0.00217
Silver	0.0023
Tungsten	0.0027
Manganese	±0.00001
Carbon	−0.00039
Electrolytes	−0.01 to −0.05
Semiconductors	−0.038 to +0.08

* These values should not be considered
absolute as they vary with the history of
the sample tested.

Resistance thermometers are commonly used as the variable resistance
in a Wheatstone bridge (see Section 4–4). It is readily seen from Eq.
(6–1) that

$$\Delta R/R_0 = \alpha \, \Delta\theta. \tag{6–2}$$

The actual thermoresistive element may take a number of different
physical forms, all being coils of some shape supported in a stress-free
manner. Some elements are flat coils, precisely like wire-resistance
strain gages, while others are coils wound on mica forms. Very small
resistive elements can follow rapid temperature variations, but tend to
have low initial resistance. On the other hand, relatively large coils
can have large initial resistance, but will exhibit relatively large time
constants τ and will measure an average temperature. Temperature
differences can be readily measured by introducing resistive elements
into adjacent arms of a Wheatstone bridge, while average temperatures
can be measured by placing resistive elements in series in one arm of
the bridge.

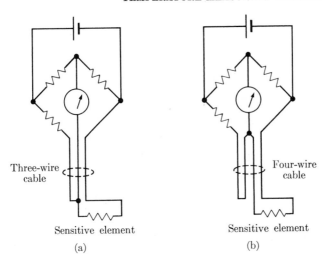

Fig. 6–1. Lead arrangements for compensation of variations in lead resistance when using thermoresistive elements.

When the temperature of the active element changes, the resistance of the leads will also change. For most precise results, the effects of variable-lead resistance must be eliminated. This is generally accomplished by introducing additional leads so that two adjacent bridge arms will both have leads as part of the total arm resistance. Figure 6–1 shows the two most used compensation systems. It is also essential that thermoelectric emf's do not affect the system. These can be eliminated by utilizing a-c excitation of the bridge, or by manually varying the polarity of the d-c supply.

Errors can also be introduced through I^2R heating of the resistive element. It is clear that the maximum I^2R heating that can be tolerated depends largely upon the heat transfer conditions adjacent to the thermometer. When the temperature to be measured is steady with respect to time, the effect of I^2R heating can be accounted for by obtaining temperature measurements at two or more currents, and extrapolating to zero current.

As in all temperature-measuring systems where the entire system is not at uniform temperature, there will be an error in resistance thermometry due to heat transfer through the leads. This can be minimized by using small-diameter leads which are in close thermal contact with the body under measurement for some distance away from the measuring point. In this manner, most of the temperature change due to lead conduction will occur at a distance from the measuring point.

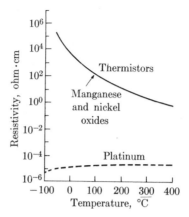

Fig. 6–2. Typical resistivity-temperature curves for a thermistor and for platinum.

Thermistors can be employed as active bridge elements, or can, because of their high inherent sensitivity, be used in a simple series circuit with inexpensive output meters. Whereas metallic resistance thermometers exhibit nominally linear characteristics, a thermistor behaves in an exponential manner, given approximately by

$$\frac{R}{R_0} = e^{\beta(1/T - 1/T_0)},\tag{6-3}$$

where T is the absolute temperature and β is a "constant." Figure 6–2 shows the variation of resistivity with temperature for a typical thermistor material. For comparison, the curve for platinum is also shown. Actual thermistors are made in a great variety of shapes and sizes, having cold (room temperature) resistance of from 100 to 500,000 ohms. The size can range from extremely small beads having the leads molded in place, and having small thermal mass, to large washers, which can have washer-type conductors clamped to each side. Thermistors are widely used in control circuits, and also find considerable application in timing and stabilization circuits where the negative characteristics give them useful time-temperature-resistance properties.

(d) *Thermocouples.* In 1821 Seebeck discovered that if two dissimilar conductors are brought into contact, a potential will be developed. Peltier and Thomson investigated this potential in greater detail and showed that it was due to two independent effects. The first effect is a voltage due only to the contact between the metals, the Peltier effect, while the second is due to temperature gradients along the conductor, the Thomson effect. The contact voltage is the major contribution to

TABLE 6–2

THERMOELECTRIC SENSITIVITY (THERMOELECTRIC POWER)
S (MICROVOLTS/°C AT 0°C) OF VARIOUS MATERIALS
RELATIVE TO PLATINUM

Material	Sensitivity S
Bismuth	−72
Constantan	−35
Nickel	−15
Platinum	0
Mercury	+0.6
Carbon	+3
Aluminum	+3.5
Lead	+4
Silver	+6.5
Copper	+6.5
Gold	+6.5
Tungsten	+7.5
Iron	+18.5
Nichrome	+25
Germanium	+300
Silicon	+440
Tellurium	+500
Selenium	+900

the potential for all the common thermocouple materials, and the Thomson effect may be neglected. However, in applications using semiconductors or other unusual conductors, the Thomson effect may be sufficiently important that the usual thermocouple rules of thumb may lead to error.

The thermoelectric voltage developed at a junction does not vary linearly with temperature, but is often considered to be linear over small temperature ranges. For precision work, a calibration curve for the materials involved must be obtained. Hence, the thermoelectric sensitivity S, (volts/°F, or volts/°C) varies with temperature. The sensitivity is often called the "thermoelectric power" (a misnomer) and is expressed in microvolts/°C at a given temperature. Thermoelectric sensitivities are often tabulated for a number of materials relative to a single standard material such as copper or platinum. The sensitivities for other combinations can be obtained directly by subtraction. Table 6–2 lists the thermoelectric sensitivity for a number of common materials relative to platinum at 0°C. To obtain the sensitivity of iron versus con-

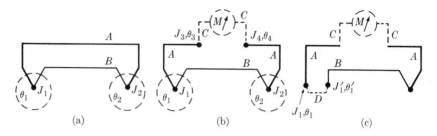

Fig. 6–3. Thermoelectric circuits: (a) basic thermoelectric circuit; (b) thermoelectric circuit with meter insert; (c) thermoelectric circuit with intermediate material at a measuring junction.

stantan, we subtract the two listed sensitivities and obtain

$$S_{\text{iron/constantan}} = 18.5 - (-35) = 53.5 \text{ microvolts/}^\circ\text{C}.$$

In order to use a thermoelectric junction to measure temperature, it is clear that the circuit must involve more than one junction. Because each junction will produce its own thermal emf, we must pay close attention to all junctions. The basic thermoelectric circuit, Fig. 6–3(a), involves only two materials A and B with the junctions J_1 and J_2 at temperatures θ_1 and θ_2, respectively. If θ_1 and θ_2 are not equal, different emfs will be developed at J_1 and J_2, and current will flow in the circuit dependent on the circuit resistance. If $\theta_1 = \theta_2$, there will be no current flow. While it is possible to have part of wire A or B formed into a galvanometer coil, and hence be able to read the current flow, this is generally not the case, and one wire, for example A, must be broken and a meter connected into the circuit. The meter may well involve wire and contacts of a third metal C, generally copper. There are now two more junctions J_3 and J_4 at θ_3 and θ_4 as shown in Fig. 6–3(b). The introduction of the meter junctions will not affect the system if either (1) the thermoelectric sensitivity between materials A and C is negligible, or (2) $\theta_3 = \theta_4$; the latter method is usually used.

It is often either desirable or unavoidable that a fourth material D be introduced at one of the measuring junctions (i.e., J_1). This is shown in Fig. 6–3(c). The net emf produced at J_1 is not altered by the presence of material D so long as its junctions J_1 and J_1' are at equal temperatures.

In order to calibrate or use a thermoelectric system (or thermocouple) it is necessary to hold one junction, J_2, at a known reference temperature. This junction is termed the reference junction. The measured voltage is then the difference between the reference emf and the emf at the measuring junction. The accuracy of the measurement can obvi-

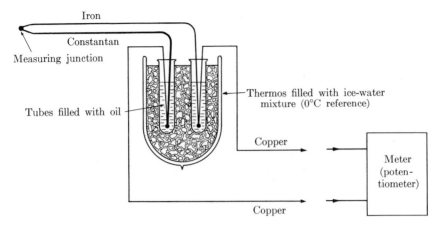

Fig. 6–4. Typical system for maintaining fixed reference temperatures.

ously be no better than the accuracy to which the reference temperature is known. Figure 6–4 shows a typical setup which will permit the use of long copper leads in conjunction with any (iron-constantan in this example) thermocouple, and which provides a reference temperature of 0°C. While any pair of materials may be used as a thermocouple, a number of materials have been standardized for convenient application. Table 6–3 gives the characteristics of the most common thermocouples.

For special purposes where high sensitivity is needed, thermocouples may be attached in series. The output is the numerical sum of the voltages expected from each of the single couples. This is commonly called a "thermopile."

When connected in parallel, a group of thermocouples will give a reading which is the numerical average of the individual ones, provided that the resistance of each individual couple is the same.

6–2. Sources of error in thermocouples

(a) *Voltaic effects.* These can be quite serious if the insulation is porous and becomes full of water. Pure water does not cause serious problems, but if any salt or acid is present, serious errors will result. The use of acid flux in soldering or welding thermocouples is especially bad if there is any chance of later contact with moisture.

(b) *Parasitic emf.* Parasitic emfs are caused by extraneous junctions at varying temperatures. Errors caused by parasitic emf can be virtually eliminated by using the thermocouple material as a lead. However, for applications where this is too expensive and copper leads are used, all

TABLE 6-3

THERMOCOUPLES AND THEIR CHARACTERISTICS

Type	Copper/constantan	Iron/constantan	Chromel/constantan	Chromel/alumel	Platinum/platinum rhodium 10	Platinum/platinum rhodium 13	Carbon/silicon carbide
Composition, percent	100Cu/60Cu 40Ni	100Fe/60Cu 40Ni	90Ni 10Cr/55Cu 45Ni	90Ni 10Cr/94Ni 2Al 3Mn 1Si	Pt/90Pt 10Rh	Pt/87Pt 13Rh	C/SiC
*Range of application, °C	−200 to +300	−200 to +1100	0 to +1100	−200 to +1200	0 to +1450	0 to +1450	to +2000
Resistivity, micro-ohm-cm	1.75 / 49	10 / 49	70 / 49	70 / 29.4	10 / 21	10 / 21	3000 / 10^6
Temperature coefficient of resistivity, per °C	0.0039 / 0.00001	0.005 / 0.00001	0.00035 / 0.0002	0.00035 / 0.000125	0.0030 / 0.0018	0.0030 / 0.0017	
Melting temperature, °C	1085 / 1190	1535 / 1190	1400 / 1190	1400 / 1430	1755 / 1700	1755 / 1700	3600 / 2700
emf, millivolts; reference junction at 0°C	100°C 4.24mv 200 9.06 300 14.42	100°C 5.28mv 200 10.78 400 21.82 600 33.16 800 45.48 1000 58.16	100°C 6.3mv 200 13.3 400 28.5 600 44.3	100°C 4.1mv 200 8.13 400 16.39 600 24.90 800 33.31 1000 41.31 1200 48.85 1400 55.81	100°C 0.643mv 200 1.436 400 3.251 600 5.222 800 7.330 1000 9.569 1200 11.924 1400 14.312 1600 16.674	100°C 0.646mv 200 1.464 400 3.398 600 5.561 800 7.927 1000 10.470 1200 13.181 1400 15.940 1600 18.680	100°C 17mv 200 46 300 75 400 106 1200 350 1300 385 1450 425
Influence of temperature and gas atmosphere	Subject to oxidation and alteration above 400°C due to Cu, above 600° due constantan wire. Ni-plating of Cu tube gives protection in acid-containing gas. Contamination of Cu affects calibration greatly. Resistance to oxid. atm. good. Resistance to reducing atm. good. Requires protection from acid fumes.	Oxidizing and reducing atmosphere have little effect on accuracy. Best used in dry atmosphere. Resistance to oxidation good to 400°C. Resistance to reducing atmosphere good. Protect from oxygen, moisture, sulfur.	Chromel attacked by sulfurous atmosphere. Resistance to oxidation good. Resistance to reducing atmosphere poor.	Resistance to oxidizing atmosphere very good. Resistance to reducing atmosphere poor. Affected by sulfur, reducing or sulfurous gas, SO₂ and H₂S.	Resistance to oxidizing atmosphere very good. Resistance to reducing atmosphere poor. Susceptible to chemical alteration by As, Si, P vapor in reducing gas (CO_2, H_2, H_2S, SO_2). Pt corrodes easily above 1000°. Used in gas-tight protecting tube.		Used as tube element. Carbon sheath chemically inert.
Particular applications	Low temperature, industrial. Internal combustion engine. Used as a tube element for measurements in steam line.	Low temperature, industrial. Steel annealing, boiler flues, tube stills. Used in reducing or neutral atmosphere.		Used in oxidizing atmosphere. Industrial. Ceramic kilns, tube stills, electric furnaces.	International Standard 630 to 1065°C.	Similar to Pt/PtRh 10, but has higher emf.	Steel furnace and ladle temperatures. Laboratory measurements.

* For prolonged usage; can be used at higher temperature for short periods.

pairs of junctions may be put in oil baths to ensure temperature equality.

(c) *Corrosion problems.* When used for a long time, especially at high temperatures, the thermoelectric properties of couples may gradually change due to oxidation or diffusion of other materials into the thermocouple itself. This may happen very quickly if wires are simply twisted together to form a junction.

(d) *Radiation effects.* For measurements where the couple is measuring gas or clear liquid temperatures, if the couple can "see" cold or hot surfaces, radiation cooling or heating of the wire can cause serious errors. For such applications a radiation shield is imperative. Measuring furnace temperatures or very low cryogenic temperatures requires this precaution.

(e) *Conduction errors.* Since all thermocouples have temperature gradients along their wires, heat will flow along the wires to or from the point where the temperature measurement is desired. These errors may be small for fine wires deeply imbedded in large metal parts, but they can be very large for heavy wires attached to light parts or exposed to still air.

(f) *Temperatures of moving gases.* There are two possible readings of significance. First, the temperature that would be indicated by a device moving with the gas and secondly a "stagnation" temperature. Since the difference between these is easily 1000°F for high-velocity flow, the exact design of the temperature probe will determine where between these extremes the indication will lie. A wide variety of special probes has been designed with various types of nozzles and shields to achieve maximum accuracy. In practice it is difficult to reliably measure anything other than stagnation temperature.

(g) *Temperature-time response.* The manner in which an element can follow rapid temperature changes depends greatly on its mass, the heat transfer conditions, and the rate of temperature change. Typical thermocouples have a time constant of the order 1 to 4 sec. However, this varies widely with ambient conditions.

6–3. Pyrometry

For temperatures above 1000°F, the radiation from a body is of sufficient intensity to be used for measuring temperature. The radiation from a hot body follows Planck's law and is distributed in wavelengths as shown in Fig. 6–5.

As the temperature changes, there are two changes useful for temperature measurement. First, the overall radiation energy increases. Second, the average wavelength of the radiation shifts to shorter wavelengths.

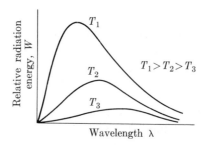

Fig. 6–5. Variation of radiant energy distribution with temperature of indicator.

The general equation for the distribution curves shown is

$$W_\lambda = \frac{C_1 \lambda^{-5}}{e^{C_2/\lambda T}},$$ (6–4)

where

$C_1 = 3.740 \times 10^{-12}$ watts-cm^2,

$C_2 = 1.4385$ cm-°C,

λ is the wavelength, cm,

T is the absolute temperature, °K, and

W is the energy level within a cavity of a body of temperature T, watts/cm^3.

If a hole is opened to a cavity with the energy distribution of Planck, a certain level of radiation will be emitted. This is given by the Stefan-Boltzmann law as

$$w = e\sigma T^4,$$ (6–5)

where

w is the radiant energy, watts/cm^2, of surface exposed,

T is the absolute temperature of surface, °K,

σ is a constant equal to 5.67×10^{-12} watts/cm^2(°K)^4, and

e is the emissivity.

The value of the emissivity varies from a low value of about 0.05 up to 1 for the theoretical "blackbody."

If two bodies face each other, the net energy transferred is the difference between the respective amounts radiated:

$$w = Ce\sigma(T_A^4 - T_B^4),$$ (6–6)

TABLE 6–4

TEMPERATURE MEASUREMENT ERRORS WHICH ARISE
DUE TO NONBLACKBODY RADIATION

Emissivity \ Actual temperature	1400°F	2000°F	2600°F	3000°F
0.1	840°F	1400°F		
0.3	380	600	870°F	
0.5	220	330	460	540°F
0.7	100	160	220	260
0.9	30	45	60	70

where

C is a geometrical factor to adjust for the relative shapes
of the two bodies,

T_A is the higher temperature (absolute), and

T_B is the lower temperature (absolute).

The total radiation pyrometer depends on Eq. (6–6) for its operation. Body B is a black surface within the pyrometer, which is heated by the radiation from body A. When B reaches equilibrium, its temperature is measured either by thermocouples or resistance thermometers. The pyrometer must be calibrated against known temperatures. In use, however, errors arise from two sources. Any filtering material such as smoke, dust, gases, windows, etc., which were not present in the calibration will reduce the energy received and hence cause an unknown error. The second source of error is surfaces having emissivities other than those used in calibration. Most calibration is done with a "blackbody" radiator. Since surface emissivities are not known very accurately, and change with time due to oxidation, the error due to unknown emissivity is not usually known. Table 6–4 gives an idea of the magnitudes of the measurement errors which can arise from this source.

In view of the troubles due to filtering and emissivity, the total radiation pyrometer is not an accurate general purpose indicator. It can be used to good advantage in fixed locations where the emissivities and optical paths are well known and constant. A typical use is a large furnace in the metals industries. The signal is electrical and therefore permits automatic control.

The optical pyrometer, which measures the shift in the Planck distribution curve, is much more useful as a general purpose instrument. This device is sighted, through an appropriate lens system, on the hot surface in question. A wire filament in the viewing system is heated by an adjustable voltage until its color matches that of the surface to be measured. A filter is employed so that only a narrow band in the red region is used. This region was chosen over a range of wavelengths where emissivity errors would be a minimum. The optical pyrometer is usually more accurate and less subject to large errors than the total radiation pyrometer. There is no upper-temperature limit, but below 1400°F the visible radiation becomes too small. The total radiation pyrometer can be used down to 100°F if an optical system is used which will pass the long-wavelength radiation.

Any pyrometer is subject to error caused by reflected radiation. A cool, painted white surface, for instance, may give a reading of 2000 to 3000°F on an optical pyrometer. Careful shielding and well-determined optical paths are necessary for meaningful results.

Pyrometry measurements are complicated by the use of windows. No material passes all wavelengths of light with the same losses. Ordinary pyrex filters out almost all radiation from sources below 1000°F. The widest-range lens materials are a group of salts such as calcium and lithium fluoride.

6–4. Other measuring techniques

Special applications have led to the development of a wide variety of temperature-measuring techniques. The heat treating industry, for instance, uses temper colors on steel surfaces. These colors are due to thin films of clear oxide which form interference colors. Since the color is determined by film thickness, and film thickness is a function of time, material, and temperature, this method is approximate at best.

The melting points of pellets, cones, crayons, and paints are used as single-point temperature indicators. Either the color or physical appearance of the material changes over some narrow temperature range. Most of these melting devices are not reversible and may be used only once.

Research people in the engine and turbine field have used the variation of sonic velocity with temperature in a gas as a measuring parameter.

Variation of magnetic properties is used as an indicator for very low temperatures near absolute zero. The variation in conductivity as a metal approaches superconductivity is a very sensitive measure near absolute zero.

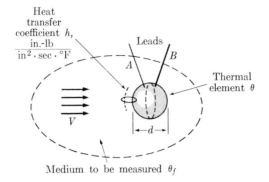

Fig. 6–6. Calculation of thermal element time constant: V = relative velocity (in./sec), k = thermal conductivity of gas (lb/sec·°F), μ = viscosity of gas (lb·sec/in²), c_p = specific heat of gas (in²/sec²·°F), and θ_f = fluid temperature; d = diameter (in.), ρc = volumetric specific heat (in.-lb/in³· °F = lb/in²· °F), and θ = average temperature of element.

6–5. Dynamics of thermal measurement

In Chapter 3, the interpretation of dynamical data was discussed, along with compensation of measuring systems to improve response. As there is no direct thermal analogy to mass, thermal systems are essentially first-order systems. However, the characteristic time constant τ of a measuring system is not a simple property of the actual thermometer. The time constant depends on the character of the material whose temperature we are measuring. Hence, the simple statement that a given thermal element has a certain time constant is meaningless without a complete description of the conditions of measurement.

The time constant of a thermal system can be estimated, but precise determination can be obtained only experimentally. Figure 6–6 shows schematically a thermal element (thermocouple junction, thermistor, resistance thermometer, glass thermometer bulb, etc.) of characteristic diameter d in a moving fluid medium of temperature θ_f. We can compute the *average* thermal element temperature θ through approximate heat transfer methods.

The rate of heat (energy) flow q into the element will be

$$q = ha(\theta_f - \theta) \quad \text{in.-lb/sec,} \qquad (6\text{--}7)$$

where h is the heat transfer coefficient from fluid to bulb [lb/(in·sec·°F)] and a is the exposed element area, in². This q must, in the absence of radiation, be equal to the increase of internal energy of the element; hence

$$q = v\rho c \frac{d\theta}{dt}, \tag{6-8}$$

where v is the volume of element, in^3,

ρc is the volumetric specific heat of element, lb/in$^2 \cdot$°F, and

$d\theta/dt$ is the rate of change of average element temperature, °F/sec.

Equating these relations gives the differential equation for the element temperature:

$$\frac{d\theta}{\theta_f - \theta} = \left(\frac{ha}{v\rho c}\right) dt. \tag{6-9}$$

For a step fluid temperature change from θ_0 to θ_f, this equation can be integrated to become

$$\frac{\theta_f - \theta}{\theta_f - \theta_0} = e^{-hat/\rho v c}, \tag{6-10}$$

which we can recognize as a first-order response equation, where the time constant τ is

$$\tau = \frac{\rho v c}{ha}. \tag{6-11}$$

All of the values necessary to calculate τ from Eq. (6–11) are easily obtainable with the exception of the heat transfer coefficient h. The empirical methods of heat transfer analysis can be used to predict the convective film coefficient h with some degree of confidence. It is found that to a good approximation, the Nusselt number (hd/k) is an exponential function of the Reynolds ($\rho V d/\mu$) and Prandtl ($c_p\mu/k$) numbers, i.e.,

$$\frac{hd}{k} = a \left(\frac{\rho V d}{\mu}\right)^m \left(\frac{c_p\mu}{k}\right)^n, \tag{6-12}$$

where h is the heat transfer coefficient, lb/in·sec·°F,

k is the thermal conductivity of fluid, lb/sec·°F,

ρ is the mass density of fluid, lb·sec^2/in^4,

V is the fluid velocity, in/sec,

μ is the fluid viscosity, lb·sec/in^2,

c_p is the specific heat of fluid, in^2/°F·sec^2, and

a, m, n are empirical constants.

For fluid flow perpendicular to a cylindrical or spherical element axis,

$$a = 0.33, \qquad m = 0.6, \qquad n = 0.33,$$

while for flow parallel to the axis,

$$a = 0.023, \qquad m = 0.8, \qquad n = 0.3.$$

For air, at Reynolds number greater than 100, an equation due to King is very useful:

$$\frac{hd}{k} = 0.30 + 0.51 \left(\frac{\rho V d}{\mu}\right)^{1/2}. \tag{6-13}$$

When the film coefficient h is large compared with the conductivity of the element divided by the element radius $(2k/d)$, the primary cause of time lag will lie within the element itself. Thus in the limiting case, the response characteristics of the system *will* be properties of the element. Carslaw and Jaeger (1948) give solutions to many heat transfer problems which can be used to estimate response. While the exact temperature-time solutions are quite complex, they can often be well approximated by simple first-order systems.

When the temperature at the outer layer of a sphere or cylinder of diameter d is varied, the temperature at the center lags in approximately first-order fashion with

$$\text{cylinder:} \ \tau \approx \frac{d^2}{20\kappa}, \qquad \text{sphere:} \ \tau \approx \frac{d^2}{30\kappa}. \tag{6-14}$$

where κ is the thermal diffusivity, $k/\rho c$. It is clear that when time constants are estimated by use of Eqs. (6-11) and (6-14), the longer τ will be controlling. We can estimate that the film coefficient time constant [Eq. (6-11)] will control when

$$\frac{hd}{k} < 1, \tag{6-15}$$

where k is the conductivity of the element, not of the surrounding fluid.

6-6. Velocity error

When a thermal probe is used to measure the temperature of a high-velocity fluid stream, the fluid will be brought to rest on the upstream area of the probe. As the fluid is brought to rest, its kinetic energy will be transformed to internal energy. The adiabatic temperature rise thus obtained is simply equal to the kinetic energy per unit mass divided by the specific heat, i.e.,

$$\Delta\theta_{ad} = \frac{V^2}{2c_p}.\tag{6-16}$$

This adiabatic temperature rise will exist only at the stagnation point; further along the probe, the temperature increase will be less. As a temperature probe normally indicates some sort of average of the surface temperature, there is always uncertainty as to the exact meaning of such a reading. To obtain the best results, high-velocity temperature probes are designed to measure the temperature as near to the stagnation point as possible. The ratio of the actual velocity correction to the ideal adiabatic increase $\Delta\theta_{ad}$ is called the recovery factor r. Ideally, r would be 1, then the indicated temperature could be simply corrected using Eq. (6–16). If r is known, then the static temperature θ_s is related to the indicated temperature θ_i by

$$\theta_s = \theta_i - r\frac{V^2}{2c_p},\tag{6-17}$$

where V is measured independently and the property c_p is that existing at the static temperature. In a "sonic-flow pyrometer," the gas is passed through a nozzle, and the thermal element located at the throat of the nozzle where the velocity will be sonic. Under this condition, a separate velocity determination is not necessary, and it can be shown that

$$\frac{\theta_s}{\theta_i} = \frac{1}{1 + (\frac{1}{2}r)(k-1)},\tag{6-18}$$

where k is the usual ratio of the specific heats. The velocity error can be quite large, amounting to about 350°F for air at 2000 ft/sec.

6–7. Radiation error

Whenever a thermal element is used to measure the temperature of a material which is "transparent" to thermal radiation, the element can either be heated or cooled by radiation to or from the surroundings. The usual case involves measuring the temperature of a hot gaseous atmosphere while the walls of the container are relatively cool. Here, the thermal element will radiate to the walls, and will indicate a temperature lower than the actual gas temperature. We note that this error is in the opposite direction from the velocity error discussed above. The heat q_r radiated *from* the element will be

$$q_r = \sigma\epsilon a(T_i^4 - T_0^4) \text{ in.-lb/sec},\qquad(6\text{--}19)$$

where σ is the Stefan-Boltzmann constant 3.09×10^{-11} in.-lb/
in^2·sec($°$R)^4,

  ϵ is the emissivity,

  a is the area of body, in^2,

  T_i is the absolute (Rankine) temperature of the element, and

  T_0 is the absolute (Rankine) temperature of the walls.

Under equilibrium (steady-state) conditions, the quantity q_r must be supplied from the gas stream according to Eq. (6–7), or

$$q_r = ha(T_f - T_i),\qquad(6\text{--}20)$$

where T_f is the actual fluid temperature and h is obtained from Eq. (6–12).

Equating the above, we obtain the radiation error

$$T_f - T_i = \frac{\sigma\epsilon}{h}(T_i^4 - T_0^4).\qquad(6\text{--}21)$$

The error can be reduced by:

(1) reducing ϵ through use of highly polished silver or aluminum coatings;

(2) increase of h by increasing fluid velocity past the element;

(3) increasing the effective wall temperature "seen" by the element by surrounding it with a cylindrical tube;

(4) increasing the actual wall temperatures.

6–8. Temperature measurement in moving and sliding members

In studies of mechanical systems, it is frequently necessary to determine the interfacial temperatures between mating, rolling, or sliding parts. Typical examples would be the contact zone between chip and tool in a machining operation, the contact between balls and races in ball bearings, contact between sliding seals, the surface temperatures of steel mill rollers, etc. These systems are generally characterized by very large temperature gradients near the contact zone. Hence, embedded thermocouples and the like are apt to give very erroneous results.

The writers feel that a brief discussion of the theoretical temperature distribution plus an indication of a method for obtaining reliable results will alert the reader to the problem, and perhaps indicate a solution.

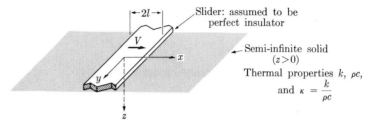

Fig. 6–7. "Band source" of length $2l$, moving at velocity V in the $+x$ direction.

Jaeger has developed particularly useful solutions to this problem for various sizes and shapes of moving contacts. Here, we shall discuss only the temperatures produced by a moving "band source" of infinite length in the y direction, length $2l$ in the x direction, sliding with velocity V in the $+x$ direction over a semi-infinite solid ($z > 0$), as shown in Fig. 6–7.

We will let heat (generally frictional heat) be produced at the interface at the rate q_a per unit area:

$$q_a = \frac{\text{heat}}{\text{area, time}} \quad \left(\frac{\text{in.-lb}}{\text{in}^2 \cdot \text{sec}}\right).$$

If we assume the slider to be a perfect insulator, all of q_a will enter the solid ($z > 0$). [*Note:* It is possible to account for nonperfect insulation by apportioning the heat rq_a into the solid, and $(1 - r)q_a$ into the slider. The average interface temperatures of the solid and of the slider are calculated separately due to their individual heat inputs. These temperatures are then equated, and the resulting equation solved for r. Generally, at high speeds, $r \to 1$ and the assumption of a perfect insulator will give satisfactory results.] If the heat is due to a frictional shear stress τ, then

$$q_a = V\tau \quad \left(\frac{\text{in.}}{\text{sec}} \times \frac{\text{lb}}{\text{in}^2}\right). \tag{6–22}$$

The solution to the moving source heat transfer problem cannot be given in closed form, but is best given in terms of graphs and numerical approximations as follows.

We can first introduce dimensionless parameters:

$$X = \frac{Vx}{2\kappa}, \quad Z = \frac{Vz}{2\kappa}, \quad L = \frac{Vl}{2\kappa}.$$

For the surface temperatures, $Z = 0$, and the results shown in Fig. 6–8

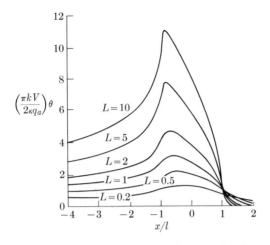

Fig. 6–8. Surface temperature due to a moving band source.

are obtained. It is clear that at high velocities (large L), the maximum temperature is at the trailing edge of the slider. For large values of L ($L > 5$) the temperature is approximated by

$$\theta\left(\frac{\pi k V}{2q_a \kappa}\right) = \begin{cases} 0 & \text{for} \quad X > L, \\ \sqrt{2\pi(L - X)} & \text{for} \quad -L < X < L, \\ \sqrt{2\pi}\,[\sqrt{L - X} - \sqrt{|X + L|}] & \text{for} \quad X < -L. \end{cases} \tag{6-23}$$

Equation (6–23) is particularly useful in determining how the surface temperature decreases behind the heat source, where we are apt to attempt temperature measurements.

The approximate average and maximum surface temperatures are: For large L ($L > 5$); both band and square source:

$$\theta_{\max} = \frac{1.6 q_a}{k} \sqrt{\frac{\kappa l}{V}}, \qquad \theta_{\text{av}} = \tfrac{2}{3}\,\theta_{\max}. \tag{6-24}$$

For small L ($L < 0.1$) we have for the band source,

$$\theta_{\max} = \frac{4}{\pi}\left(\frac{q_a \kappa L}{k V}\right)\ln\left(\frac{3.05}{L}\right), \qquad \theta_{\text{av}} = \frac{4}{\pi}\left(\frac{q_a \kappa L}{k V}\right)\ln\left(\frac{2.52}{L}\right). \tag{6-25}$$

For the square source ($L < 0.1$):

$$\theta_{\max} = 1.12\,\frac{q_a l}{k}, \qquad \theta_{\text{av}} = 0.95\,\frac{q_a l}{k}. \tag{6-26}$$

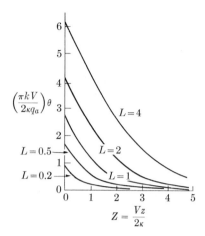

Fig. 6–9. Temperature versus depth at trailing edge of a moving band source.

The variation of temperature with depth into the semi-infinite solid is shown for a limited set of conditions in Fig. 6–9. It is clear that the temperature gradients are very strong.

The temperatures referred to above are all "steady-state" interface temperatures. Jaeger also considers the time required to achieve essentially steady-state conditions. While the results are rather complex, they can be reduced to the approximation that steady-state conditions at $Z = 0$ are reached after sliding $1\frac{1}{2}$ band widths. This is, indeed, very rapid.

6–9. Sliding temperature measurement

While numerous methods have been used to measure moving surface and interface temperatures, there are few methods that give reliable results. At very high temperatures, radiation measurement can be useful, but at lower temperatures, we must resort to various contact methods. The steep gradients indicated in Fig. 6–9 show that embedded thermocouples will not be useful for certain types of measurement. Sliding or rolling contact thermocouples can be useful if the temperature rise due to the frictional heat is not significant. The previous analyses permit calculation of such temperature rises.

Probably the best method for conducting such measurements on electrically conducting surfaces is to use the moving member as one side of a thermocouple, and have a rolling or sliding member act as the other part. It is usually necessary to calibrate the thermal emf-temperature characteristics of the two materials, but this is relatively easy.

PROBLEMS

1. An idealized mercury in glass thermometer is shown in Fig. 6–10: $D = 0.5$ in., $L = 10$ in., $d = 0.4$ in., $x_{0°C} = 2$ in., $E = 0.25$ in., $e = 0.02$ in., $\alpha_{Hg} = 34 \times 10^{-6} \,°F^{-1}$, $\alpha_{glass} = 5 \times 10^{-6} \,°F$, $k_{Hg} = 1.0$ lb/sec·°F, $k_{glass} = 0.1$ lb/sec·°F, $\rho c_{Hg} = 151$ lb/in^2·°F, $\rho c_{glass} = 140$ lb/in^2·°F. (a) Estimate the sensitivity $dx/d\theta$ (in./°F) of the thermometer when it is totally immersed. [*Ans.* 0.0095 in./°F] (b) Estimate the time constant τ for the thermometer when it is used to measure water moving at 10 ft/sec (totally immersed). [*Ans.* 5 to 10 sec] (c) If the thermometer is calibrated at 32°F totally immersed, and then withdrawn from the fluid in various amounts until only the bulb is immersed, estimate the deviation from the original calibrated ice point (32°F) if room temperature is 70°F. [*Ans.* For 1 in. Hg exposed, thermometer reads 0.36°F high.]

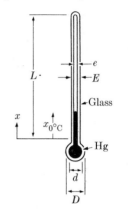

Figure 6–10

2. A bimetallic strip is made by joining two strips, each $6 \times \frac{1}{2} \times 0.020$ in.; one of 18-8 stainless, and one of pure iron (see Fig. 6–11). Determine (a) the motion δ of the free end per unit temperature change (in./°F); (b) the force F required to hold the strip such that $\delta = 0$ as the temperature increases a unit amount (lb/°F). (c) Estimate the time constant of

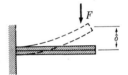

Figure 6–11

such a device in room-temperature air moving at 1 ft/sec.

3. It is desired to design a resistance thermometer to be made of nickel wire of 0.001 in. diameter. The thermometer resistance at 70°F is to be 25 ohms. [Nickel wire: resistivity $= 8.7 \times 10^{-6}$ ohm-cm (at 70°F), temperature coefficient of resistance $= 0.0037/°F$.] (a) How long should the wire be? [*Ans.* 5.73 in.] (b) Design a form for holding the coil in a relatively stress-free fashion.

4. A platinum thermoresistive element has the following reported characteristics: range, $-200°$ to $+500°C$; sensitivity, 0.099 ohm/°C at 0°C; resistance, 25 ohms at 0°C; maximum current, 10 milliamperes. The element is to be used in a bridge as shown in Fig. 6–12. The unit will be used to measure temperatures in the 200°C to 300°C range. The potentiometer R will be used to adjust the output to zero at 0°C. The fixed resistances are all $\pm 1\%$, and all resistances have a temperature coefficient of $+0.00001$. We wish to measure to a precision of 0.1°C. (a) Determine the maximum supply voltage V_0. [*Ans.* $\frac{1}{2}$ volt] (b) Determine the value of R to assure zero adjustment. [*Ans.* 2000 ohms] (c) What range and resolution must the meter have? [*Ans.* Range $= 0.03$ volt; res. $= 10^{-5}$ volt] (d) Can you suggest improvements to

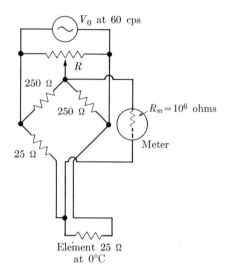

Figure 6–12

the circuit? [Zero suppression.] (e) How large a temperature variation can be tolerated in the bridge circuit? [*Ans.* 40°C]

5. An iron-constantan thermocouple has its reference junction in a large copper block whose temperature is measured (by a mercury thermometer) to be 73°F. The output is recorded as 7.21 mv. What is the hot-junction temperature?

6. A simple thermocouple circuit is shown in Fig. 6–13. The two reference junctions are attached to a copper block to maintain their temperature equal at room temperature (θ_r). If the hot junction is at 400°C, how much error will be caused as room temperature varies from 20°C to 25°C without our knowing it?

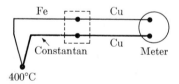

Figure 6–13

7. A thermistor exhibits a resistance of 100,000 ohms at the ice point. The constant β, Eq. (6–3), is 3500°K. Estimate the best linear relationship between resistance and temperature over the range 0° to 100°C. What will be the maximum deviation from linearity? Show plot.

8. A thermistor bead, composed principally of manganese oxide, is 0.1 in. in diameter. It is to be used to measure small, rapid fluctuations in the tem-

perature of air moving in a duct. The air is at atmospheric pressure, and about 70°F. The air velocity is 10 ft/sec. (a) Estimate the time constant for the system. (b) Assuming that the thermistor has the characteristics listed in Problem 7, design a suitable Wheatstone bridge circuit. The maximum thermistor current is 5 ma. (c) Add to the circuit of (b) a compensating network to decrease the time constant by a factor of 10. If an oscilloscope is available having a maximum sensitivity of 1 mv/cm, what will be the sensitivity of the system in cm/°F? (d) What will the system time constant be [as in part (a)] if the temperature of water moving at 10 ft/sec is to be measured?

9. We have seen [Eq. (6–16)] that the adiabatic temperature rise is $\Delta\theta_{ad} = V^2/2c_p$ when consistent units are employed. It can be shown that

$$\frac{T_{tot}}{T_{stat}} = 1 + \frac{(k+1)M^2}{2},$$

where T_{tot} is the absolute total impact temperature,

T_{stat} is the absolute true, or static, temperature, that is,
$T_{tot} = T_{stat} + \Delta\theta_{ad}$,

k is the ratio of the specific heats for the gas, and

M is the Mach number.

Derive the above relationship.

10. The surface temperature of a moving iron member is to be measured by having a strip of constantan shim stock slide on it as shown in Fig. 6–14. The shim is $\frac{1}{4}$ in. wide (perpendicular to the page), and wears to give a contact length $2l$ of 0.01 in. The normal force between the two surfaces is approximately 0.1 lb, and the friction coefficient is estimated to be 0.3. Calculate the additional interface temperature, which is caused by the frictional energy, and is measured by the thermocouple (a) when $V = 100$ ft/min, (b) when $V = 3000$ ft/min. (c) If the actual iron surface temperature is approximately 300°F, is this a satisfactory method of measurement?

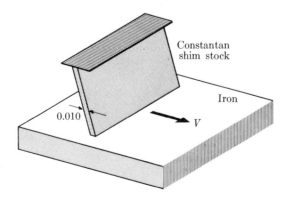

Figure 6–14

11. A temperature probe having a recovery factor $r = 0.9$ projects ahead of a fast-moving aircraft. When traveling at Mach 0.7, the probe indicates a temperature of 40°C. What is the true air temperature?

12. A bare, shiny thermocouple bead is used to indicate temperature of a high-velocity, high-temperature gas. The gas is an air jet, at atmospheric pressure, and the surroundings are at room temperature. The velocity is expected to be 800 ft/sec, and the thermocouple indicates a temperature of 1400°F. Assume that the bead emissivity $\epsilon = 0.2$, and that the recovery factor $r = 0.7$. Estimate the true gas temperature. If ϵ or r are in error by $\pm 20\%$, how much will the temperature be in error?

REFERENCES

BECKWITH, T. G. and N. L. BUCK, *Mechanical Measurements*, Addison-Wesley Publishing Co., Reading, Mass., 1961. Comprehensive description of apparatus and techniques used in physical measurements.

CARSLAW, H. S. and J. C. JAEGER, *Conduction of Heat in Solids*, Clarendon Press, Oxford, 1948. Extremely helpful for estimating time constants of thermal systems.

HARRISON, T. R., *Radiation Pyrometry and its Underlying Principles of Radiant Heat Transfer*, Wiley and Sons, New York, 1960.

JAEGER, J. C., "Moving Sources of Heat and the Temperature at Sliding Contacts," *Proc. Roy. Soc., New South Wales*, **56**, 1942. Complete, highly useful analysis of temperatures produced by moving sources of various types; i.e., square sources, band sources, etc.

LION, K. I., *Instrumentation in Scientific Research*, McGraw-Hill Book Co., New York, 1959. Description of wide variety of transducers.

ROHSENOW, W. M. and H. Y. CHOI, *Heat, Mass and Momentum Transfer*, Prentice-Hall, Englewood Cliffs, New Jersey, 1961.

SWEENEY, R. J., *Measurement Techniques in Mechanical Engineering*, Wiley and Sons, New York, 1953. Complete description of International Temperature Scale. Discussion and analysis of measurement errors.

CHAPTER SEVEN

Measurements on Fluids

Measurement problems in the field of fluid mechanics generally involve the measurement of temperature, velocity, and pressure at various points in liquid, gaseous, or multiphase media. In Chapter 6, we discussed temperature measurements as they occur within a limited temperature range. Measurements at extremely high, or extremely low, temperature are still sufficiently controversial to preclude concise description and analysis. In this chapter, we will discuss the other aspects of fluid measurement, namely velocity (or flow) and pressure (or vacuum). The greater part of this chapter will be descriptive, and general, because there are so many devices which could be discussed and analyzed that an entire volume would be required. However, there are certain classifications, generalizations, and common problems which are useful in the selection and use of flow- and pressure-measuring devices.

7-1. Flow measurement

Flow-measurement problems may cover a wide variety of areas involving steady or unsteady flow, liquids, gases, or two-phase media, and laminar or turbulent flow. Two basic approaches are taken to measure flow.

      (1) Direct quantity measurements
          (a) weighing or volume tanks
          (b) positive displacement meters
      (2) Indirect, or rate, measurements
          (a) obstruction devices
          (b) velocity probes
          (c) special methods

In this section an attempt will be made to outline the principal types of devices available, pointing out their major advantages and drawbacks. One example will be analyzed in more detail in order to illustrate the type of theory which is available.

7-1.1. Direct methods

(a) *Tanks.* The basic reference device for steady-flow measurement is usually a tank of known volume which is filled, and the times of filling noted. For liquids of known density, weight measurements may replace volume. The basic accuracy of these methods can be very high when using precise tanks or scales. However, there are many rather old devices still in use which give the illusion of high accuracy, but due to accumulated paint layers, dents, dirt accumulation, inaccurate weights, etc., may be significantly in error. For accurate calibration of many modern rate meters these old installations may no longer be accurate enough. They do give values of high reproducibility, but often contain significant systematic errors.

(b) *Displacement meters.* A wide variety of displacement meters are basically positive-displacement hydraulic motors used to measure volume flow. They all chop the flow into "pieces" of known size and then count the number of "pieces." Their accuracy can be very good even at the low end of the flow range. Since they are devices with moving parts, wear may alter their accuracy. Measurement of liquids with entrained vapors can be a problem unless a good vapor trap is used. Most of these devices are totalizers and do not attempt to measure instantaneous flow rates. Some of the configurations currently in use include reciprocating piston, reciprocating diaphragm, revolving vane, rotating drum, nutating disc, and lobed impellers.

7–1.2. Indirect methods

(a) *Variable-head meters.* This group includes all meters which measure the pressure drop across a restriction in a pipe line. For incompressible fluids, the flow rate is given by an equation of the type

$$q = CA \sqrt{\frac{2g}{\gamma} \Delta p}, \qquad (7\text{--}1)$$

where q is the volume flow rate, in³/sec,

g is the acceleration due to gravity, 386 in./sec²,

γ is the density, lb/in³,

Δp is the pressure drop across the constriction, lb/in²,

C is the flow coefficient, depending upon geometry and slightly on Reynolds number, and

A is the minimum restriction area, in².

Three types of constriction meters in fairly common use are the venturi, the flow nozzle, and the orifice. The venturi offers the best accuracy, least head loss, and best resistance to abrasion and wear from dirty fluids. It is, however, expensive and occupies substantial space.

The nozzle type offers all the advantages of the venturi to a slightly lesser extent but does take considerably less space. The nozzle is difficult to install properly. The orifice is very cheap, easy to install, and takes almost no space. It suffers from considerable head loss and is very sensitive to abrasion or other damage. All three can be used without calibration if made to standard dimensions.

All three types of restrictors suffer from a limited useful range because of the square root relationship between pressure drop and flow. It is not practical to measure flow below, say, 20% of meter capacity. The *ASME Power Test Code* (1959) gives extensive data and specifications for these three types of meters.

Restriction meters are used for compressible fluids in the subsonic region by a simple correction for expansion of the fluid.

Restriction meters are not too useful for measuring flow at small Reynolds numbers (Re < 15,000) as the discharge coefficient begins to depend strongly on Reynolds number. This is due to viscous effects becoming important. For very viscous fluids or very small flow rates, a capillary-type meter is used to overcome this problem. The Hagen-Poiseuille law governs this type of viscous flow:

$$q = \left(\frac{\pi a^4}{8\mu L}\right) \Delta p, \tag{7-2}$$

where q is the flow, in^3/sec,

Δp is the pressure drop, lb/in^2,

μ is the viscosity, lb·sec/in^2,

a is the tube radius, in., and

L is the tube length, in.

The tube length required to make errors small increases with Reynolds number, but an $L/a > 100$ is usually adequate.

(b) *Drag-body meters.* The insertion of an appropriately shaped fixed body into a flow stream can serve as a meter. The drag force on the body becomes a measure of flow rate after suitable calibration. The force is often measured using a strain-gage instrumented support. This meter works on essentially the same principle as the restriction meters and its output follows the same square law. It can be the most accurate of the differential pressure-flow meters, and with a symmetrical body can work for flow in either direction.

(c) *Pitot tube.* The well-known pitot tube is often used to measure fluid velocity distributions in large passages. The flow rate is then found by averaging the velocities over the area. This is tedious work, but very little flow energy is wasted. The accuracy of this method is not as good as those mentioned above.

(d) *Variable-area meters.* These meters also measure a differential pressure. One type uses a weight suspended by the flow in a tapered glass tube. The pressure difference is caused by the weight and is relatively constant. The area depends upon the height which the weight assumes. The vertical location of the weight in the tapered tube indicates the flow rate.

A second variable-area type consists of a ported piston-cylinder arrangement. As the flow increases, the weighted piston is raised exposing more port area for the flow.

Both of these types have the advantage of being direct reading on a linear scale. They handle almost all fluids and are quite accurate over wide ranges of flow. However, they must be mounted vertically and are subject to oscillations in pulsating flow.

(e) *Mass flow meters.* There are several designs of flow meters which measure true mass flow. These are based on changes of angular momentum. In one device the fluid is directed axially through an impeller rotating at constant speed. The torque required to drive the impeller is a function of the mass of fluid passing through. A second device directs the flow through radial channels in a rotating member. The resulting gyroscopic couple is a measure of the flow rate. Both of these devices are expensive but do measure mass flow accurately, and independently of changes in density, pressure, viscosity, temperature, and compressibility.

(f) *Magnetic flow meters.* These meters can be used only with conducting fluids, although fluids having conductivities as low as that of water can be used. An electromagnet, either a-c or d-c, or a permanent magnet, is placed around a nonconducting length of pipe. Electrodes are then placed in the pipe at right angles to the magnetic field. As the conducting fluid flows, a potential is generated according to Faraday's law:

$$e = BlV \times 10^{-8}, \tag{7-3}$$

where B is the flux density, gauss,

l is the length of the conductor, cm,

V is the fluid velocity, cm/sec, and

e is the induced voltage, volts.

These meters are expensive but can handle a wide variety of fluids with no substantial pressure loss.

(g) *Sonic flow meter*. These meters again offer no obstruction to the flow and are based on the variation in sonic velocity propagating upstream versus downstream. They are expensive but unaffected by density variations. The read-out can easily be analog or digital.

(h) *Thermal meters*. These meters add a fixed amount of energy to the fluid stream. The temperature rise of the fluid is sensed by a differential thermocouple. The voltage output is generally a logarithmic function of flow velocity, decreasing asymptotically to zero at high flow rates.

(i) *Turbine flow meter*. A turbine wheel is mounted axially on bearings in the pipe. The speed of the wheel is proportional to the flow and is indicated by magnetic pickups. Accuracy is very good over the design range, with good response. Bearing maintenance problems are always present, and accuracy drops off greatly at low flow rates.

(j) *Hot-wire anomometer*. Most of the devices described above are normally bought as commercial units. The average engineer, unless he meets a very special situation, will not attempt to build his own. The performance depends in large part upon the skill of the manufacturer. Hot-wire anomometers, however, are so simple in construction that many engineers build their own, although they do use commercial read-out equipment.

The basic principle of the hot-wire anomometer is that heat transfer rates from a hot wire to a fluid depend on the flow velocity. The loss (or gain) of energy by a wire or cylinder is

$$q = ha(\theta_\omega - \theta_r), \tag{7-4}$$

where q is the heat flow, in.-lb/sec,

a is the wire surface area, in^2,

θ_ω is the wire temperature,

θ_r is the recovery temperature; $\theta_r = \theta_s + r\,\Delta\theta_{ad}$ (see Chapter 6), and

h is the film coefficient, lb/in.·sec·°F.

The heat flow is known from information on electrical input and resistance. The geometry is fixed. The wire temperature is measured by observing the wire resistance and knowing its resistance as a function of temperature. The recovery temperature is somewhat uncertain, but is usually close to the isentropic stagnation temperature or total temperature θ_t of the fluid. In any event, if the wire is much hotter than the stream, errors in recovery temperatures are not important. Taking these known numbers, we may use the above equation to calculate a film coefficient h. The film coefficient h will depend strongly on flow velocity and fluid properties. However, a large amount of experimental data has been collected and correlated. Equations (6–12) and (6–13) can be used to determine an approximate h-V relationship.

For values of Re $> 10^2$, a formula due to King is widely used. For air, King's formula is Eq. (6–13):

$$\frac{hd}{k} = 0.30 + 0.51 \left(\frac{\rho V d}{\mu}\right)^{1/2}. \tag{7–5}$$

The hot wire may be used to measure flow velocity in two ways. The first uses an electric circuit which is adjusted to feed a constant current to the hot wire. A knowledge of this current and the resistance of the wire defines the power being fed to the wire. This power is all transferred from a wire of known geometry so that an experimental value of h is determined.

The hot wire has a small time lag in making readings, due to its thermal capacity. For most wires a time constant of 1 millisec is common. For faster signals the hot wire may be treated as a first-order system, and compensated if necessary (see Chapter 3).

The second technique for hot-wire operation is to adjust the current to give constant wire resistance (constant temperature). The current (or voltage) is then a measure of the heat transfer rate.

The constant-temperature design has the advantage that the wire is inherently protected against burnout. However, the associated electronic devices have upper limits of frequency response beyond which the system becomes unstable and the wire temperature oscillates. The system works very well all the way down to zero velocity; however, more refined relationships between the film coefficient h and the velocity V must be employed.

The constant-current system is limited in its range of velocity for any given current level. However, for electronic stability and amplification reasons, it can be used at higher frequencies and with smaller signals than the constant-temperature wire. However, it is subject to burnout with large changes in flow rate or with vapor inclusions.

The wires are usually made of platinum, nickel, or tungsten. They need to be strong enough to resist impinging dirt, yet fine enough to give adequate electrical resistance. Accumulated dirt on a wire can lead to serious heat transfer errors in only a few minutes of operation at high velocities unless the fluid is exceptionally clean.

Most hot-wire devices are used in gas flow measurements, but a few results have been reported lately in liquid streams. Troubles can arise

TABLE 7–1

OPERATING CHARACTERISTICS OF
FLOW METERS BY BASIC GROUPS

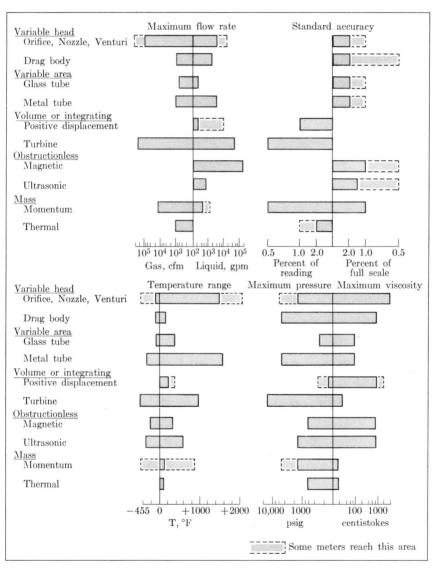

TABLE 7-2

PERFORMANCE CHARACTERISTICS OF FLOW METERS BY BASIC GROUPS [MIESSE AND CURTH, 1961]

Meter type		Fluid	Range of max. flow: Liquid, gpm / Gas, cfm	Useful range	Max. pressure, psig	Temp. range, °F	Max. viscosity, centistokes	Scale	Indication	Accuracy	Construction materials	Pressure loss, psi	Line size, in.	Special piping considerations	Typical power requirement	Relative cost
				Fluid factors					**Application Factors**					**Installation factors**		
Variable head	Orifice	Liquid / Gas	0.2-3500 / 50-100,000	5:1	6000	-455 to 2000	4000	Sq. rt., rate	Remote, diff. press.	1-2% full scale diff. press.	Most metals	0.1-30	1½-12 and larger	Straight pipe: 10 dia. upstream; 3 downstream	None	1.0
	Flow nozzle	Liquid / Gas	0.5-15,000 / 100-500,000	5:1	1500	-60 to 1500	4000	Sq. rt., rate	Remote, diff. press.	1-2% full scale diff. press.	Bronze, iron, steel, stainless stl.	0.1-20	1-24 and larger	Straight pipe: 10 dia. upstream; 3 downstream	None	1.4
	Venturi	Liquid / Gas	0.5-15,000 / 100-500,000	5:1	1500	-60 to 1500	4000	Sq. rt., rate	Remote, diff. press.	1-2% full scale diff. press.	Bronze, iron, steel, stn. stl., plastic	0.1-15	1-24 and larger	Straight pipe: 10 dia. upstream; 3 downstream	None	1.5
	Drag body (var. force)	Liquid / Gas	0.5-2000 / 5-1000	5:1	5000	-60 to 180	1000	Sq. rt., rate	Remote, electric	½-2% full scale	Steel, stn. stl.	2-50	½-12	Vertical or horizontal	115 v 60 cps 20 w	1.0-4.0
Variable area	Glass tube rotameter	Liquid / Gas	10^{-3}-250 / 10^{-2}-700	10:1	250	-50 to 400	100	Linear, rate	Local or remote, electric or pneumatic	1-2% full scale	Most metals, plastics and ceramics	0.01-1.0	¼-4	Vertical only	None	1.0
	Metal tube rotameter	Liquid / Gas	0.5-4000 / 0.6-1000	10:1	5000	-300 to 1600	100	Linear, rate	Local or remote, electric or pneumatic	1-2% full scale	Most metals, plastics and ceramics	0.05-10	½-12	Vertical only	None	1.2

	Type	Fluid	Range	Rangeability		Temp. range		Flow readout	Readout location	Accuracy	Materials	Pressure loss		Position	Power	
Volume or integrating	Reciprocating piston	Clean liquids	0.002–200,000	10:1 to 20:1	250	0 to 250	1000	Linear, total	Local or remote, electric	1% reading	Bronze, iron, steel, stn. stl.	1–20	$\frac{3}{4}$–3	Horizontal recommended	None	1.0–2.0
	Rotary piston	Clean liquids	5–8750	10:1 to 20:1	3000	0 to 300	2000	Linear, total	Local or remote, electric	1% reading	Bronze, iron, steel, stn. stl.	1–20	$\frac{5}{8}$–16	Horizontal recommended	None	1.0–2.0
	Nutating disc	Clean liquids	0.25–1000	10:1	150	0 to 300	2000	Linear, total	Local or remote, electric	1% reading	Bronze, iron, steel, stn. stl.	1–20	$\frac{1}{2}$–6	Horizontal recommended	None	1.0
	Diaphragm	Gas	0.25–500	20:1	100	−30 to 180	all gas	Linear, total	Local	1% reading	Steel, aluminum, syn. rubber	0.05–1.5	$\frac{1}{4}$–4	Horizontal recommended	None	1.0
	Turbine or propeller	Clean liquid or gas	0.004–50,000 0.5–300,000	15:1 10:1	15,000	−455 to 1000	30	Linear, total	Remote, electric	$\frac{1}{2}$% reading	Aluminum, stn. stl.	2–10	$\frac{1}{8}$–36	Any position	115 v 50 w	5.0
Obstructionless	Magnetic	Conductive liquids only	0.002–50,000	20:1	600	−200 to 360	1000	Linear, rate	Remote, electric	$\frac{1}{2}$–1% full scale	Plastic, stn. stl. with nonconductive liner	Nil	$\frac{1}{10}$–78	Any position	115 v 200 w	6.0
	Sonic or ultrasonic	Liquid	0.1–800	20:1	1500	−300 to 600	1000	Linear, rate	Remote, electric	1–1$\frac{1}{2}$% full scale	Bronze, steel, stn. stl.	Nil	$\frac{1}{4}$–2	Any position	115 v 100 w	10
Mass	Momentum gyroscopic	Liquid Gas	100–4000 lb/in² 20–600 lb/in²	10:1	1500	0 to 165	20	Linear, total, rate	Local or remote, electric	1% full scale	Bronze, steel, stn. stl.	1–10	1–3	Horizontal recommended	115 v 50 w	4.0–5.0
	Momentum axial	Liquid Gas	40–100,000 lb/in² 10–15,000 lb/in²	10:1	5000	−430 to 850	20	Linear, total, rate	Remote, electric	$\frac{1}{4}$% reading	Aluminum, stn. stl.	5–20	1–12	Horizontal recommended	115 v 50 w	6.0–8.0
	Thermal	Gas	1.0 gm/min to 80 lb/in²	20:1	600	0 to 100	all gas	Logarithmic rate	Remote, electric	1–2% reading	Bronze, steel, stn. stl.	Nil	$\frac{1}{8}$–6	Any position	115 v 10 w	1.0–4.0

due to local boiling or the tendency of entrained bubbles to collect on the wires, thereby changing the calibration.

(k) *Summary.* The various types of velocity and flow meters discussed above are each most useful in particular regions of flow, pressure, temperature, etc. Tables 7–1 and 7–2 outline the general operating areas and characteristics of the commercially available devices.

7–2. Pressure measurement

Pressure measurements can be qualitatively divided into three ranges:
(1) Very low pressures (vacua)
(2) Moderate pressures (10^{-1} to 10^4 psi)
(3) Very high pressures (greater than 10^4 psi).
Very low pressures are measured relative to absolute zero pressure (perfect vacuum), and are expressed in terms of the height to which a column of mercury would be raised by the pressure (mm or microns). Moderate pressures can be referred to zero pressure (absolute pressure) or can be referred to standard atmospheric pressure (gage pressure). For very high pressures, the difference between absolute and gage pressures is academic. Figure 7–1 shows the relationship of the various common pressure scales, and also shows the ranges of various types of gages to be considered later.

7–2.1. Moderate pressures

Pressures in this range are generally measured either by noting the height to which a liquid column is raised by the pressure, or by measuring the elastic deflection of a spring element, which is caused by the pressure. Liquid-column gages are inexpensive, and sensitive, but must be maintained at a known angle relative to vertical, and have very poor time response. The more common elastic gages (Bourdon gages, metal bellows, etc.) utilize the pressure to cause a substantial elastic deflection, which can be mechanically amplified (through gears and levers) to produce a direct dial reading. Due to the mass of the physical elements, and due to the relatively large fluid flow associated with a pressure change, these devices, too, are slow responding and hence suited only to static determinations. Most pressure devices suited for rapid transient measurement involve extremely small elastic deformations, which are measured electrically through use of the various electrical displacement-measuring devices discussed in Chapter 4. The two most used configurations involve either a tubular pressure cell with wire-resistance strain gages attached, or a diaphragm whose motion is measured with standard (R, C, or L) displacement-measuring devices. Ap-

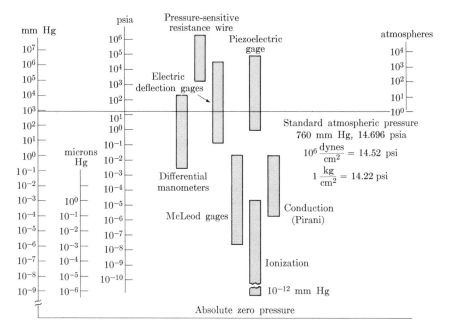

Fig. 7–1. Comparison of pressure scales and the range of various types of gages.

proximate analysis of such devices is straightforward and will not be discussed here.

Numerous piezoelectric crystals will produce a charge when subjected to hydrostatic pressure, and hence they are suited to dynamic pressure measurement. As in all piezoelectric devices, the response will fall to zero at very high and very low frequencies.

7–2.2. High pressures

Pressures up to a limit of about 10^5 psi can be readily measured using elastic devices.

Another device, particularly suited to high-pressure measurement is the pressure-sensitive resistance (Bridgman) gage. All conductors when subjected to hydrostatic pressure will undergo an alteration of resistivity. When a fine resistance wire (generally in the form of a loosely wound coil) is subjected to hydrostatic pressure, it will undergo an elastic size change, and a change of resistivity. The net result is a variation of total resistance, the largest effect generally being due to the variation of resistivity. Two materials which are commonly used are listed in Table 7–3.

TABLE 7–3

MATERIALS FOR USE IN BRIDGMAN GAGES

(PROPERTIES FOR SMALL-DIAMETER WIRES)

	Manganin wire (84 Cu, 12 Mn, 4 Ni)	Gold wire (2.1 Chrome)
Pressure sensitivity, (ohm/ohm)/psi	1.692×10^{-7}	0.673×10^{-7}
Temperature sensitivity, (ohm/ohm)/°F	1.7×10^{-5}	0.8×10^{-6}
Resistivity, ohm·cm	45×10^{-6}	2.4×10^{-6}

Since the variation of resistance is associated with elastic movements within the wire, it occurs within the time required for a sound wave to travel the wire radius. For a wire of 0.001-in. radius, this is of the order of 10^{-8} sec, or essentially instantaneous for any mechanical measurement. The resistance gage is normally used in a Wheatstone bridge, which has been discussed in detail.

7–2.3. Vacuum measurement

Vacuum measurements and vacuum technology are generally not well understood by the average practicing engineer. Hence, we will briefly discuss the theoretical background necessary to make and understand vacuum measurements.

(a) *Theoretical background.* One usually assumes that the gas in a vacuum system behaves as a "perfect gas," as described by kinetic theory. The basic assumptions are: (1) the molecules are of negligible size compared with the volume available; (2) no forces exist between the molecules except at the instant of collision. All real gases and those vapors which do not follow these assumptions at atmospheric pressures are very well described by "perfect gas" predictions at even modest vacuums. Using these assumptions, and assuming a Maxwellian distribution of velocities for the molecules, we can draw several useful relationships. First, we have the equation of state for a perfect gas:

$$pV = NKT, \tag{7–6}$$

where N is the number of molecules,

K is Boltzmann's constant,

T is the absolute temperature,

V is the volume, and

p is the pressure.

Secondly, for a mixture of gases, the total pressure is the sum of the individual pressures as predicted by the equation of state:

$$p = \Sigma p_i, \tag{7-7}$$

where $p_i V = K N_i T$.

Third, the root-mean-square velocity of the molecules within a perfect gas is given by

$$\overline{V} = \sqrt{\frac{8KT}{\pi m}}, \tag{7-8}$$

where m is the mass of a molecule. The values for velocity are large, on the order of 0.2 to 2 km/sec at 15°C for most gases. This very high velocity is helpful in leak detection.

Fourth, the mean free path, or the average distance, λ that these high-speed molecules move before collision is given by

$$\lambda = \frac{KT}{\pi\sqrt{2}\, p\sigma^2}, \tag{7-9}$$

where σ is the diameter of a molecule. For air at 15°C, Eq. (7–9) reduces to

$$\lambda_{\text{air}} = \frac{5}{p_\mu}, \tag{7-10}$$

where p_μ is the pressure, microns Hg, and λ is the mean free path, cm. If values of p_μ are substituted in Eq. (7–10) to obtain values for λ, we see that at pressures of 10^{-6} mm Hg ($10^{-3}\ \mu$) a value of $\lambda = 50$ meters is obtained. This means that for practical vacuum systems, most collisions are between walls and molecules rather than between molecules.

7–2.4. Thermal conductivity of gases

Heat transfer in gases at normal pressures is mostly due to convection, but as the pressure is reduced, the convective transfer gradually disappears. Heat transfer then is due only to molecules colliding with the hot surface, and after several intermediate collisions with other molecules, finally transferring the energy to a cold surface. Analysis of this process leads to an approximate expression for the thermal conductivity k:

$$k = \frac{C}{\sigma^2}\sqrt{\frac{T}{m}}, \tag{7-11}$$

where C is a constant, and, k is the thermal conductivity.

Note that the conductivity is independent of pressure when this mechanism is the principal mode of heat transfer. This conclusion has been experimentally verified down to pressures of $100\,\mu$ Hg (microns Hg). Thus when hot objects are cooled by admitting a gas to a chamber, little is gained by raising the pressure above 1 mm Hg, since without considerable convection there is little increase in heat conduction above this pressure.

Further reductions in pressure below $100\,\mu$ Hg, however, enter into the region where the mean free path of molecules will generally exceed the size of the container. Heat is then transferred by molecules hitting the hot surface and traveling without collision to the cold surface. Analysis of this process shows that the heat transfer is now dependent on pressure and drops off fairly rapidly with falling pressure. This feature is used to make several vacuum gages, which will be discussed later.

Radiation has been ignored in the discussion but will always be present and may contribute significantly if the temperature differences are large, such as with liquid air traps.

7–2.5. Flow through apertures (leaks)

In vacuum systems it is convenient to define the flow rate Q as the product of the volumetric flow rate (liter/sec) and the pressure (microns Hg). Thus, in this section, we shall let

$$Q_\mu = p_\mu \frac{dV}{dt}, \tag{7–12}$$

where
$\qquad Q_\mu$ is the flow rate, micron·liter/sec,

$\qquad p_\mu$ is the pressure, microns Hg, and

$\qquad dV/dt$ is the volumetric flow rate, liter/sec.

If we combine Eq. (7–6) and (7–12), we have

$$Q = KT \frac{dN}{dt}, \tag{7–13}$$

where dN/dt is the molecular flow rate, molecules/sec. Note that

$\qquad$ 1 micron Hg $= 1.333$ dynes/cm^2,

$\qquad$ 1 liter $= 1000$ cm^3,

$\qquad K = 1.38 \times 10^{-16}$ erg/°K,

$\qquad T = $ °K $=$ °Kelvin $=$ °C $+ 273.16$.

We can rewrite Eq. (7–13) as

$$Q_\mu = 1.33 \times 10^{-3} KT \frac{dN}{dt}.$$ (7–14)

In this section, we want to describe the flow rate Q_μ through a tube or orifice of radius a and length L. We find that the flow takes on different characteristics depending on whether most collisions are intermolecular, as in *continuous flow*, or between the walls and molecules as in *molecular flow*. The type of collision depends largely on the ratio of the mean free path λ to the tube radius a. For

$$0 < \lambda/a < 0.01 \quad \text{the flow is continuous,}$$

$$0.01 < \lambda/a < 1.0 \quad \text{the flow is transitional,}$$

$$1.0 < \lambda/a < \infty \quad \text{the flow is molecular.}$$

Through use of Eq. (7–9) or (7–10), we can estimate the type of flow.

(a) *Continuous flow.* A typical example of continuous flow would be atmospheric air leading into a vacuum system. Flow of this type is characterized by the usual orifice equations. For all practical systems, the ratio of outlet pressure p_2 to inlet pressure p_1 will be less than 0.525, and the flow will be sonic at the throat. Hence, the flow rate will depend only upon inlet pressure $p_{\mu 1}$, and is approximated by

$$Q_{\mu,\text{air}} = 20\pi a^2 p_{\mu,1}.$$ (7–15)

When the flow is continuous through a "long" tube at low Reynolds number, the usual Poiseuille equation holds. If entrance conditions are taken into account,

$$Q = \frac{\pi a^4 \bar{p}(p_1 - p_2)}{8\mu L[1 + 1.14(m/8\pi\mu kT)(Q/L)]},$$ (7–16)

where $\bar{p}$ is the average pressure in the tube, and μ is the gas viscosity. For air

$$Q_{\mu,\text{air}} = \frac{2.84a^4(p_{\mu,1} - p_{\mu,2})\bar{p}_\mu}{L(1 + 3.83 \times 10^{-4}Q_\mu/L)},$$ (7–17)

where a and L are in centimeters.

(b) *Molecular flow.* When the mean free path λ is large compared with a, molecular flow analysis gives (approximately)

$$Q_\mu = \frac{3.64\pi a^2(p_{\mu,1} - p_{\mu,2})}{1 + 3L/8a}\sqrt{\frac{T}{M}},$$ (7–18)

where M is the gram molecular weight, i.e., gm/mole. For air, $M_{air} = 28.98$. For air at 20°C when $l \gg a$,

$$Q_{\mu, air, 20°C} \approx \frac{97a^3}{L} (p_{\mu,1} - p_{\mu,2}). \tag{7–19}$$

For transitional regions and pipes of noncircular cross section there is an extensive literature of both theoretical and experimental results.

If we can determine Q, the above equations are useful for calculating the error introduced by remote location of a pressure gage. Often the pressure gage is connected near the pump, while the pressure we wish to measure is in a chamber connected by piping. If a valve is located so that the chamber can be sealed off from the pump, closing this valve will isolate the chamber except for pressure rises due to leaks. The gas flow is then given by

$$Q = V\frac{dp}{dt}, \tag{7–20}$$

where V is the volume of the system, liters, and dp/dt is the rate of pressure change. If dp/dt is in microns per second, then Q is in micron·liters per second.

The exact location of all the leaks may not be known, but if it is assumed that all inflow is at the most remote location from the gage, an upper limit on error can be calculated.

7–2.6. Pumping components

There are numerous types of vacuum pumps on the market, each with particular advantages that are best explained by the manufacturer. These pumps may be divided into three classes as follows.

(a) *Mechanical pumps.* Most mechanical pumps are the fixed-displacement type, using a variety of eccentric or vane designs. The better quality pumps will produce a vacuum down to 0.2 micron gas pressure. However, there will be an additional vapor pressure of 1 to 20 microns due to the pumping oil. The performance of these pumps can be very poor, however, if the oil becomes contaminated by volatile components such as water.

(b) *Diffusion pumps.* This type is an adaption to high-vacuum practice of the jet, or aspirator, pump. The jet is generated by boiling a suitable oil through orifices. The molecules to be pumped are picked up by the jet and swept into the higher-pressure region, where the mechanical backing pump removes them, as shown in Fig. 7–2.

The typical operating range for the oil-diffusion pump is from 10^{-3} down to 10^{-8} mm Hg. Under favorable conditions, pressures of

Molecules
from system

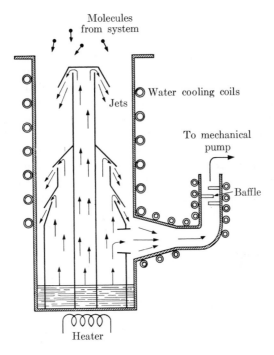

Water cooling coils

Jets

To mechanical
pump

Baffle

Heater

Fig. 7–2. Oil-diffusion pump.

10^{-10} mm Hg can be obtained. Within its operating range, the pump does not operate by allowing molecules to follow a pressure gradient, but rather picks up those molecules which happen to enter the pump section because of their thermal motion. The final performance of diffusion pumps depends upon the geometry, location and number of jets, as well as the type of oil used and cooling provisions.

(c) *Ion pumps.* A recent entry into the high-vacuum pumping field is the ion pump. Electrons in space are oscillated by a combination of magnetic and electric fields. The high-velocity electrons ionize any gas molecules present. These ionized molecules are then attracted to a cathode, usually titanium, where they are trapped. This pump works well with the gases in air, most of which form chemical compounds with titanium. It pumps very slowly, however, with oil vapors and other large molecules. Under ideal conditions it can achieve pressures down to 10^{-9} to 10^{-10} mm Hg. [*Note:* At this point we may note that quantities like 10^{-9} mm Hg involve a contradiction of physical meaning, since the diameter of a mercury atom is of the order of 10^{-7} mm. Accordingly, we do well to adopt a new unit, the *torr*, which has the magnitude of 1 mm Hg (e.g., 10^{-9} torr $\equiv 10^{-9}$ mm Hg) but does not carry the same physical connotation.]

(d) *Cold traps.* Cold surfaces in the vacuum system at dry ice or liquid nitrogen temperatures can be very effective pumps for removing condensable vapors of water, oil, etc. The pumping rate is very great until the vapor pressure of the vapor at the temperature of the surface is approached. A liquid nitrogen trap for instance can reduce the vapor pressure of water to 10^{-18} torr. Traps are often designed much like optical baffles. Since molecules at low pressures travel in straight lines, a trap which provides no direct paths without collision on a cold surface will trap most molecules. Traps must always be used to prevent oil vapor from mechanical or diffusion pumps from reaching the chamber being evacuated.

7–3. Vacuum gages

The theoretical discussion given above forms the basis for the design of most vacuum gages.

(a) *McLeod gage.* This type of gage is essentially a sophisticated mercury U-tube. A large volume of gas is trapped at a low pressure and compressed to a small volume at a pressure high enough to read with a mercury manometer. The perfect gas law is then assumed, so that the low pressure can be calculated. The practical range for McLeod gages is 1 mm Hg to 10^{-6} mm Hg. However, any single instrument will have a much smaller range. A serious limitation of the McLeod gage is that it measures only the pressure of the perfect gases present. Any condensable vapors in the chamber will probably condense upon compression, and will therefore be ignored. A typical example of this occurs when an indication of $0.2\,\mu$ Hg is obtained from a mechanical pump although the vapor pressure of the oil is $20\,\mu$ Hg.

(b) *Thermal conductivity gages.* The operation of both the Pirani and the thermocouple gages depends on the variation of thermal conductivity of a gas with pressure. This restricts them to an upper limit of about 1 mm Hg, above which conductivity is constant. A lower limit of about 10^{-4} mm Hg is due to the very small heat conduction at lower pressures.

The Pirani gage employs a very fine resistance wire, electrically heated and connected in a Wheatstone bridge. The equilibrium temperature, and hence resistance, of the wire depends upon the pressure. The thermocouple gage uses an electric resistance wire with a fine thermocouple mounted on it to measure temperature.

Neither of these gages gives an absolute reading and each must be calibrated. Aging effects can change the wire surfaces, altering emis-

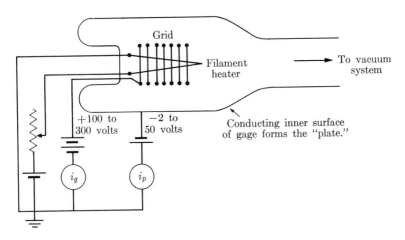

Fig. 7–3. Schematic view of thermionic ionization gage.

sivity and efficiency in heating colliding molecules. As a result these gages are only approximate in their reading, and usually are used where order of magnitude readings are desired and ruggedness in service is important. They are sensitive to all gases as well as condensable vapors. The calibration depends upon the type of gas present.

(c) *Ionization gages.* Ionization gages all work on the principle that the current flow between electrodes in a low-pressure gas is proportional to the concentration of ionized molecules. A low-pressure gas is bombarded by various means to provide a reasonable number of ionized molecules to carry current. With a fixed bombarding source, the percent of ionized molecules remains the same regardless of pressure. The gages have the advantage of being linear with pressure. However, they must be calibrated with some absolute standard such as a McLeod gage. Once these gages are calibrated, the calibration may be extrapolated to pressures as low as 10^{-10} to 10^{-12} torr, a region where no other gage operates.

Three methods are used for forming the ions. The most common uses thermionic electrons accelerated by a potential of 100 to 300 volts. The physical arrangement of the elements is shown in Fig. 7–3. The electrons are accelerated from filament to grid and ionize some of the molecules between the grid and the plate. The number of bombarding electrons available is measured by the grid current i_g. The positive ions in the space between grid and plate will migrate to the plate causing a plate current i_p. The pressure is thus proportional to the ratio of the plate to grid currents. At pressures greater than 1 μ Hg, the ions hitting the cathode tend to overheat and destroy it.

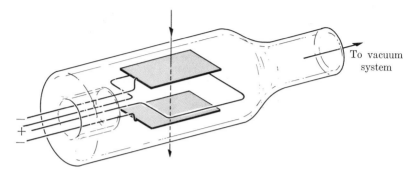

Fig. 7–4. Cold discharge ionization gage.

A second technique replaces the hot filament by a radium source which furnishes the ionizing particles. The concentration of ions produced is less than with the thermionic method, so that the resolution is limited usually to about 10^{-4} mm Hg.

The third type of ionization gage depends on cold discharge in a magnetic field. The mechanical arrangement is as shown in Fig. 7–4.

The cold cathodes emit few electrons, but any electrons in the space between the cathodes and the ring-type anode are accelerated by the magnetic field. The electrons oscillate back and forth between the two equipotential cathodes passing through the ring anode. By this technique, a few electrons can do a good deal of ionizing. The ionization current between the cathode and anode can then be measured as a measure of pressure. Pressures down to 5×10^{-6} mm Hg can be measured. More sophisticated versions can measure to 10^{-12} mm Hg.

All these ionization-type gages are linear in their response, but they do have varying sensitivity, depending upon the type of gas present. Various gases are ionized with greater or less ease so that a calibration is really necessary for each gas. Manufacturers usually label a gage for air but give conversion factors for other gases.

7–4. Cleanliness considerations

A recurrent practical problem with any high-vacuum system is the prodigious volume of gas which is released from various surfaces in the system. Any porous materials containing water, solvents, oil, etc., can take months to dry out even under high vacua. For all practical purposes, they will limit the pressure of the system to the vapor pressure of the material present. Particularly troublesome are certain polymer parts which contain considerable volatile plastizer. Fingerprints can cause trouble if the vacuum desired is low enough. In general, the better the vacuum desired the more care and pumping time are needed. Down to 10^{-6} mm Hg with a leak-free system there is not too serious a problem. However, each succeeding decade is harder to attain. Beyond 10^{-9} torr, an all metal system, preferably of stainless steel to minimize adsorbed gases at the surface, will be necessary. The speed of outgassing can be accelerated in any system if provision is made for heating the parts while pumping. Upon recooling a much better vacuum will be obtained.

Designing vacuum chambers to provide a minimum of sharp inside corners which easily collect dirt is desirable. Where possible all weld beads should be on the inside to avoid cracks where mating parts meet.

7–5. Leak detection

The simplest leak-detection technique is compressed air inside the system plus soapy water on the outside.

For glass systems a spark coil passed over the surface will show a purplish-white glow near a leak, where the pressure will be in the glow discharge region.

If we paint the outside of a system with acetone, alcohol, amyl acetate, etc., this liquid will temporarily seal a leak from the air and feed vapor into the system. As ionization gages, cold traps, thermocouple gages, etc., have varying sensitivity depending upon the vapors or gases present, a sudden change in gage reading is observed.

The most sensitive leak detector employs a small mass spectrometer with dimensions exactly correct for helium atoms. This is connected to the discharge of the system pump. The leak detection probe is then a stream of helium gas played over suspicious areas on the outside of the system. The detector can sense one part helium in 200,000 parts air.

7–6. Dynamics of pressure measurement

When a pressure-sensing element can be directly exposed to the fluid pressure to be measured, as in certain piezoelectric devices, the system dynamic characteristics are simply those of the element itself. However, probably the great majority of pressure measurements involve *fluid transmission* of the pressure signal through various tubes and chambers from the point of interest to the sensing element. For static measurements, the transmission path has no effect on the system (except in vacuum as described previously). However, when we wish

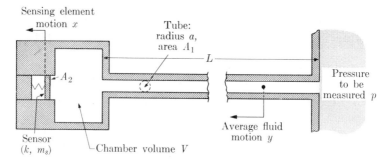

Fig. 7–5. Schematic view of fluid transmission system.

to measure pressure transients, the total transmission path acts as a complex filter, and will very often completely control the system dynamic response characteristics. There are so many possible transmission configurations that we could not hope to analyze or describe them in detail. Indeed, the best analyses can only be considered as general guides, as there are numerous incalculable effects. When there is serious question regarding frequency response, direct calibration under operating conditions must be resorted to if possible.

In this section, we shall treat the cases of incompressible and compressible fluid transmission lines from a very elementary point of view. The literature provides more complete analyses; however, these must also be considered as only approximate.

Figure 7–5 shows schematically the fluid transmission system. The pressure transient p to be measured must be transmitted by the fluid through the tube (area A_1, length L) to a chamber (volume V), and to the pressure sensor. The motion x of the sensor will be accompanied by motion y of the fluid in the tube. In many instances, the chamber may not exist at all.

For the case of incompressible flow, our primary concern is with the fluid mass which must move whenever the sensor moves, and with the fluid friction at the walls. When the frequency ω of the pressure variation is small, the flow in the tube will be laminar, and the velocity distribution across the tube section will be parabolic. It is readily shown that under these conditions, the effective fluid mass m_e is $\frac{4}{3}$ of the actual fluid mass m_f:

$$m_e = \tfrac{4}{3}m_f, \tag{7–21}$$

and that the tube resistance at zero frequency is

$$R_0 = \frac{8\mu}{\pi a^4} \frac{\text{lb} \cdot \text{sec}}{\text{in}^6}, \tag{7–22}$$

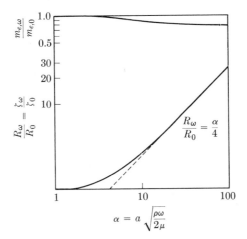

Fig. 7–6. Variation of effective mass and tube resistance with frequency-incompressible fluids.

where the tube resistance is defined according to

$$q = \frac{1}{R}\frac{dp}{dL}.$$ (7–23)

When the frequency is high, the flow is no longer parabolic; the central portions of the fluid move almost as a solid slug, with high-velocity gradients at the tube walls. Thus, both the effective mass and the wall friction will vary with frequency. It has been shown that an appropriate parameter for separating "high" from "low" frequencies is α, where

$$\alpha = a\sqrt{\frac{\rho\omega}{2\mu}},$$ (7–24)

where a is the tube radius, in.,

ρ is the fluid mass density, lb·sec^2/in^4,

ω is the frequency of pressure change, rad/sec, and

μ is the fluid viscosity, lb·sec/in^2.

Figure 7–6 shows the variation of the effective mass and the tube resistance with variation in the frequency parameter α. It is seen that the mass decreases by only 25%, while the resistance may increase many-fold.

Referring to Fig. 7–5, we see that because the effective sensor area A_2 is not generally equal to the tube area A_1, the fluid velocity $\dot{y}$ will differ from the sensor velocity $\dot{x}$ due to continuity:

$$\frac{\dot{y}}{\dot{x}} = \frac{A_2}{A_1}. \qquad (7\text{-}25)$$

The kinetic energy of the fluid, $\frac{1}{2}m(\dot{y})^2$, will then become $\frac{1}{2}m(A_2/A_1)^2$ $(\dot{x})^2$. If we want to refer the fluid motion to the sensor coordinate x, we can define an effective mass m_e, where

$$m_e = \left(\frac{A_2}{A_1}\right)^2 m = \left(\frac{A_2}{A_1}\right)^2 \rho A_1 L. \qquad (7\text{-}26)$$

Thus, referred to the sensor, the total mass will be the sensor mass m_s plus the effective fluid mass m_e, and the system natural frequency ω_n is

$$\omega_n = \sqrt{\frac{k}{m_s + (A_2/A_1)^2 \rho A_1 L}}. \qquad (7\text{-}27)$$

Frequently, the sensor mass is insignificant relative to the effective fluid mass, and we can reduce Eq. (7–27) to

$$\omega_n = \frac{a}{A_2} \sqrt{\frac{\pi k}{\rho L}}. \qquad (7\text{-}28)$$

Thus, to a good approximation, the natural frequency is proportional to the tube diameter, and inversely proportional to the square root of its length. The "natural frequency" is almost independent of the frequency parameter α.

The damping constant c, expressed in lb/(in./sec), when referred to the sensor motion x is given by

$$c_0 = 8\pi\mu L \left(\frac{A_2}{A_1}\right)^2 \qquad \text{(low } \alpha \text{ only)}, \qquad (7\text{-}29)$$

and

$$\zeta_0 = \frac{4\pi\mu L(A_2/A_1)^2}{\sqrt{k[m_s + (A_2/A_1)^2 \rho A_1 L]}}, \qquad (7\text{-}30)$$

again, when $m_s \ll m_e$:

$$\zeta_0 = \frac{4\mu A_2}{a^3} \sqrt{\frac{L}{\pi \rho k}}. \qquad (7\text{-}31)$$

As frequency increases, Fig. 7–6 shows that the damping will also increase. For sufficiently high frequencies ($\alpha > 10$),

$$\zeta_\omega \approx \frac{A_2}{a^2} \sqrt{\frac{\mu \omega L}{2\pi k}}. \qquad (7\text{-}32)$$

The theory for compressible fluid pressure transmission is considerably more complex, as we are concerned with acoustical resonances, and subresonance signal attenuation. The compressibility of gases is such that we can generally obtain or design a sensor whose motion x is completely insignificant relative to the fluid motion. We then must estimate the lowest frequency at which acoustical resonance is likely to occur. For the system of Fig. 7–5, there are two primary resonances. The first is a resonance associated with standing waves in the tube itself. The fundamental frequency (ω_1) for such oscillations is simply

$$\omega_1 = \frac{\pi c}{2L}, \tag{7-33}$$

where c is the speed of sound in the gas (in./sec).

There are higher harmonics, but for measurement purposes, we are generally limited by the fundamental. The second resonance occurs when the cavity volume V acts as a spring and the fluid in the tube acts as a mass. This system is termed a Helmholtz resonator, and has its resonant frequency ω_H at

$$\omega_H = \sqrt{\frac{c^2 A_1}{V(L + \pi a/2)}}. \tag{7-34}$$

As a general rule of thumb, we will be limited by the Helmholtz condition whenever

$$V_{\text{chamber}} > \tfrac{1}{2} V_{\text{tube}}. \tag{7-35}$$

When the chamber volume is relatively large, and the transmission tube of very small diameter, the system characteristics will approach those of a first-order system, where the chamber is analogous to a capacitor, and the tube analogous to a resistor. Such a system (acoustical filter) can be designed to attenuate frequencies above any given value.

PROBLEMS

1. A venturi flow meter, of the type shown in Fig. 7–7 is highly efficient (little total energy loss), and measures flow according to the following equation:

$$Q = C \frac{A_2}{\sqrt{1 - (A_2/A_1)^2}} \sqrt{\frac{2(p_1 - p_2)}{\rho}},$$

where C is the empirically determined "discharge coefficient" (0.975 to 0.990, for Reynolds number greater than 10^5), and ρ is the mass density of the "incompressible" fluid. Derive the above flow equation.

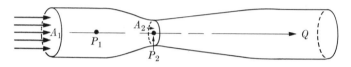

Figure 7–7

2. Water at an unknown pressure is flowing in a 2-in. diameter tube. Two simple water-level manometers are attached as shown in Fig. 7–8. A static pressure tube, flush with the side wall, shows 10 in. of water. The impact, or pitot tube, at the pipe axis shows 40 in. of water. What is the average water pressure, and what is the flow rate q (in^3/sec)?

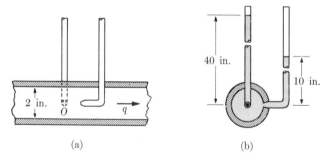

(a)   (b)

Figure 7–8

3. A spherical ball is suspended by a fine string from a fixed point as shown in Fig. 7–9. The wind, moving at velocity V causes the string to be at some angle ϕ relative to the vertical. Determine the relationship between ϕ (degrees) and V (mph).

4. A simple liquid flow meter consists of a circular bend of radius R in a pipe as shown in Fig. 7–10. Static pressure is measured in the straight section p_1 and then in the curved section p_2. Determine the relationship $q = f(\rho, R, p_1, p_2)$. What are the probable sources of error? (Neglect gravity.)

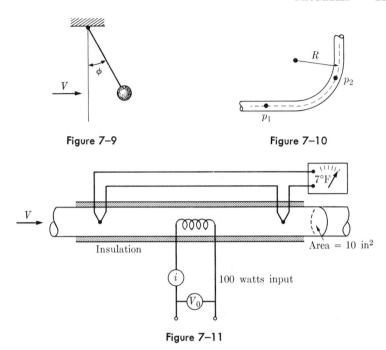

Figure 7–9   Figure 7–10

Figure 7–11

5. Dry air, at essentially atmospheric pressure and room temperature, flows through a thermally insulated pipe having a flow area of 10 in², as shown in Fig. 7–11. An electric heater inside the pipe dissipates 100 watts. A differential thermocouple, arranged as shown, indicates a temperature difference of 7°F. Estimate the average flow velocity. What are the primary sources of error in such a system?

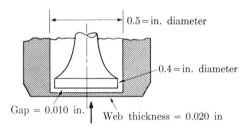

Figure 7–12

6. A partial section of a variable-capacitance pressure gage is shown in Fig. 7–12. The diaphragm and housing are machined from a single piece of steel. Estimate (a) the natural frequency of the diaphragm, (b) the pressure sensitivity $(\Delta C/C_0)$/psi, and (c) the maximum pressure allowable.

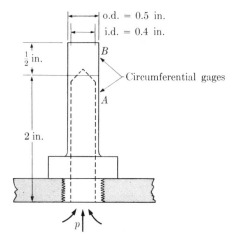

Figure 7-13

7. A pressure cell is made from 18-8 stainless steel to the pertinent dimensions shown in Fig. 7-13. Four circumferential gages are applied; two at A for measuring circumferential strains, and two at B to afford temperature compensation. (a) What will be the strain sensitivity (in./in.)/psi? (b) What is the maximum pressure that can be applied before damage results. (c) Estimate (crudely if necessary) the natural frequency of the system when used to measure oil pressure.

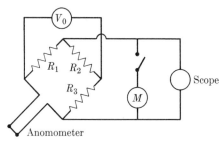

Figure 7-14

8. A hot-wire anomometer is constructed from nickel wire (resistivity, 8.6×10^{-6} ohm·cm at 20°C; temperature coefficient 0.0037°F^{-1}), 0.001 in. diameter and 1 in. long. It will be used to measure velocity transients in air moving at an average velocity of 800 ft/sec, at atmospheric temperature and pressure. The wire will be used as one arm of a Wheatstone bridge as shown in Fig. 7-14. The input voltage V_0 will be manually adjusted until the long-time-constant meter M reads zero. Then fluctuations will be observed on the oscilloscope. Determine the expected circuit parameters (resistances and voltages) and estimate the sensitivity of the system in volt/(ft/sec).

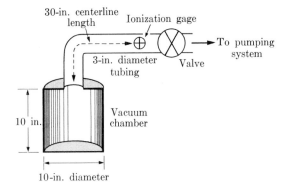

Figure 7–15

9. A vacuum chamber is connected to a pumping system as shown in Fig. 7–15. When the valve is closed, the ionization gage indicates 10^{-7} mm Hg. After 10 min, the pressure has risen to 10^{-6} mm Hg. Estimate the greatest probable error between the actual chamber pressure and that indicated by the gage.

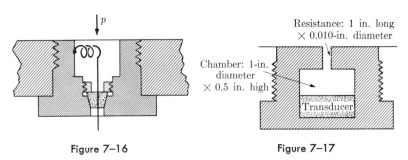

Figure 7–16   **Figure 7–17**

10. It is proposed to construct a Bridgman-type pressure gage for purposes of measuring short-duration pressure pulses in gas. The pulses will be as large as 50,000 to 100,000 psi. The pressure pulse will be accompanied by a temperature pulse of the order of 1000°F. The active element is to be 0.001 in. diameter manganin wire, 1 in. long, in a channel $\frac{1}{2}$ in. in diameter by $\frac{1}{2}$ in. deep (Fig. 7–16). (a) Design a Wheatstone bridge circuit for the unit and estimate the system sensitivity. (b) Estimate the frequency response (i) with the system as shown, (ii) with the cavity filled with a silicone grease. (c) What problems would you be concerned about in this system?

11. A very sensitive pressure transducer is to be used to measure small variations in pressure. In order that the unit not be damaged by relatively rapid high-pressure pulses, an acoustical filter is employed. For the dimensions given in Fig. 7–17, and for air at room conditions, estimate the frequency response of the device (assuming that mechanical response is not limiting).

Note that for small pressure changes, the gas flow in the tube can be approximated by incompressible flow.

12. In a gas-flow application it is necessary to measure the differential pressure between two points (nominally at room temperature and pressure) which are 8 ft apart. This is to be done using two 4-ft sections of copper tubing, 0.1 in. inside diameter, connecting to a differential pressure transducer having an enclosed volume of $\frac{1}{2}$ in^3 on each side of an actuating diaphragm. Estimate the first resonant frequency of this system.

REFERENCES

ASME Power Test Code, ASME, New York, 1959. Restriction-type flow meters.

ASME Symposium on Measurement in Unsteady Flow, ASME, New York, 1962. Coverage of hot-wire anomometry.

MIESSE, C. C., and O. E. CURTH, "How to Select a Flowmeter," *Product Engineering*, May 8, 1961 p. 35.

SWEENEY, R. J., *Measurement Techniques in Mechanical Engineering*, Wiley and Sons, New York, 1953. General coverage.

"Attenuation of Oscillatory Pressures in Instrument Lines." *J. of Research, Nat. Bu. Stand.* RP2115, Vol. 45, July 1950.

CHAPTER EIGHT

Radiotracer Techniques

8-1. Introduction

One of the most versatile techniques available to the experimenter is that involving the use of radioactive isotopes as tracers. The practical applications of this technique are characterized by their extreme diversity, simplicity, and directness. It is impossible, within the scope of a brief treatment, to do more than give some of the general considerations governing the production and use of radioisotopes, to discuss the accompanying experimental techniques, and to describe a few of the practical applications.

8-2. The constitution of atoms

Matter is made up of atoms, and every atom consists of a central nucleus surrounded by a swarm of orbiting electrons. Each nucleus is made up of different numbers of two elementary nuclear particles, neutrons and protons. These particles have essentially equal mass (this is defined as unit mass), but they differ in that, while the neutrons are electrically neutral, the protons are electrically charged (the charge on one proton is defined as unit positive charge). Nuclei differ among each other in the total number of elementary particles they contain, and the way this total number is made up among neutrons and protons. Using standard nomenclature, there are in each nucleus Z protons and $A - Z$ neutrons (where A, as we shall see below, is the atomic weight of the nucleus). Outside the nucleus there are Z electrons, each electron having essentially zero mass and unit negative charge. This simple picture of the atoms is summarized in Table 8-1.

Now the chemical properties of an atom are determined exclusively by the number Z of electrons orbiting around it. This number Z is called the atomic number of the atom, and it may vary from 1 for hydrogen, the first element in the periodic table, up to 92 and beyond for uranium and the transuranic elements.

Although all the atoms of a chemical element have the same number Z of electrons and protons, they may have, in their nuclei, different numbers $(A - Z)$ of neutrons. Thus, iron, the 26th element in the periodic table, has an atomic number of 26, and every nucleus of iron

TABLE 8–1

CONSTITUTION OF AN ATOM

	Number of particles	Mass	Charge
Inside the nucleus	$\begin{cases} A - Z \text{ neutrons} \\ Z \text{ protons} \end{cases}$	$\begin{matrix} A - Z \\ Z \end{matrix}$	$\begin{matrix} 0 \\ +Z \end{matrix}$
Outside the nucleus	Z electrons	0	$-Z$
Total		A	0

has 26 protons in it. The number of neutrons, however, may vary in different nuclei of iron, and each constitutes a separate nuclear species, or nuclide. They are also referred to as *isotopes* of iron.

Atoms of iron are known whose nuclei contain 28, 30, 31, and 32 neutrons, giving atomic weights A of 54, 56, 57, and 58, respectively. We write these as $_{26}^{28}\text{Fe}^{54}$, $_{26}^{30}\text{Fe}^{56}$, $_{26}^{31}\text{Fe}^{57}$, and $_{26}^{32}\text{Fe}^{58}$, where the bottom left-hand corner denotes the number Z of protons, the top left-hand corner the number $A - Z$ of neutrons, and the top right-hand corner the total atomic weight A. This leaves the bottom right-hand corner for the chemists, who wish to indicate the degree of chemical combination of the atom as, for example, in $_{26}^{30}\text{Fe}_{2}^{56}\ _{8}\text{O}_{3}^{16}$, which is one form of the familiar rust Fe_2O_3.

Actually, we may simplify our notation considerably, since iron is known to have an atomic number of 26, and hence we may omit this fact from our notation. Also, knowing the atomic weight and the atomic number, we may obtain, by simple subtraction, the number of neutrons. Hence, the nuclear species is defined uniquely by the symbol of the element and the value of its atomic weight. These are written in the form Fe^{56}, etc., or more simply as Fe-56.

8–3. Stability of nuclides: radionuclides.

We now proceed to a new question. Given that a nucleus of 26 protons and any number of neutrons whatever constitute an isotope of iron, how many isotopes of iron are there? In other words, what number of neutrons may be combined with 26 protons to form a stable nucleus. In Fig. 8–1 is a plot of all the stable nuclei, showing the number of neutrons as a function of the number of protons. We see that all the stable nuclei lie within a narrow band, which for light elements follows a line of slope 45° (number of protons approximately equal to the number of neutrons), but for heavy nuclei there are considerably more neutrons

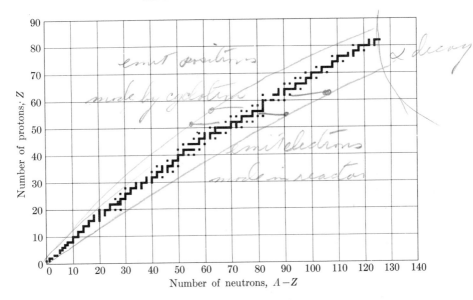

Fig. 8–1. Plot of the stable nuclei.

than there are protons. Not all combinations of neutrons and protons, even within the narrow band, form stable nuclei, since complicated nuclear interaction selection rules operate. These discriminate especially severely against nuclei with odd numbers of both protons and neutrons.

If we try to produce a nucleus by throwing together a totally unsuitable number of protons and neutrons (e.g., 26 protons, 46 neutrons), it falls apart immediately, and ejects most of the excess neutrons in a time of the order of 10^{-20} sec. However, if we form a nucleus which consists of a ratio of neutrons to protons near the stable ratio, (e.g., 26 protons, 33 neutrons), then a nucleus is produced which, although it is unstable, does have a reasonably long life. In fact the combination of 26 protons and 33 neutrons, namely Fe-59, will remain, on the average, about 46 days before it breaks up.

This behavior is illustrated in Fig. 8–2, which shows a small section of the neutron-proton plot of Fig. 8–1, but with the unstable as well as stable nuclei indicated. It will be seen that the unstable nuclides, otherwise known as radionuclides, all have neutron/proton proportions close to those which produce stability. Further, it will be noted that the unstable nuclides are several times more common than are the stable isotopes. Iron has six radioisotopes: Fe-52, Fe-53, Fe-55, Fe-59, Fe-60, and Fe-61, as Fig. 8–2 shows.

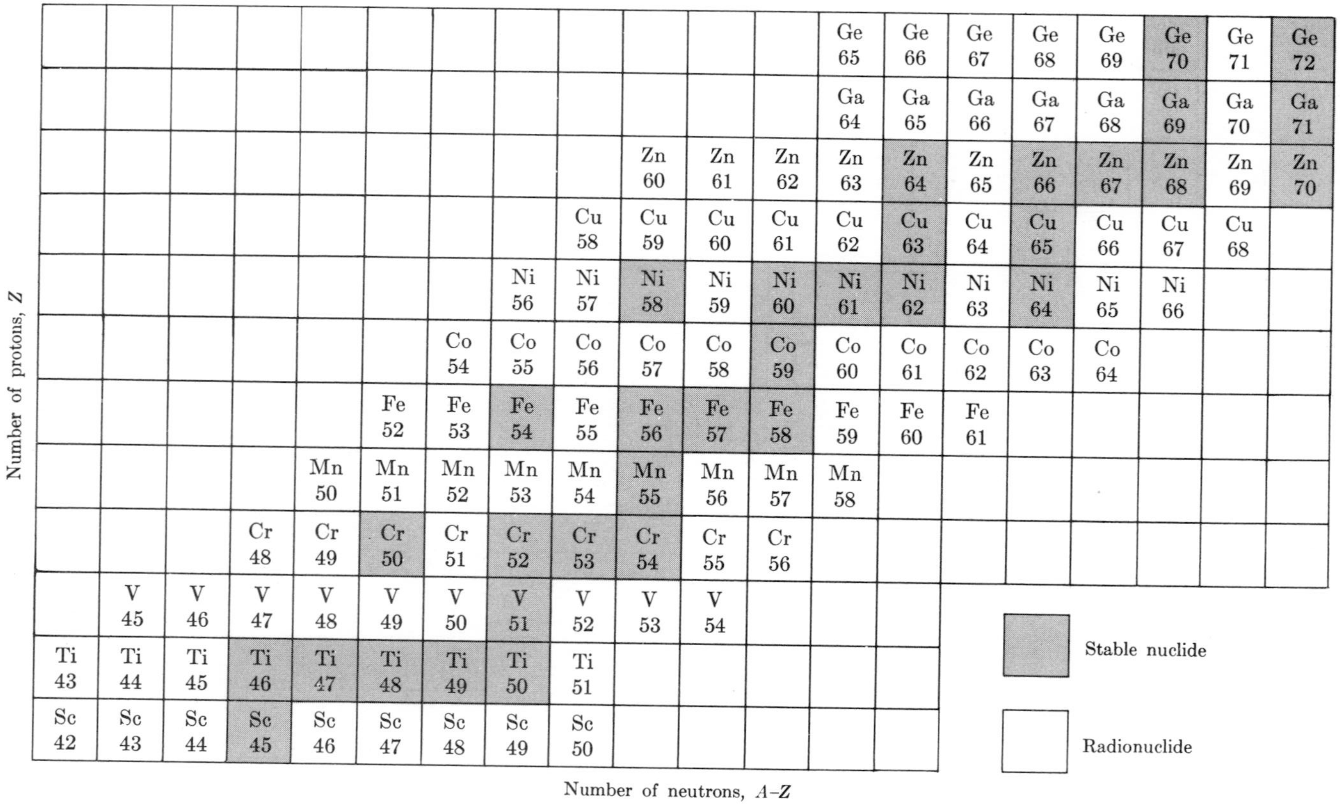

Chart of stable and radioactive nuclides. The vertical axis is "Number of protons, Z"; the horizontal axis is "Number of neutrons, $A-Z$." Shaded cells denote stable nuclides; unshaded cells denote radionuclides.

Legend:
- Stable nuclide (shaded)
- Radionuclide (unshaded)

Nuclides shown (by element, with mass numbers; stable nuclides shown in **bold**):

Element (Z)	Nuclides
Ge (32)	Ge 65, Ge 66, Ge 67, Ge 68, Ge 69, **Ge 70**, Ge 71, **Ge 72**
Ga (31)	Ga 64, Ga 65, Ga 66, Ga 67, Ga 68, **Ga 69**, Ga 70, **Ga 71**
Zn (30)	Zn 60, Zn 61, Zn 62, Zn 63, **Zn 64**, Zn 65, **Zn 66**, **Zn 67**, **Zn 68**, Zn 69, **Zn 70**
Cu (29)	Cu 58, Cu 59, Cu 60, Cu 61, Cu 62, **Cu 63**, Cu 64, **Cu 65**, Cu 66, Cu 67, Cu 68
Ni (28)	Ni 56, Ni 57, **Ni 58**, Ni 59, **Ni 60**, **Ni 61**, **Ni 62**, Ni 63, **Ni 64**, Ni 65, Ni 66
Co (27)	Co 54, Co 55, Co 56, Co 57, Co 58, **Co 59**, Co 60, Co 61, Co 62, Co 63, Co 64
Fe (26)	Fe 52, Fe 53, **Fe 54**, Fe 55, **Fe 56**, **Fe 57**, **Fe 58**, Fe 59, Fe 60, Fe 61
Mn (25)	Mn 50, Mn 51, Mn 52, Mn 53, Mn 54, **Mn 55**, Mn 56, Mn 57, Mn 58
Cr (24)	**Cr 48**, Cr 49, **Cr 50**, Cr 51, **Cr 52**, **Cr 53**, **Cr 54**, Cr 55, Cr 56
V (23)	V 45, V 46, V 47, V 48, V 49, **V 50**, **V 51**, V 52, V 53, V 54
Ti (22)	Ti 43, Ti 44, Ti 45, **Ti 46**, **Ti 47**, **Ti 48**, **Ti 49**, **Ti 50**, Ti 51
Sc (21)	Sc 42, Sc 43, Sc 44, **Sc 45**, Sc 46, Sc 47, Sc 48, Sc 49, Sc 50

Fig. 8–2. Chart of stable and radioactive nuclides.

8-4. Decay of radioactive nuclei

All unstable nuclei sooner or later undergo spontaneous disintegration, with the emission of a ray or particle from the nucleus, and the formation of a different nucleus. The important decay mechanisms are detailed below.

(a) *Beta-particle emission.* The nucleus undergoes an internal reaction, in the course of which one neutron is converted into a proton and an electron. This process conserves charge and, essentially, mass. The electron does not belong in the nucleus and is ejected as a β-particle:

$$_{26}^{33}\text{Fe}^{59} \rightarrow\ _{27}^{32}\text{Co}^{59} + \beta^-. \qquad (8\text{-}1)$$

This process generally occurs in nuclei which have an excessive number of neutrons, i.e., those below the stable band of Figs. 8–1 and 8–2.

(b) *Positron emission.* The positron is a positively charged electron. It is produced by a nuclear process which is the exact converse of the one specified above. In nuclei which have an excessive number of protons, one proton changes into a neutron and a positron, and the positron is ejected:

$$_{26}^{26}\text{Fe}^{52} \rightarrow\ _{25}^{27}\text{Mn}^{52} + \beta^+. \qquad (8\text{-}2)$$

(c) *Gamma-ray emission.* Gamma-rays are a form of electromagnetic radiation, just as are radio waves, visible light, and x-rays. As such, each ray has no intrinsic mass, and no charge, and represents a pulse of pure energy. Gamma-rays are given off in many nuclear processes, whenever a nucleus is formed in a state other than its lowest energy state. Most of these processes are instantaneous. Thus, the Co-59 produced in Eq. (8–1) is formed in an excited state (written Co-59*) and undergoes gamma-ray emission:

$$\text{Co}^{59^*} \rightarrow \text{Co}^{59} + \gamma. \qquad (8\text{-}3)$$

Two gamma-rays also result from the formation of every positron, since positrons interact strongly with electrons, and there are always plenty of electrons about. This reaction may be written as

$$\beta^- + \beta^+ \rightarrow 2\gamma. \qquad (8\text{-}4)$$

(d) *K-capture.* In this reaction, an electron from outside the nucleus is captured by the nucleus, and takes part in a reaction in which a proton plus an electron is turned into a neutron. The captured electron is almost invariably one that was circling the atom in the closest orbit, or

K-orbit. For this reaction, we have

$$\,_{26}^{26}\mathrm{Fe}^{52} + \beta^- \to \,_{25}^{27}\mathrm{Mn}^{52}. \tag{8–5}$$

We see that K-capture produces the same nuclear change as does positron emission. One clear difference is that in K-capture, a characteristic x-ray is always formed, resulting from the energy released as an outside electron orbiting the atom falls into the empty K-orbit. In general, nuclei lying above the stable band undergo β^+-decay or K-capture.

(e) *Alpha-particle emission.* In this process a package of two protons and two neutrons (constituting the nucleus of He-4) is emitted simultaneously, and lightens the nucleus accordingly:

$$\,_{88}^{138}\mathrm{Ra}^{226} \to \,_{86}^{136}\mathrm{Rn}^{222} + \alpha. \tag{8–6}$$

This is the famous disintegration of radium into radon. Although, historically, alpha-decay is of great importance, it actually is of little significance in radiotracer work, since very heavy elements are those which mainly show alpha-decay, and they are not generally those of interest. Moreover, it is difficult to produce alpha-emitting isotopes starting with nonradioactive material. On the other hand, the beta-emitting and gamma-emitting radioisotopes are generally easy to prepare, and are often isotopes of common engineering materials.

8–5. Multiple decay

The presentation given above is something of an oversimplification, since not all radionuclides turn into stable species after undergoing but one disintegration, and not all radionuclides decay in but one way.

In regard to the first part, we must note that many radionuclides decay into other radionuclides, which themselves decay. For example,

$$\,_{88}^{138}\mathrm{Ra}^{226} \to \,_{86}^{136}\mathrm{Rn}^{222} \to \,_{84}^{134}\mathrm{Po}^{218} \to \,_{82}^{132}\mathrm{Pb}^{214}$$

$$\to \,_{83}^{131}\mathrm{Bi}^{214} \to \cdots \to \,_{82}^{124}\mathrm{Pb}^{206}.$$

The other complication is the property of some radionuclides of being able to decay in two different ways. For example,

$$\,_{29}^{35}\mathrm{Cu}^{64} \to \,_{30}^{34}\mathrm{Zn}^{64} + \beta^-, \tag{8–7}$$

or

$$\,_{29}^{35}\mathrm{Cu}^{64} \to \,_{28}^{36}\mathrm{Ni}^{64} + \beta^+. \tag{8–8}$$

8–6. Half-life of radionuclides

Each radionuclear species decays in a characteristic way, in which the number of nuclei decaying in a short interval of time is proportional to the number of nuclei N present at that time. The constant of proportionality, generally denoted by λ, is known as the decay constant and has the dimensions of inverse time. We have

$$\frac{dN}{dt} = -\lambda N,$$

or

$$\frac{dN}{N} = -\lambda \, dt. \tag{8–9}$$

Equation (8–9) may be integrated from the time $t = 0$, at which time N_0 nuclei were present, to a later time t when N nuclei of this species remain. Thus we have

$$\ln N - \ln N_0 = -\lambda t$$

or

$$N = N_0 e^{-\lambda t}. \tag{8–10}$$

This relationship is plotted in Fig. 8–3. There are two features of interest in this figure. The first is the half-life $t_{1/2}$, the time required for the number of nuclei to drop to one-half their initial value. From Eq. (8–10), we may calculate that $t_{1/2}$ has a magnitude of $0.693/\lambda$. Secondly, we note that the initial rate of decay is such that if it continued at a constant rate, the number of nuclei would drop to zero in a time equal to $1.44 \times t_{1/2}$. Actually, the rate of decay slows down as the number of radioactive nuclei diminishes, so that the number of

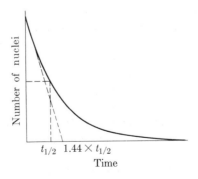

Fig. 8–3. Plot of radioactive decay.

nuclei remaining drops by a factor of 2 whenever the time increases by one half-life.

Although the decay constant λ is the quantity which is used in decay calculations, it is almost never quoted in tables, or indeed kept in mind by anyone, this honor being reserved for the half-life. The reason for this strange situation lies in the preference of the human mind for comprehending a time rather than a reciprocal of a time.

The rate of decay of a radioactive species is the most important parameter which determines its potential usefulness for radiotracer experiments. If the radioactivity is too short-lived (less than a few hours, for example), then by the time the experiment is well under way the radioactivity will be almost gone. Conversely, if the rate of decay is low (half-life more than 100 years), then measurements of the disintegration will be difficult.

8–7. Penetrating power of radioactive decay particles

Besides the half-life, two other parameters determine the potential usefulness of radioactive species. These are the type of particle emitted and the particle energy. These parameters govern the penetration of the radiation, which in turn affects our ability to extract information from a radiotracer experiment. As will be seen below, the type of particle or ray emitted is of prime importance, since alpha-particles have but a very short range, beta-particles have an intermediate penetrating power, while K-radiation and gamma-rays have the greatest ability to penetrate matter. (In this chapter, we generally refer to electromagnetic radiation such as x-rays and γ-rays as *rays*, while other emitted substances are labelled *particles*. This distinction is rather arbitrary, since all these products of radioactive decay show both wave and corpuscular properties.)

The information on the various forms of radioactive decay is summarized in Figs. 8–4 and 8–5 in the form of two graphs for each particle, one denoting the penetration as a function of distance for a particle of typical energy passing through a typical species of matter, the other showing the thickness of matter required to cut the amount of radiation to $1/e$, as a function of particle energy. In general, if matter different from that indicated is used to cut down the radiation, then its effectiveness is roughly proportional to its density, i.e., aluminum (density 2.7) has about $\frac{1}{3}$ the stopping power per unit thickness of copper (density 8.5).

The difference in stopping power between alpha-particles, beta-particles, and gamma- and x-rays should be carefully noted. To quote

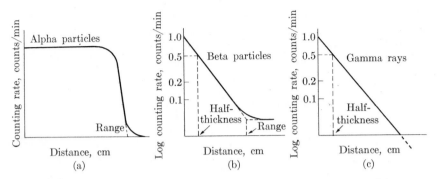

Fig. 8–4. (a) Range of alpha-particles in air; (b) range of beta-particles; (c) range of gamma-rays.

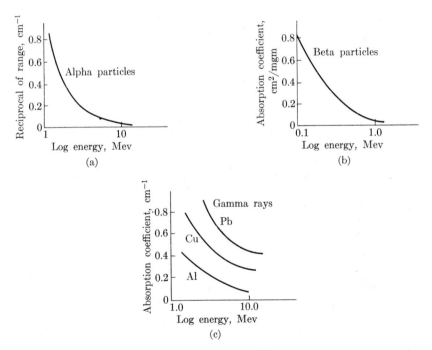

Fig. 8–5. (a) Range-energy plot for alpha-particles in air; (b) absorption coefficient-energy plot for beta-particles; (c) absorption coefficient-energy plot for gamma-rays stopped by lead, copper, and aluminum.

data for particles of average energy, alpha-particles are stopped by thick but not by thin aluminum foil, beta-particles are stopped by a thick coin but not by a thin one, and gamma-rays go through a half-inch of steel but not through more than a few inches.

8–8. Detection of radiation

The particles given off by decaying nuclei are all distinguished by great specific energy, but by very small overall size, so that the total energy per particle is quite small. In order for one particle to make much of an impact in the world, it is necessary for us to use an amplifying system with very high gain. Also, we chose a system which minimizes spurious signals from other charged particles with much lower energies which are widely prevalent everywhere. A number of systems of this kind are shown in Fig. 8–6, but we shall concentrate on but two of the most widely used ones, namely the Geiger-Mueller counter, generally referred to as the geiger or G-M counter, and photographic film.

8–9. The geiger counter

If two conducting plates are separated by a small distance and an ever-increasing potential difference is applied to them, then it is found that essentially no current passes until the voltage reaches a critical value, known as the breakdown voltage. Thereafter, a large current passes continuously (Fig. 8–7). It has been found that if the voltage applied is a little less than the breakdown voltage, and then a radioactive particle passes through the gap, breakdown occurs. In this way one tiny particle of radiation can produce a very large effect.

A device incorporating this principle of detection is known as a geiger counter. Practical counters differ from the simple charged plates in several ways. Firstly, the geometry is always that of a fine charged wire inside a cylinder, as this arrangement has been found to be most effective. Secondly, the counter is fully enclosed, so that odd ions from the atmosphere are kept out, and variations in the atmospheric moisture content will not affect the counter performance. Thirdly, the electronic circuit supplying the counter is arranged so that as soon as a discharge occurs, the voltage across the plate rapidly drops, thus cutting off the current and allowing the counter to charge up again in time to detect the next particle. Last, the gas inside the counter is not ordinary air, but a mixture of argon and various organic vapors, the function of the latter being to neutralize charged particles in the counter, thus cutting

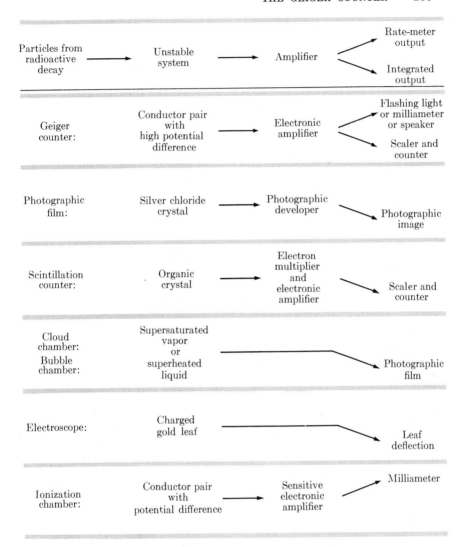

Fig. 8–6. Schematic diagrams of radioactivity detectors.

off the discharge current more quickly after the particle has passed through the counter.

We may evaluate the performance characteristics of the geiger counter in a number of ways. Suppose that we place a geiger counter near a radioactive source of long life and measure the counting rate as a function of potential difference. A curve such as is shown in Fig. 8–8 results. It will be seen that if the voltage is below a minimum value, no particles

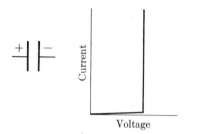

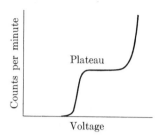

Fig. 8–7. Operating characteristics of
two conducting plates.

Fig. 8–8. Operating characteristics of
a geiger tube.

are detected; that within a certain voltage range known as the plateau, the counting rate is almost independent of the voltage, while at higher voltages the counting rate increases very rapidly. Geiger counters are operated within the plateau, usually at a voltage just below the middle of the plateau. At this voltage essentially all particles within it are detected, while at lower voltages many particles are missed; whereas at much higher voltages many of the counts which are measured are spurious.

One of the important features of geiger counters is their *dead time*, which is an interval of time, after a particle is detected, during which the counter is not in a position to record any new particle that may have arrived. Clearly, this dead time corresponds to the time required to discharge the counter, extinguish the current, and recharge the counter. The dead time is a function not only of the counter construction but also of the surrounding circuitry. A typical value might be 2×10^{-4} sec. The existence of the dead-time phenomenon limits the counting rate at which a geiger counter will operate effectively to something less than about 100,000 counts/min.

At counting rates above 10,000 counts/min the observed counting rate must be corrected for the fact that some counts are being missed, and the corrections become steadily more difficult to make as the counting rate approaches 100,000 counts/min.

The information from a geiger counter may be used in a number of ways. The simplest method is that of feeding the signal into an amplifier connected to an earphone or loudspeaker or a flashing light. In this case each discharge of the counter will correspond to the production by the counter of one "blip" or pulse. The geiger counter with this simple "blip" output finds many uses, as in monitoring to detect the presence of radioactive contamination, or in prospecting, to detect the presence of uranium ores. It suffers as a quantitative device from the fact that counts coming close together are apt to be missed, also there is the tediousness involved in the counting process.

These defects can be remedied in two ways. The simpler procedure consists of allowing the counts to be averaged out by an electric storage circuit, and producing an average reading to be displayed on a meter. A more accurate and satisfactory system is that of having the counts recorded on a digital adding device. Since mechanical recorders have a response time of at least 10^{-1} sec, while the geiger counter has a response time of but 10^{-4} sec, a serious mismatch occurs if the counts are recorded mechanically. However, it is universal practice to use electronic addition using a series of electronic scale-of-two or scale-of-ten counters, which record the counts up to some reasonably large number such as 1000 and 1024, and then the units of 1000 or 1024 are recorded mechanically.

The geiger counter has a low efficiency for recording gamma-rays, because it is filled with a low-density gas, and most of the rays pass through without triggering off the counter. In fact, the gamma efficiency of most counters is as low as 1 or 3%. The efficiency to beta-rays is determined by the penetrating power (i.e., the energy) of the particle, and by the wall thickness of the counter. However, efficiencies of 50% and above are quite common.

8–10. Photographic film

Radioactivity was first recorded on photographic film, and since that time the popularity of this system of detecting radioactivity has had its ups and downs. It is of interest to note that while the actual method of use of photographic film is quite different from that involving geiger counters, the basic principle of operation does show some similarity.

It will be remembered that the basic problem in detecting radioactivity is that of making a macroscopically observable phenomenon out of the tiny amount of energy possessed by one radioactive particle. In the geiger counter, this effect is achieved through the use of an electric system which is close to instability. In photography, use is made of a crystal of silver chloride whose atomic arrangement is close to instability. If a crystal of silver chloride within the emulsion of a photographic film is placed in a developing solution which is, chemically, mildly reducing, then the crystal is unaffected and remains in the chemical form of silver chloride. This compound may be washed from the emulsion by a solution of sodium thiosulfate. However, if the crystal has been traversed by a particle from a radioactive disintegration, then a slight rearrangement of its structure occurs, so that the developing solution is able to reduce the whole crystal to silver. Silver is not soluble in sodium thiosulfate. The overall effect is that one radioactive particle is made observable in the form of one silver lump in a photographic emulsion.

It is worth pointing out that the way in which radioactive particles affect photographic film is closely analogous to the way that light rays (themselves electromagnetic waves just like x-rays and γ-rays) act in the standard photographic process. Practical differences between light photography and radiation photography arise mainly from the fact that radioactive particles cannot be readily refracted and focused in the way that light rays can.

In the typical use of photographic film in radiotracer work, the material containing radioactive material is placed close to the photographic film and allowed to remain there for a substantial period of time, generally in the range of a few minutes to a few days. Thereafter, the film is developed, and the regions in the film which were close to the radioactive material come out as blackened patches, while the regions which were remote from any radioactive material remain clear and transparent.

8–11. Comparison of geiger counters and photographic film as radioactivity detectors

It will be seen that photographic and counter methods of detecting radioactivity differ in very many respects, which we will itemize below.

(1) The geiger counter method is much more rapid. A level of radioactivity which may readily be detected in a few seconds with the geiger counter may require an exposure of hours with photography.

(2) Surprisingly, in view of the above, autoradiography is often a more sensitive way of detecting radiation than is counting. This occurs when the radioactive material is in the form of small compact lumps which can be brought right up to the film, and which have long half-lives, so that exposures of a week or more become possible. The resolution of photographic film is about 10^5 particles/mm^2. It is generally impossible to carry out geiger counting for more than a few hours, since the expensive equipment may be needed for another count determination, and in any case the background needs frequent rechecking. This background problem does not arise in autoradiography, since those areas of the film remote from radiation give the level of the background count.

(3) The geiger counter method is much more accurate than is autoradiography. A typical value for the accuracy obtainable with geiger

counting is 0.3%, while with radiography a value of 10% is close to the best that is practical.

(4) The geiger counter determines the radioactivity from only one region at one time, while autoradiography provides information simultaneously about many different regions.

(5) A serious limitation of radiography is the time required to finish the experiment, to develop the film, and then to examine it, before being able to use the result obtained in devising the next experiment. No such limitation applies to the counting method.

(6) A serious limitation of the counting method is the expense involved in obtaining a good counter and scaler unit, compared with the great economy which accompanies autoradiography. It is quite easy to carry out a hundred autoradiographic determinations of radioactive intensity at the same time, while that number of geiger measurements could not be handled simultaneously. This becomes of great importance when we are working with a radioisotope with a short half-life.

Perhaps this distinction can be made particularly clear when we consider the matter of the detection of radiation for health purposes. People working with radiotracers use both methods; a geiger counter as part of a portable unit known as a health monitor, and a piece of photographic film as the active element of a film badge. The geiger counter is used as a monitor, and is moved around the laboratory to indicate at which points, if any, there is a high concentration of radiation. This may indicate that it is unsafe to work in this location, unless the level of radiation is first reduced, or alternatively, it will detect the accidental spillage of some radioactive material which must be carefully removed to prevent hazard to health and contamination of other equipment.

The film badge, on the other hand, is attached to the arm of the worker in a radioactive laboratory by a wrist band, or in some other way. A new film is supplied weekly, and the old film is developed and examined for excessive blackening. This serves as a record of the total amount of radiation received by the wearer of the film badge. Similarly, a film badge may be mounted in a fixed location (near an x-ray unit, for example) to give an indication of the amount of stray radiation emitted by the machine. Film badges generally consist of photographic film, parts of which are covered by pieces of foil, and the whole is placed in a light-tight envelope. Thus, one piece of film can indicate, not only the total amount of radiation, but also its nature: beta-ray, gamma-ray, or neutron.

A little thought will show that the photographic film cannot fulfill the role of the counter, and conversely, the counter cannot do what a few pieces of film can do. The two devices are complementary, rather than competitive. Similarly, in carrying out radiotracer experiments, both forms of detection have their part to play.

8–12. Obtaining radioactive material

Fifty years ago there was only one source of radioactive material, namely that resulting from the decay of natural radioisotopes like uranium-238 and thorium-232. The isotopes available were all of heavy elements such as radium and lead, mostly alpha-emitters, and their use in experimental work was limited.

The next development, in the 1930's, is associated with the invention and perfection of the charged-particle accelerators, of which the cyclotron is the best-known example. In a typical reaction, the cyclotron would be used to accelerate protons to high energies (many million electron volts) and hurl them into a surface of chromium. The resultant reaction would be

$$\ce{^{50}_{24}Cr} + p \rightarrow \ce{^{51}_{25}Mn} + \gamma. \tag{8–11}$$

Clearly, this so-called p-γ reaction (a proton in and a gamma-ray out) produces radioisotopes above the stable band of Fig. 8–1.

If the accelerated particles were deuterons (i.e., nuclei of the heavy form of hydrogen, deuterium), then a typical reaction would consist of the deuteron being absorbed and a proton emitted from the target nuclei. This d-p reaction is written as

$$\ce{^{114}_{48}Cd} + d \rightarrow \ce{^{115}_{48}Cd} + p. \tag{8–12}$$

As a net result of this reaction, the target nucleus has gained a neutron, and thus this reaction is used for preparing nuclei below the stable band.

Although cyclotrons and similar high-energy devices are very versatile in their ability to produce large varieties of radioisotopes, they have serious practical disadvantages, since an expensive cyclotron can irradiate only one target specimen at a time. Also, since protons and deuterons have limited penetrating power in solid matter, only the surface of a specimen can be irradiated.

The big step forward came with the building of nuclear piles in the 1940's. In these piles, nuclei of uranium break up and undergo fission as a result of reaction with neutrons, and the two resulting nuclei are so far from the stable band that they emit neutrons as they decay toward the stable band. These neutrons are slowed down by carbon or heavy water moderators, whereupon they are in a position to react with further nuclei of uranium, and continue the chain cycle. Materials placed in the pile are exposed to these neutrons which are present in large amounts, and hence nuclear reactions can occur. These are usually of the n-γ type. Thus

$$_{48}^{66}\mathrm{Cd}^{114} + \mathrm{n} \rightarrow \,_{48}^{67}\mathrm{Cd}^{115} + \gamma. \tag{8--13}$$

This reaction is the same one as that produced by the d-p process in cyclotrons, but the advantage in using a pile is that the pile is basically a cheaper method of irradiation, since one pile can irradiate many hundreds of specimens at one time; also, the pile irradiates solid specimens evenly, since neutrons have large penetration distances in most solids. The basic disadvantage of the pile is that it only produces isotopes below the stable band of Fig. 8-1, but not above the band. To obtain them, a particle accelerator must still be used.

8-13. Quantitative aspects of irradiation

In this section we shall confine ourselves to the problems posed by irradiation in nuclear piles, since this is the mode used in the great majority of practical applications. First, we must define the quantitative unit of radioactivity, the curie. If a nuclear species is decaying at the rate of 3.7×10^{10} disintegrations per second, it has a radioactive strength of 1 curie. (This peculiar unit stems historically from the fact that radium, the first radioisotope available in pure form, decays in such a way that 1 gm undergoes 3.7×10^{10} disintegrations per second.) Similarly, one millicurie corresponds to 3.7×10^7 disintegrations per second, while a microcurie amounts to 3.7×10^4 disintegrations per second.

Next, mention must be made of the way that nuclear piles are rated. Reactors are rather like furnaces in that just as furnaces are hottest in the middle and cooler toward the sides, so piles have the highest neutron densities in the center, and lower densities toward and through the massive shielding. However, the intensity near the center is fairly uniform. The unit of intensity is the number of neutrons passing through an area of 1 cm^2/sec. The neutron flux at the center of a pile varies in practice from about 10^{11} to about 10^{14} neutrons/cm^2/sec, depending on the construction and nature of the pile.

The operators of piles generally publish tables giving the activity produced by irradiating 1 gm of various elements in their pile at a given flux level for stated periods of time, and these data are given in Table A5-7. From these data, it is quite easy to calculate the activity

TABLE 8–2

RADIOACTIVITY INDUCED IN VARIOUS ELEMENTS

Isotope	Activity, mc/gm	Half-life	Radiation
W-185	6.6	73 d	β^-
W-187	420	24 h	β^-,γ
Cr-51	39	28 d	K,γ
Fe-59	0.4	45 d	β^-,γ
Fe-55	0.15	2.9 y	K

attained by any material irradiated for any time at any flux level. We may best see this by carrying out a real calculation of this kind.

Suppose that we intend to place a piece of tool steel in a pile for two weeks. The flux intensity of our location in the pile will be 10^{13}. The chemical composition of the steel is given as 18% tungsten, 4% chromium, 1% vanadium, and 77% iron. It will be assumed that the steel contains no impurities whose irradiation might produce radioisotopes of appreciable intensity. From Table A5–7, we take the data shown in Table 8–2. Note that this table was derived for an irradiation of 28 days at an assumed flux of 5×10^{11}.

Note that no radioactive isotope derived from vanadium is listed, since this metal does not form a radioactive isotope of appreciable half-life in the pile. The tungsten and the iron each form two radioisotopes, these being derived from different stable isotopes of the starting material. In the case of the iron, for example, the Fe-55 and Fe-59 are derived from Fe-54 and Fe-58 present in ordinary iron. The activities attained in the pile are computed on the basis that the gram of iron used as the starting material has the isotopic proportions characteristic of natural iron, as listed in Section 8–2. These proportions are known to be characteristic of iron from all sources, in whatever state of chemical combination, unless it has been given a special and fearfully expensive isotope separation treatment.

The intensity of the radioactivity is given on the basis of a 28-day irradiation, and to calculate the effect of a different irradiation time we must take account of the way radioactivity builds up during irradiation. If we assume that the rate dN/dt at which radioactive atoms are formed is constant with time, and this is in all cases a very good approximation, while the rate at which they decay is $-\lambda N$, where λ is the

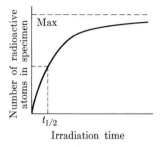

Fig. 8–9. Radiation buildup in a nuclear pile.

decay constant, Eq. (8–9), then we have

$$\frac{dN}{dt} = k - \lambda N,$$

which we may rewrite in the form

$$\frac{-\lambda\, dN}{k - \lambda N} = -\lambda\, dt. \tag{8–14}$$

Integrating, we obtain

$$\ln (k - \lambda N) = -\lambda t + c.$$

When t is zero, N is also zero, and hence c is equal to $\ln k$. Thus, our final solution becomes, after some rearranging

$$N = \frac{k(1 - e^{-\lambda t})}{\lambda} = \frac{k t_{1/2}(1 - e^{-0.693 t/t_{1/2}})}{0.693}. \tag{8–14a}$$

This relation is plotted in Fig. 8–9. We see that at times smaller than one half-life, the amount of radioactive matter formed is nearly proportional to the time of irradiation; while at times greater than twice the half-life, the amount of activity is almost independent of the time of irradiation. After a time of irradiation corresponding to one half-life, the activity has reached half of its final value.

We are now in position to return to Table 8–2 and to compute the effect of a 2-week irradiation of a flux of 10^{13} neutrons/cm^2/sec. Thus, the tungsten-185 would receive an activity of 20 times the stated 6.6 mc/gm if the flux is 20 times as great as the 5×10^{11} for which the table was compiled, and if the irradiation time is cut from 4 weeks to 2, so will the radioactivity be cut in half (note that the half-life, 73 days, is much greater than the irradiation time). Thus, the final result is that

TABLE 8–3

ACTIVITIES AFTER REMOVAL FROM PILE, IN MC/GM STEEL

Isotope	After irradiation	After 1 day	After 1 week	After 1 month	After 1 year	After 5 years
W-187	1500	750	12	0	0	0
Cr-51	19	19	15.5	9.5	0	0
Fe-59	3.1	3.1	2.7	2.1	0	0
W-185	12	12	11.4	10.0	0.4	0
Fe-55	1.2	1.2	1.2	1.0	0.9	0.4
Total	1535	785	42.8	22.6	1.3	0.4

the activity of W-185 becomes 66 mc/gm. Similarly, values for Fe-59 and Fe-55 increase by factors of 10 to 4.0 and 1.5 mc/gm, respectively. On the other hand, the reduction from 4 weeks to 2 does not affect the activity of the W-187, since both values are far greater than its 24-hour half-life. Hence, its activity becomes 8400 mc/gm. The chromium-51 represents a difficult problem, since 4 weeks is just about equal to its half-life. If, however, we assume that its activity is directly proportional to its irradiation for the first half-life time, we find an intensity of 390 mc/gm, as with the long-lived isotopes above. An exact solution based on Eq. (8–14a) yields 460 mc/gm.

Having found the amount of radioactivity induced in 1 gm of each of the elements in our steel, we must now calculate the activity in 1 gm of the steel itself. To do this, we multiply the activities of each of the isotopes by the percentage of the steel that each element represents. This produces the activities shown in the first column in Table 8–3.

Lastly, we must evaluate the fact that some time must elapse from the moment that our specimen is taken out of the pile to the moment at which our tracer experiment can get under way. The change in radioactivity with time is given by Eq. (8–10). Typical values of radioactivity at stated moments after removal from the pile are shown in Table 8–3.

8–14. Amount of radioactivity required for tracer experiments

Having considered in some detail the calculation of how much radioactivity is produced during irradiation, we shall now turn to the other aspect of the problem and consider how much radioactivity is needed during a tracer experiment. In general, we need a quite high degree of radioactivity in the typical tracer experiment, because such a small

percentage of the total activity gets to our radiation-detecting device. There are three main ways that radioactive intensity is lost:
   (a) the dilution loss inherent in the tracer experiment,
   (b) geometric loss,
   (c) shielding loss and detector inefficiency.
The dilution involved in the experiment depends greatly, of course, on the nature of the experiment. Let us consider two possible experiments. In the first case, it is required to find the amount of blood in a person by injecting 1 ml of blood containing radioactive iron, allowing it to mix thoroughly with the rest of his blood, then drawing off 1 ml and analyzing this. Clearly, the dilution factor here is the ratio of 1 ml to the total volume of the person's blood. If the total volume is 5000 ml, then the dilution ratio is a factor of 5000.

As a second example, we may consider a wear experiment in which a radioactive cutting tool is used to cut chips of a nonradioactive steel. It is found that in 1000 gm of chips there are 10^{-4} gm of radioactive material from the cutting tool. Clearly, the dilution factor here is a factor of 10^7.

The geometric efficiency is the solid angle which the counter subtends at the sample, or $A/4\pi x^2$ approximately, where A is the area of the counter and x its distance from the sample. In practice, efficiencies of a few percent are the best that can be attained.

The shielding loss varies from close to 0% where thin samples emitting gamma-rays are involved, up to 90% and above when weak beta-rays are being detected by a geiger tube with a fairly thick window.

The counter detection losses also depend on the nature of the particle being detected and on the counter. Geiger counters have efficiencies close to 100% for beta-rays, but only about 2% for gamma-rays. However, other types of counters are available which are much more effective in detecting gamma rays. Thus *scintillation counters*, in which the gamma rays are stopped in an organic crystal and give off a flash of light, which hits a screen and emits an electron which is amplified, may have efficiencies of nearly 100% for gamma-ray detection.

8–15. The statistics of radiotracer measurements: Poisson statistics

The emission and detection during a limited time of any one ray or particle as a result of the decay of a radioactive atom is a rare event, and, moreover, is independent of the presence of other radionuclides.

In analyzing this process, we must apply a statistical treatment applicable to rare, random events. This is generally known as *Poisson* statistics, namely the statistics associated with the Poisson distribution.

Suppose that we have a large number M of radioactive atoms, and that there is a small but finite probability λ that any of them will decay in unit time. Then the probability that it will decay in a small interval of time t will be λt, which we define as p; while the probability that it will not decay will be $(1 - p)$ or q. The probability that all the M atoms will decay in time t is p^M, the probability that none will decay is q^M, and the probability that exactly s atoms will decay is represented by the $(s + 1)$th term of the binomial expansion $(q + p)^M$, namely $M! q^{M-s} p^s / (M - s)! s!$. The first few terms of this expansion are

$$q^M, \ Mq^{M-1}p, \ \frac{M(M - 1)}{2!} q^{M-2}p^2, \ \frac{M(M - 1)(M - 2)}{3!} q^{M-3}p^3.$$

(8–15)

We may simplify these terms by applying the conditions that p is very small, so that q may be considered equal to 1, while M is very large, so that $(M - 1)$, $(M - 2)$, etc., will be nearly as large as M. Thus the terms of (8–15) become

$$1, \ Mp, \ (Mp)^2/2!, \ (Mp)^3/3!, \ \text{etc.}$$

(8–16)

It will be seen that M and p always occur together, so that we may replace them by another symbol, say m. The individual terms of (8–16) represent the expansion of e^m, so that their sum must equal e^m. Hence, to normalize the terms of (8–16) so that their sum becomes equal to 1, and each term constitutes a probability, we must multiply each term by e^{-m}. Thus, the Poisson expansion becomes

$$e^{-m}\{1, \ m, \ m^2/2!, \ m^3/3! \ldots\}.$$

(8–17)

In Fig. 8–10 are shown the Poisson distributions for $m = 0.5$ and for $m = 2$. The first of these has but one tail; the second one has a peak and two tails, one tail being more pronounced than the other. Poisson distributions for high values of m (say 5 or above) look very similar to normal distributions.

We may readily calculate the mean and standard deviation of a Poisson distribution using for this purpose the unnormalized form (8–16). For the means, we have (2–30)

$$\bar{x} = \frac{\sum y \cdot x}{\sum y} = \frac{\sum(1 \times 0 + m \times 1 + m^2 \times 2/2! + m^3 \times 3/3! \ldots)}{\sum y}$$

$$= \frac{m\sum(1 + m + m^2/2! + \cdots)}{\sum(1 + m + m^2/2! + m^3/3! + \cdots)} = m.$$

(8–18)

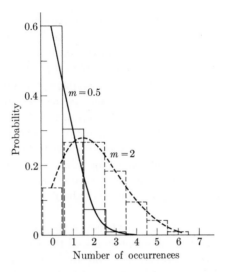

Fig. 8–10. Histogram of Poisson distribution for m = 0.5 and m = 2.0.

For the standard deviation, we have

$$\sigma^2 = \frac{\sum y(x - \bar{x}^2)}{\sum y} = \frac{\sum yx^2}{\sum y} - \frac{2\bar{x}\sum yx}{\sum y} + \frac{\bar{x}^2\sum y}{\sum y}. \qquad (8\text{--}19)$$

The first of these terms is

$$\frac{\sum(1 \times 0^2 + m \times 1^2 + m^2 \times 2^2/2! + m^3 \times 3^2/3! + \cdots)}{\sum y}$$

$$= \frac{\sum m(1 + 2m + 3m^2/2! + 4m^3/3! + \cdots)}{\sum y}$$

$$= \frac{m\sum\{(1 + m + m^2/2! + m^3/3! \ldots) + m(1 + m + m^2/2! \ldots)\}}{\sum(1 + m + m^2/2! + m^3/3! \ldots)}$$

$$= m + m^2. \qquad (8\text{--}20)$$

The second term of Eq. (8–19) is [see Eq. (8–18)] equal to $-2m^2$ and the third term is m^2.

Hence

$$\sigma^2 = m + m^2 - 2m^2 + m^2 = m,$$

or

$$\sigma = m^{1/2}. \qquad (8\text{--}21)$$

The Poisson distribution is thus seen to be simpler than the normal distribution, since the normal distribution has three independent variables, or adjustable degrees of freedom (the height of the curve, the mean, and the standard deviation), while the Poisson distribution has but two (the height of the curve and the mean). The distribution can be met with in many ways; for example, the number of times some specified letter occurs on each line or each page of a book, or the number of accidents in any community in some specified period of time, or the number of cosmic rays which register in a geiger counter in a period of time, all obey Poisson statistics. In some of these cases, the quantities M (the total population), and p (the probability that a quantity will be enumerated), whose product makes up m, are both fairly well defined; but in some cases, for example in the case of the cosmic rays, it is not known how large M might be, and only the product Mp can be evaluated.

Many people have the habit, whenever they encounter a statistical distribution with one tail more pronounced than the other, of referring to it as "resembling a Poisson distribution." It must be pointed out that every true Poisson distribution must have as ordinate a dimensionless number, namely the number of times some event happened. This fundamental property arises from the fact that for a Poisson distribution

$$\sigma = (\bar{x})^{1/2}, \qquad (8\text{--}22)$$

and for any distribution σ and $\bar{x}$ must have the same dimension. The relationship of Eq. (8–22) constitutes a very useful feature of Poisson statistics. In the process of obtaining one quantity x, we obtain at the same time an internal estimate of its error without having to take repeat readings. This property is of great use to us in evaluating the accuracy and the resolution of radiotracer techniques.

8–16. Resolution and accuracy of radiotracer counting methods

In a typical radiotracer experiment, the number At of particles we may expect to detect in a counter in a time t may be written in the form

$$M \times \lambda \times (\text{overall detection efficiency}) \times t = At. \qquad (8\text{--}23)$$

The production and detection of particles satisfies the criteria of rarity and independence, and hence this process obeys Poisson statistics. Consequently, if during a certain time interval t a number of particles At may be expected to be detected, then the actual number detected will be $At \pm \sqrt{At}$. This makes it very easy to estimate the accuracy of a radioactive measurement (insofar as this accuracy is determined by statistical fluctuations in the counting rate), since the standard error ϵ_I may be expressed in the form

$$\epsilon_I = \frac{\sqrt{At}}{At} = \frac{1}{\sqrt{At}}. \tag{8–24}$$

If an accuracy of 1% is required, we must have $1/\sqrt{At}$ equal to 1%, and thus have to have an At value of 10,000. If we want an accuracy of 0.1% or better, we need to take 1,000,000 counts or more.

Note that Eq. (8–24) does not consider the counting rate A and the time t separately, but only their product. If 3% accuracy is required, we can achieve it with a counting rate of 1000 counts/min and a counting time of 1 min, or at a counting rate of 20 counts/min for 50 min. In practice, the problem is more complex, owing to the presence of background radiation. If we take a count for time t in the absence of our radioactive source, we will get a count of Bt, where B is the background rate, and corresponding to it an uncertainty of $\sqrt{Bt}$. Now we introduce our radioactive source and again take a count of time t, and get a reading of $(A + B)t$ with an uncertainty of $\sqrt{(A + B)t}$. The real signal is obtained by subtracting the background from the total count, and the uncertainty in the real signal as discussed in Appendix A2–4 will be the square root of the sum of the squares of the two uncertainties, namely $\sqrt{(A + 2B)t}$.

We can get an idea of the magnitude of the effect of the background by considering a case where the signal counting rate A is 20 counts/min, and the background counting rate B is 30 counts/min. As we saw earlier, if there were no background, we could achieve 3% accuracy by counting for 50 min. In the presence of background, we have

$$\epsilon_I = \frac{\sqrt{(A + 2B)t}}{At} = \frac{3}{100}. \tag{8–25}$$

This gives a counting time of 200 min. Naturally, the effect of background would have been less pronounced if the signal-to-background ratio had been higher.

An important calculation to perform is that of the minimum detectable signal or resolution. If there were no background, this would clearly be one count. However, if there is background, then we must have a signal substantial enough to be detectable above background. Since we may write the true signal in the form

$$\text{signal} = At \pm \sqrt{(A + 2B)t}, \tag{8–26}$$

we might regard the least signal as one which is twice as great as its standard deviation, so that there is only one chance in 20 that we detect a signal which turns out to be spurious. Clearly, we might decide to work at the 3σ level without affecting the argument except to change the numerical values somewhat.

If we apply the 2σ criterion to Eq. (8–26), we have

$$At = 2\sqrt{(A + 2B)t},$$
$$A^2t^2 = 4 \times (A + 2B)t. \tag{8–27}$$

If the background is fairly high and the time of counting fairly long, it will be found that $B \gg A$, so that we may simplify (8–27) to

$$A = \left(\frac{8B}{t}\right)^{1/2}. \tag{8–28}$$

By substitution, we find for the case $B = 30$ counts/min, that if

$$\begin{aligned}
t &= 1 \text{ min}, & A &= 15 \text{ counts/min}, \\
t &= 10 \text{ min}, & A &= 5 \text{ counts/min}, \\
t &= 100 \text{ min}, & A &= 1.5 \text{ counts/min}, \\
t &= 1000 \text{ min}, & A &= 0.5 \text{ counts/min}.
\end{aligned} \tag{8–29}$$

Analogous to the case of many other statistical relationships, we find that the resolution becomes better as the square root of the total counting time increases.

Unfortunately, the counting time cannot be made much larger than a few hours, because the background rate changes with time (electric devices shut off at night), while the counters, too, tend to drift in their response. Thus, a reasonable minimum counting rate (for an 8-hr count), might be 0.8 count/min. If the background rate can be drastically reduced, by enclosing the counter in thick lead walls, lower counting rates become feasible, in accordance with Eq. (8–28).

8–17. Experimental uses of radioactivity: nontracer uses

Although the uses of radioactivity have been many and varied, and have received close study, it has not as yet proved possible to arrive at a comprehensive classification. As we have seen, radioactive materials have distinct and unusual properties, and this makes it possible for us to use them in many different ways. Perhaps it is easiest to classify the uses in terms of the property which makes that use possible. (The reader is warned that before he tries out these and other uses, he may have to fulfill a variety of safety and legal requirements, which are discussed in detail in the references cited in the bibliography. In general, if the amount of radioactive material exceeds certain specified limits, then all experiments with it must be carried out in a special room equipped with adequate facilities, and competent supervision must be provided. In practice, we have found that these requirements are not difficult to meet).

(a) *As a source of electric power.* Many radioactive materials emit charged particles, either beta- or alpha-rays. It might be possible to use this electrical energy directly in some applications, but the voltages are too high (in the 100,000 to 1,000,000-volt range, usually) and the currents so small (~0.01 microamp for a source operating at one curie) that this does not appear to be practical. However, it has been found possible to build batteries which incorporate radioactive material and semiconductors, and in these systems, the semiconductors use the energy of the radioactive decay to derive low voltages and relatively high currents. Batteries built on this idea are compact, light, and have a long life, limited only by the decay of the radioactive material. This life may be quite great, using for example strontium-90 with an 28-year half-life. These batteries have found an important role in the exploration of space.

(b) *As a method of ionizing matter.* The fact that radiation from radioisotopes causes the breakup of molecules through which it passes has been used in a number of ways. We shall mention just three of them. The first arises in the chemical industry, when plastics of unusual properties, the cross-linked polymers, are produced by allowing ordinary polyethylene to be exposed to the radiation from powerful radioactive sources. Secondly, there is the use of radiation in the food industry to sterilize bacteria in food, thus making it possible to store the food for long periods of time. This use is based on the fact that radiation passing through living matter tends to break up and rearrange some of the molecules in the living cells, thus upsetting their functioning. The danger of radiation to humans is due to just this effect. Thirdly, there is the use of small radioactive sources in chemical balances, to keep the air ionized and prevent the buildup of electric charges at various points in the system, thus avoiding spurious weight readings.

(c) *Use of radiotracers in gaging.* The fact that the intensity of radioactive radiation passing through matter drops off in a regular way as the thickness of the matter is increased may be utilized to form a thickness gage of considerable effectiveness. To control a process in which material in strip form is produced, we need a source of radiation (generally beta), a counter (generally a geiger), and some system for converting the reading of the counter into feedback instructions to the machine producing the strip (Fig. 1–5).

In this application, beta-rays have taken over from x-rays, which at one time were used exclusively for gaging purposes. The advantage of beta-ray gaging is mainly that of lower cost and greater constancy of the source of penetrating particles.

The rays from radioactive particles have taken over from x-rays in a number of other applications; for example, in the detection of flaws in castings. In this application, analogous to the ordinary x-ray photograph which utilizes the differences in x-ray stopping power of human flesh and bones, a point source of radiation is placed on one side of a metallic body, and photographic film on the other, and cracks and flaws show up as black regions of enhanced ray transmission on the photograph.

(d) *Characteristic features of the nontracer uses.* As will be seen by considering the uses detailed above, there are several common features in all the nontracer uses of radioisotopes. Thus, the isotope is never diluted in the course of its application, and may be used over and over until it decays. Furthermore, it does not matter what radioactive species is used, so long as its half-life is sufficiently long, the nature of its radiation is suitable, and the radioactive intensity in terms of curies has a suitable value.

As we turn to the tracer applications, we find that requirements put on the tracer are made much more severe. In some cases it is necessary only that the tracer be physically compatible with some other substance in which it is dispersed. In other applications, the chemical species of the tracer and its dispersing medium must be identical.

8–18. Tracer applications of radiotracers

(a) *The measurement of wear.* In this application, one member of a sliding system is made radioactive. After sliding has taken place, it is possible to detect the transfer of material to other surfaces, to a liquid lubricant which may be present, or to the atmosphere. The radiotracer method has great resolution ($\sim 10^{-13}$ gm), and for example will detect the material transfer of contacting bodies (Rabinowicz, 1952). It is widely used, for example, in the study of engine wear, because it greatly shortens the testing time. The component whose wear is to be measured is made radioactive either by being placed in a pile, or by being cast from a melt into which a radioactive component was introduced.

(b) *The measurement of flow.* A problem of some importance is that of detecting the flow in pipelines. A typical pipeline may run many hundreds of miles, and transport, in turn, a number of petroleum products, which may be owned by different oil companies. It is found that if the flow in the pipeline is turbulent, not laminar, then not too much mixing of adjacent layers occurs. However, the material near the interface of two different products does undergo some mixture, and must be drawn off separately and processed to separate the components.

It is a task of some difficulty to decide quickly, and accurately, while the liquid is moving through the pipeline, just when the mixed region reaches the end of the pipeline. If, however, some radioactive material is introduced into the pipeline between the adjacent layers, then the demarcation region can be readily detected by means of a geiger counter immersed in the pipeline. All the radioactive liquid is assumed to constitute the mixed region.

In this application, it is necessary that the radioactive material be in a form which is soluble in petroleum products, but no more complex requirements are involved.

A similar use is that involving radiotracers to detect leaks in a hot water heating system whose pipes are buried in a concrete slab foundation. In this case some radioactive matter is introduced into the water, and the foundation is monitored for excessive radiation.

(c) *The measurement of the growth of living matter.* Many problems of importance to the biologist are concerned with the way that food and other products circulate in a living system. These problems are readily studied by introducing radioactive material at some point into the system, and then noting where the radioactivity goes. In this case it is necessary to specify the chemical nature of the radiotracer, in all cases concerning the element to be used, and in some cases concerning the chemical compound, since living species have a habit of accepting only the materials they are used to, and in rejecting imitations.

(d) *Measurement of the volume of a liquid.* We have already discussed the measurement of the volume of blood in a person by injecting some radioactive blood, allowing it to mix thoroughly, and then drawing off a sample and measuring a dilution ratio. This method can be extended to measure the volume of any liquid.

8–19. Calibration of radioactive materials

An important problem which arises after many radiotracer measurements is that of calibration. Taking a simple example, we consider a surface on which there are some radioactive fragments, place it near the window of a geiger counter, and obtain a count above background of A counts/min. What is the mass of the fragments?

In order to find the mass, we take the counting rate and multiply it by a factor for the counter inefficiency, by another factor for the geiger window stopping power, another factor for the counting geometry, and then compare the corrected count with the known radioactivity of the material, as given by the pile operator, and corrected for decay since the irradiation.

This is a difficult project, since in general the counter efficiency and window stopping power are not known (they vary with the nature of the radiation being detected), the activity as given by the pile operator is subject to variation of the order of 25%, while the other variables can be calculated, although tediously.

A simple method, which avoids all these difficulties, is to irradiate, at the same time as the original specimen was obtained, a thin piece of foil of the same material, and of known weight. If this is placed in front of the counter, in the same position as the sample, and gives a count A', then the mass of the sample is to the known mass of the standard as A is to A'.

This simple calibration method avoids all difficulties produced by the unknown factors, since the sample and the standard have the same radioactive characteristics and are placed in the same geometric situation. The only difficulties likely to arise are those caused by the standard's being so powerfully radioactive that it overloads the geiger counter. In that case we must either move the foil farther from the counter than was our specimen, and to correct for this using the inverse square law, or else allow the standard to decay for a few half-lives longer than the specimen and correct for this using the decay equation, or else reduce the weight of the standard by cutting out a small piece and using this as the standard, correcting for the change in geometry from spread out source to point source where necessary.

In cases where thin foil is not available, a known amount of the radioactive material is spread out in the same geometric form as the sample, and this is used as the standard. In order to do this, it is often necessary to dissolve a sample of radioactive material in acid, and, after chemical precipitation, obtain a uniform thin deposit on filter paper.

The need for having a thin standard. Several times above we have emphasized the need to keep the standard thin. This is done to avoid an effect known as self-shielding, in which the outer layers of a thick foil prevent radiation from the inner layers from penetrating through to the counter. Under these circumstances, the count obtained from the standard is lower than it should be, and thus inaccurate calibration will occur.

In special circumstances it is desirable to make the geometry of the standard the same as that of the source. Thus, in immersion counting, if the sample to be counted is a liquid of volume 500 cc in a 1000-cc beaker, then the standard should be made up as a 500-cc solution in a 1000-cc beaker, and the counter should be placed in exactly the same way in each liquid.

PROBLEMS

1. It is known that uranium-238 decays to thorium-234 with a half-life of 4.5×10^{10} years and the emission of an α-particle; that thorium-234 decays to protactinium-234 with a half-life of 24 hours and the emission of a β-particle; and that protactinium-234 decays to uranium-234 with a half-life of 2 min and the emission of a β-particle. The uranium-234 has such a long half-life that it may be regarded as stable. If at a certain time a sample of 10^{23} atoms of pure uranium-238 is present in a system, discuss the distribution of isotopes 1 day later. Make all reasonable simplifying assumptions.

2. A radioactive γ-emitting sample of very small size is placed 4 cm from the face of an end-window geiger tube. The window is circular, having a diameter of 2 cm, and the specimen is placed symmetrically along the axis of the tube cylinder. The scaler connected to the geiger counter registers 519 counts after 5 min of counting. When the sample is moved to a new position, still symmetrically from the window but 7 cm away, the count after 5 min is 374. Calculate what the count would be if the specimen were placed right up against the counter window. State explicitly any simplifying assumptions. [*Ans.* 7180 counts/min]

3. One gram of cobalt attains a radioactive intensity of 250 millicuries after being exposed in a pile to a certain neutron flux for 28 days. (a) If the half-life of the radioactive isotope of cobalt is 5.3 years, calculate the intensity which would be reached if the cobalt was left in the pile for 10 years. (b) The cost of an irradiation is $50, plus 50 cents/day. Estimate how long an irradiation should last so that the millicurie/dollar ratio is as high as possible

4. It is required to find the amount of blood in a student, without causing him a fatal injury. Into his veins are injected 2 cc of blood, some of the iron of which has previously been made radioactive, so that the activity of this blood is 0.005 microcuries/cc. A few hours later, after the blood has become thoroughly mixed, 200 cc of blood are withdrawn from the student, and placed in a beaker into which an immersion-type geiger counter is inserted. It is found that this increases the rate of the counter from a background rate of 25 counts/min to a rate of 30 counts/min. If the geometry and efficiency of the arrangement is such that 1% of the total activity of the sample is recorded, calculate the total blood content of the student.

5. In a plant, a careful check is made on how many accidents (major or minor) each worker has over a 2-year period. The following data are obtained.

No. of accidents	No. of workers
0	364
1	376
2	218
3	89
4	33
5	13
6	4
7	3
8	2
9	1

Compare this distribution with the corresponding one of the Poisson type, and deduce whether any of the workers are "accident prone," or whether the large number of accidents suffered by some of them is attributable to statistical fluctuation. [*Ans.* About 6 workers seem to be accident prone.]

6. It is known that radioactive C^{14} is formed in the outer layers of the atmosphere as result of cosmic ray action on N^{14}. This C^{14} eventually reaches the ground, enters the bodies of plants and animals, and decays back to N^{14} with a half-life of 5560 years. Thus, recently formed wood products have a higher radioactivity than do wood materials of ancient origin. (a) In an experiment, it was found that modern wood gave a counting rate of 12.5 counts/min/gm of carbon (above background), while similarly, wood from an Egyptian tomb gave 7.04 counts/min/gm. How old is the tomb? (b) Using all your knowledge of radiotracer techniques, estimate the age of the oldest wood which can be "dated" in this way.

7. In a friction experiment, a copper rider containing Cu^{64} is slid on a well-lubricated surface of steel, and copper is transferred to the wear track of diameter 1 in. at a rate of 10^{-10} gm/sec of sliding. If the half-life of the copper is 12.8 hours, how long should the experiment be run so that the activity of the steel specimen is at a maximum? At this point the experiment is stopped and the steel plate held in front of a geiger counter. Make an order-of-magnitude estimate of the counting rate, assuming that the copper has an initial radioactive intensity of 1 millicurie/gm, and that it decays by β-emission.

8. It is required to monitor the thickness S of a sheet of rubber being formed in a rolling mill by mounting a geiger counter on one side of the sheet and a source of β-radiation on the other side. Owing to safety regulations, the strength of the β-source to be used (in curies) is fixed. Assume that the law for β-radiation passing through the rubber is of the type $I = I_0 \exp(-kx)$, where x is the sheet thickness and k is a constant dependent on the energy of the β-particles emitted by the radioisotope, and a variable in that we may choose a different radioisotope giving a different value of k. What should be the relation between k and S which will make the percentage

error in measuring the thickness of the rubber sheet a minimum. [*Ans.* $kx = 2$]

9. It is proposed to manufacture Hg^{198} for use in a mercury arc lamp by irradiating Au^{197} in a pile (this gives Au^{198}, which decays with a 2.7-day half-life to Hg^{198}). Reference to a nuclear table shows that if gold is placed in the middle of a certain pile for 1 week, the Au^{198} has an activity of 150 milli-curies/gm. How much gold must be irradiated in the pile to produce 1 gm of Hg^{198} during a 2-month irradiation. [*Note:* 198 gm of Hg^{198} contain 6×10^{23} atoms.] [*Ans.* 100 kg of gold]

10. Mercury normally consists of seven isotopes. For optical interference measurements, it is desired to use mercury lamps in which the mercury consists of but one isotope. This is done by irradiation of gold (Au^{197}) with neutrons from a pile. The product is Au^{198} with a half-life of 2.7 days, decaying to Hg^{198}. The Hg^{198} is very satisfactory as a spectroscopic standard. Unfortunately, as the Au^{198} accumulates in the pile, a small percentage of it is reacted by neutrons to form Au^{199}, which decays with a half-life of 3.3 days to form Hg^{199}. This is an undesirable contaminant of the Hg^{198}. Discuss this situation quantitatively, and evaluate whether, in order to minimize the Hg^{199} concentration, it is better to irradiate the Au^{197} for 1 month at a high neutron flux, or for 10 months at a neutron flux $\frac{1}{10}$ as great. [*Ans.* 10 months at low neutron flux]

11. In an old English coal mine, it is required to determine the spatial relationship between two tunnels. It is proposed to place 100 kilocuries of radioactive cobalt at a specified point in one tunnel, and to test the intensity of irradiation at various points in the other tunnel. The point giving the largest intensity will be the closest point to the radioactive source. Estimate the greatest distance apart of the two tunnels for which this method is practical, and the time required to carry out the experiment. Assume that the natural background in the tunnel produces a count of 0.1 count/min in a geiger counter and of 0.5 count/min in a scintillation counter and that γ-rays from cobalt have their intensity halved on traversing a 3 in. thickness of ground. [*Ans.* About 12 ft]

12. An automotive engineer is given the assignment of discovering the production rate of a competitor's factory. He takes a job in the repair shop for new cars attached to the production line. In his first week of work he notices that 774 cars are brought into the repair shop needing one major repair, 42 cars need two major repairs, 2 cars need three major repairs. From these figures, estimate the production rate of the plant. State clearly your assumptions and reasonings. [*Hint:* Try to fit these data to a Poisson distribution.]

REFERENCES

BRADFORD, J., ed., *Radioisotopes in Industry*, Reinhold, New York, 1953. Applications of radioisotopes.

GLASSTONE, S., *Sourcebook on Atomic Energy*, Van Nostrand, Princeton, N. J., 1950. A good introductory text.

KOHL, J., R. D. ZENTNER, H. R. LUKENS, *Radioisotope Applications in Engineering*, Van Nostrand, Princeton, N. J., 1961. This is a very comprehensive compilation.

RABINOWICZ, E., "Metal Transfer during Static Loading and Impacting," *Proc. Phys. Soc. (London)*, B, **65**, 630–640, 1952.

Radioactive Materials and Stable Isotopes, Catalogue No. 4, Isotope Division, Harwell, Berks, England, 1957.

The Radiochemical Manual, Part I, Physical Data, Her Majesty's Stationary Office, London, 1962. Contains a large amount of well-presented data on radioisotopes.

Radioisotopes: Catalog and Price List, Oak Ridge National Laboratory, Oak Ridge, 1960. Information on radioisotope irradiations.

Time-Variant Physical Quantities: The Use of Complex Numbers

Many of the dynamic analyses of electrical and mechanical systems could be made simpler, and more easily extended to complicated situations, through the use of Laplace transforms. However, many readers will not be familiar with the Laplace transform system for solving time-dependent differential equations. For our purposes here, a representation of the system behavior through complex number analysis is satisfactory. Hence, we will not use the Laplace methods. There are many good texts on circuit theory and control systems analysis that can give the reader a clear insight into the usefulness of the Laplace method.

While it is certainly possible to analyze the characteristics of systems through the use of sine and cosine notation, a much clearer picture of what actually happens is obtained if we represent sinusoidal-type oscillations through the use of complex numbers.

The concept of complex numbers is really very simple. If we have any cyclically varying quantity which repeats at fixed time intervals, we can plot that quantity on rectangular coordinates and obtain sine waves, cosine waves, etc. Because the cycle repeats, we need only observe one cycle. Now if we plot the quantity on polar coordinates where $\theta = 2\pi$ corresponds to exactly one cycle, and let the length of the vector from the origin to the curve represent the magnitude of the quantity, we have again represented the cycle. The handling of the mathematics and the physical concepts become much clearer if instead of letting the radius to a point on the curve be equal to the magnitude of the quantity in question, we let the *horizontal component* or *real* part of the radius vector represent the magnitude. The vertical component is then the imaginary part of the vector. The simplicity of the system becomes clear when we look at Fig. A1–1. Here a vector of length R is rotating counterclockwise about the origin with angular frequency ω (radians/sec). The angle $\theta = \omega t$. The *real* part a of R is numerically equal to

$$a = R \cos \theta = R \cos \omega t. \tag{A1–1}$$

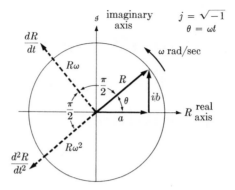

Fig. A1–1. Complex number representation of periodic functions and their derivatives.

Hence, the circle of unit radius represents a cosine function, while a circle of radius R represents R times the cosine function. The vector **R** can be specified in many ways. If the unit vector along the imaginary axis is $j = \sqrt{-1}$, we can set

$$\mathbf{R} = \mathbf{a} + \mathbf{jb}, \tag{A1-2}$$

or we can say

$$\mathbf{R} = |R|, \; |\theta|. \tag{A1-3}$$

The quantity $e^{j\theta}$, where e is the base of natural logarithms ($e = 2.7183 \ldots$), is represented on the complex plane as a vector of unit length at angle θ; therefore

$$\mathbf{R} = Re^{j\theta} = Re^{j\omega t}$$
$$= \sqrt{a^2 + b^2}\, e^{j\theta}. \tag{A1-4}$$

The derivative of R with respect to time is

$$\frac{dR}{dt} = Rj\omega e^{j\omega t},$$

$$\frac{dR}{dt} = (R\omega)(j)(e^{j\omega t}),$$

but

$$j = e^{j\pi/2},$$

thus

$$\frac{dR}{dt} = R\omega e^{j(\omega t + \pi/2)}. \tag{A1-5}$$

TABLE A1–1

SIMILAR QUANTITIES

Mechanical	Electrical	Thermal
Force F, lb	Voltage V, volts	Temperature T, degrees
Velocity v, in/sec distance/time	Current i, amps Coulombs/sec charge/time	Heat flow q, in·lb/sec energy/time
Spring k, lb/in force/distance	Capacitor C, $1/C$ = volts/Coulomb voltage/charge	Specific heat ρC_p, $1/\rho C_p$ = degrees/(in·lb/in^3) temperature/unit stored energy
Dashpot c, lb/(in/sec) force/velocity	Resistor R, ohms volts/amp voltage/current	Conductivity k, $1/k$ = degrees/(in·lb/sec·in) temperature/rate of energy transferred
Mass m, lb/(in/sec^2) force/rate of change of velocity	Inductor L, henries volts/(amp/sec) voltage/rate of change of current	

Physically, this means that dR/dt has magnitude $R\omega$ and also rotates at an angular velocity of ω, but *leads* R by 90°.

Similarly, as shown in Fig. A1–1,

$$\frac{d^2R}{dt^2} = -R\omega^2 e^{j\omega t}. \qquad (A1\text{–}6)$$

Whether we are discussing mechanical, electrical, or thermal phenomena, there are many instances when they satisfy very similar equations. Tables A1–1 and A1–2 show the analogous situations that exist among these three areas. The tables also give the basic cause-effect relationships among the various system parameters. It is evident that force, voltage, and temperature perform similar causal roles, while velocity, current, and rate of heat flow are similar effects. We do not mean that they can be equated, rather they perform similar functions in the system.

When discussing a-c electrical transducers and networks, it will be necessary to consider the phase relationships between various circuit voltages.

TABLE A1–2

SYSTEM PARAMETERS
SHOWING ANALOGY BETWEEN MECHANICAL,
ELECTRICAL AND THERMAL SYSTEMS

Type	Static energy storage	Energy dissipation or transfer	Dynamic energy storage
Mechanical	Spring (k)	Dashpot (c)	Mass (m)
	$F = kx = k \int v \, dt$	$F = c \dfrac{dx}{dt} = cv$	$F = m \dfrac{d^2 x}{dt^2} = m \dfrac{dv}{dt}$
	$x = F/k; \quad v = \dfrac{1}{k} \dfrac{dF}{dt}$	$\dfrac{dx}{dt} = \dfrac{F}{c}$	$v_2 - v_1 = \dfrac{1}{m} \int F \, dt$
Electrical	Capacitor (C)	Resistor (R)	Inductor (L)
	$V_1 - V_2 = \dfrac{1}{C} \int i \, dt$	$V_1 - V_2 = iR$	$V_1 - V_2 = L \dfrac{di}{dt}$
	$i = C \dfrac{d(V_1 - V_2)}{dt}$	$i = \dfrac{V_2 - V_1}{R}$	$i = \dfrac{1}{L} \int (V_2 - V_1) \, dt$
Thermal	Specific heat (c_p)	Conductivity (k)	
	$T_2 - T_1 = \dfrac{1}{\rho c_p A l} \int q \, dt$	$T_2 - T_1 = \dfrac{ql}{Ak}$	
	$q = \rho c_p A l \dfrac{d(T)}{dt}$	$q = kA \dfrac{(T_2 - T_1)}{l}$	

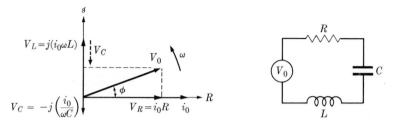

Fig. A1–2. Simple series *RCL*-circuit.

If we let the alternating current be

$$i = i_0 e^{j\omega t}, \tag{A1-7}$$

then, from Table A1–2, the voltage change across a resistor will be

$$V_R = R i_0 e^{j\omega t}. \tag{A1-8}$$

The voltage drop V_L across an inductor will be

$$V_L = L \frac{di}{dt} = L(j\omega) i_0 e^{j\omega t}. \tag{A1-9}$$

That across a capacitor V_C is

$$V_C = \frac{1}{C} \int i \, dt = \frac{i_0 e^{j\omega t}}{j\omega C}, \tag{A1-10}$$

$$V_C = \frac{-j}{\omega C} (i_0 e^{j\omega t}). \tag{A1-11}$$

Thus R, $j\omega L$, and $-j/\omega C$ all have the units of ohms. In a series circuit, the vector sum of these three quantities is the *impedance* of the circuit. Figure A1–2 shows a simple *RCL* series circuit with an a-c voltage applied. If we plot the current along the positive real axis (for convenience only) we see from Eqs. (A1–5), (A1–8), (A1–9), and (A1–11) that the voltages across the various components will be as shown: V_R in phase with the current; V_L leading the current by 90°; and V_C lagging the current by 90°. The applied voltage V_0 must be the vector sum of V_R, V_L, and V_C and will lead or lag the current by a phase angle ϕ.

When we discuss mechanical systems, we can see by analogy that when an alternating force F_0 is applied simultaneously to a mass, a spring, and a dashpot, as shown in Fig. A1–3, the applied force F_0 will be the vector sum of F_m, F_c, and F_k and will lead the displacement vector x_0 by a phase angle ϕ.

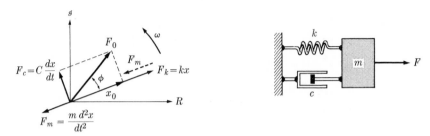

Fig. A1–3. Simple *m, k, c,* systems.

Throughout this book, when we make detailed use of phase plots such as Fig. A1–2 or A1–3, we will see that this spatial representation of time variables can give us a very clear picture of a measuring system's operational characteristics.

Experiments with Random Numbers

A2-1. Introduction

In Chapter 2 we discussed the laws which govern the behavior of experimental data subject to statistical variation. Some of these laws we deduced, others we quoted. In any case these relations are subject to experimental verification, just as are other scientific laws and equations. Often, this verification is made difficult in that great care must be taken to arrange the experiment so that we satisfy the conditions under which the statistical law applies. In particular, it is often difficult to arrange matters so that data are obtained in a random way, without any of the bias which would contravene the assumptions underlying the statistical law. In these circumstances, we may make effective use of tables of random numbers.

Many mathematical and statistical compilations contain a table of random numbers. These may be obtained by using a type of roulette wheel with ten slots, marked zero to nine, and recording the sequence in which digits are produced by this machine. Alternatively, an electronic device equivalent to a roulette wheel might be used (for example, a scaler unit attached to a geiger counter). Numbers have sometimes been selected from telephone books. Very careful evaluation of the roulette wheel or other source of the numbers, and many statistical tests of the table of digits, are required to assure us that a table is, indeed, random.

Included in this appendix will be found a table of 1500 digits. These are not, strictly speaking, random digits, in that the digits form part of a larger pattern (the reader is invited to discover the nature of this pattern). However, for the uses to which random digits are generally put, our table will serve admirably, and moreover, it is digits of this type, pseudo-random, which a high-speed computer normally generates and uses when it wishes to work with random digits.

Tables of random numbers are useful in many ways besides their use in testing statistical laws. First they enable us, without resort to the roulette table, to get a true picture of the way random phenomena occur. Reproduced below is the 16th line from our table:

51870 72113 49999 99837 29780 49951 05973 17328 16096 31859

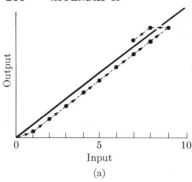
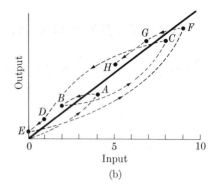

Fig. A2–1. (a) In systematic testing, it may take ten calibration points to reveal hysteresis; (b) in random testing, hysteresis is revealed with the second calibration point.

This line has six adjacent 9's and twelve 9's in all. Certainly, this extreme local abundance of one digit is uncommon, but repeated digits, and other apparent systematic behavior, are quite frequent, more frequent than appears to us to be associated with the concept of randomness. The reader is urged to bear this fact in mind in his experimental work. Often he will come across something, for example repeated unusual readings, which are caused not by something systematic, but merely by a quirk of the process of randomness.

A second use of random number tables is in the selection of data. If we have carried out a considerable number of repeat experiments (say 100), and wish to select a few of them (say 10) for intensive examination, the problem is that of picking the 10 experiments in the best way. For most purposes, a random selection process is best. For the observer to pick out experiments himself is dangerous because his subjective bias may be present. For him to pick out every tenth experiment may also be bad, if, for example, he did ten experiments a day so that the first experiment of each day, which might be quite uncharacteristic, would get chosen. The best procedure is to number the data from 00 to 99, and then to find two-digit numbers at random in a table. Starting with the fifth line of our table, we have 44288, 10975, etc., and hence choose experiments number 44, 28, 81, 09, 75, etc.

Often, we may use this same system to avoid errors such as hysteresis in measuring the response of an instrument (c.f. Fig. 1–22a). Instead of first applying inputs which increase regularly, say from 0 to 9, and then decreasing them regularly from 9 to 0, which is the normal procedure, we might apply the inputs in amounts, 4, 2, 8, 1, 0, 9, 7, 5, etc. In this way we reach some of the inputs on the upside and some on the downside, and detect the presence of hysteresis earlier (Fig. A2–1).

In the pages that follow, we shall concentrate on the third use of random numbers, and carry out a number of "experiments" with them. These have the purpose either of confirming some statistical relationship, or else of demonstrating why some statistical relationship is true, or else of testing some model of a physical situation. The experimental use of random numbers is sometimes referred to as the "Monte-Carlo Method."

A2–2. Test of our table for digit randomness

A number of tests may be applied to a table of digits to see if it is a random number table. Thus, it is possible to count how often repeat digits occur, or to see how far we have to go, starting at any arbitrary place, before we have encountered all the ten digits. Here we shall check another characteristic of a random number table, namely the frequency of occurrence of the various digits. We shall use the first 250 digits, having determined how frequently the digits 0 to 9 occur (Fig. A2–2). The data may then be analyzed by the χ^2 method (Section 2–13), as shown in Table A2–1.

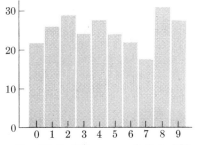

Fig. A2–2. Histogram of first 250 digits of Table A2–2.

TABLE A2–1

DISTRIBUTION OF THE FIRST 250 DIGITS OF TABLE A2–2 AND THEIR χ^2 ANALYSIS

Digit	n_0	n_e	$|n_0 - n_e|$	$(n_0 - n_e)^2$	$(n_0 - n_e)^2/n_e$
0	22	25	3	9	.36
1	26	25	1	1	.04
2	29	25	4	16	.64
3	24	25	1	1	.04
4	28	25	3	9	.36
5	24	25	1	1	.04
6	22	25	3	9	.36
7	17	25	8	64	2.56
8	31	25	6	36	1.44
9	27	25	2	4	.16
	Sum = 250	Sum = 250			$\chi^2 = 6.00$

TABLE A2–2

RANDOM DIGITS*

14159	26535	89793	23846	26433	83279	50288	41971	69399	37510
58209	74944	59230	78164	06286	20899	86280	34825	34211	70679
82148	08651	32823	06647	09384	46095	50582	23172	53594	08128
48111	74502	84102	70193	85211	05559	64462	29489	54930	38196
44288	10975	66593	34461	28475	64823	37867	83165	27120	19091
45648	56692	34603	48610	45432	66482	13393	60726	02491	41273
72458	70066	06315	58817	48815	20920	96282	92540	91715	36436
78925	90360	01133	05305	48820	46652	13841	46951	94151	16094
33057	27036	57595	91953	09218	61173	81932	61179	31051	18548
07446	23799	62749	56735	18857	52724	89122	79381	83011	94912
98336	73362	44065	66430	86021	39494	63952	24737	19070	21798
60943	70277	05392	17176	29317	67523	84674	81846	76694	05132
00056	81271	45263	56082	77857	71342	75778	96091	73637	17872
14684	40901	22495	34301	46549	58537	10507	92279	68925	89235
42019	95611	21290	21960	86403	44181	59813	62977	47713	09960
51870	72113	49999	99837	29780	49951	05973	17328	16096	31859
50244	59455	34690	83026	42522	30825	33446	85035	26193	11881
71010	00313	78387	52886	58753	32083	81420	61717	76691	47303
59825	34904	28755	46873	11595	62863	88235	37875	93751	95778
18577	80532	17122	68066	13001	92787	66111	95909	21642	01989
38095	25720	10654	85863	27886	59361	53381	82796	82303	01952
03530	18529	68995	77362	25994	13891	24972	17752	83479	13151
55748	57242	45415	06959	50829	53311	68617	27855	88907	50983
81754	63746	49393	19255	06040	09277	01671	13900	98488	24012
85836	16035	63707	66010	47101	81942	95559	61989	46767	83744
94482	55379	77472	68471	04047	53464	62080	46684	25906	94912
93313	67702	89891	52104	75216	20569	66024	05803	81501	93511
25338	24300	35587	64024	74964	73263	91419	92726	04269	92279
67823	54781	63600	93417	21641	21992	45863	15030	28618	29745
55706	74983	84054	94588	58692	69956	90927	21079	75093	02955

* These numbers were taken from a table published by D. Shanks and J. W. Wrench, *Mathematics of Computation*, **16**, No. 7, 76–99, Jan. 1962.

There are 10 summed terms making up χ^2, but we must subtract one because we have assumed a distribution for n_e of the type

$$n_e = \frac{N}{10},$$

which has one adjustable constant or constraint, namely N.

The data point $\chi^2 = 6.00$, degrees of freedom $= 9$, falls well within the "no reason to suspect hypothesis" region of Fig. 2–8. Hence, this test does nothing to make us doubt the randomness of the digits in our table.

A2–3. An experiment to study the way random effects combine

This experiment is an investigation of the shape of the histogram of a quantity whose variation is due to a number of random, independent effects. The histogram of the resultant quantity is compared with that of the effects.

As random effects, we take the first 250 digits from a table of random numbers. As the quantity which is dependent on them, we select the mean of five consecutive random digits, i.e.,

$$\bar{x} = (x_1 + x_2 + x_3 + x_4 + x_5)/5.$$

We have already determined the histogram of random digits. It is the rectangular distribution of Fig. A2–2. What is the shape of the mean of five digits? Is it also rectangular, or does it have some other shape?

The answer is given in Fig. A2–3, which plots the means of five digits for the digits shown in Fig. A2–2. It will be seen that the distribution is bell-shaped, approximating a normal distribution. A little thought will show how this has come about. For the average of five numbers to be between 8.5 and 9.5, it is necessary that all the digits be high. For

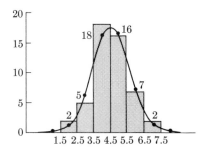

Fig. A2–3. Histogram of means of five consecutive digits of the data of Fig. A2–2; also, the best fitting normal distribution.

an average between 4.5 and 5.5, all may be average, or some high and some low, etc. Clearly, this is the more common situation.

We may take the argument a step further. As we have seen, it has taken only five random errors to produce a distribution which follows a normal one quite closely. Hence, we are justified in assuming that in the average experiment in which there are more than five error-causing factors, the distribution will be still closer to the normal one, provided that the various factors contribute, to more or less the same extent, to the error. This result, that the distribution of means tends to be a normal distribution, even when the data points themselves are not distributed normally, is a very important one.

If the errors are not of comparable magnitude, the distribution is likely not to be normal. Consider the function

$$F = (100x_1 + x_2 + x_3 + x_4 + x_5)/104.$$

The error in F is again caused by the errors in x_1 to x_5, but all terms except x_1 are negligible. Hence the histogram of F will resemble the histogram of x_1. If we calculate F from groups of 5 adjacent digits of our table, it will be essentially rectangular, as is the distribution of the individual digits themselves.

A2–4. An experiment to measure the standard deviation of a sum or a difference

In this experiment we shall try to demonstrate experimentally the important statistical law which states: "If a quantity x_1 with standard deviation σ_1, is added to, or subtracted from, an independent quantity x_2 with standard deviation σ_2, then the resultant, either $x_1 + x_2$ or $x_1 - x_2$, will have a standard deviation $(\sigma_1^2 + \sigma_2^2)^{1/2}$. This law is used, for example, in Section 8–16. The reader is invited to prove this law using Eq. (2–9).

We can best generate the required quantities x_1 and x_2 from a table of random numbers. For example, let x_1 be the number of times either the digit 8 or the digit 9 occurs in a set of 50 random digits. Clearly, the average value of x_1 is 10, and, since x_1 is made up of a number of rare random events, it will obey Poisson statistics so that its standard deviation σ_1 will be $\sqrt{10}$. Now let x_2 be the number of times some other digit, e.g., 7, occurs in a set of 50 random digits. Then x_2 will have an average value of 5 and a standard deviation of $\sqrt{5}$. If the individual values of x_1 and x_2 are either added or subtracted, then the sums and differences will have values averaging 15 and 5, respectively, with, according to our law, a standard deviation of $\sqrt{15}$ in either case.

Instructions to experimenters. Obtain a large number of values of x_1 and x_2 as outlined above (say 50 of each). Confirm that $\bar{x}_1$ is 10 and $\bar{x}_2$ is 5 with but minor variation due to statistical fluctuations. Confirm that σ_1 is $\sqrt{10}$ and σ_2 is $\sqrt{5}$ with, again, but minor variation. Then set up the 50 values of $x_1 + x_2$ and $x_1 - x_2$ and calculate their standard deviations. Are these equal to $\sqrt{15}$?

Illustrative Experiments

The experiments that can be devised to illustrate and help teach the various sections of this book are very numerous, and will in general depend strongly upon the particular physical equipment that is available, in sufficient quantity, in a given laboratory. Because of this rather strong dependence of experiment upon equipment, we have not tried to outline in detail a wide variety of experiments. Rather, we have simply described what we have done in a number of instances with our equipment. Similar experiments can easily be devised using similar equipment.

A3–1. Size distribution of wear particles

As experimental work associated with Chapter 1, we have in the past carried out an investigation to measure the size of wear particles. This problem not only is of some theoretical interest and practical importance, but also illustrates the ideas discussed in that chapter.

The wear particles are conveniently produced in the simple apparatus shown in Fig. A3–1, which uses a geometry of two crossed cylinders of copper ($\frac{1}{4}$ in. rod), one of which is stationary, the other driven at about 2000 rpm by a $\frac{1}{10}$ h.p. electric motor. The stationary rod is pressed against the rotating one with a load of 200 gm, the rods are cleaned with emery paper before the test is started, and then wear particles are produced at a rate of about 0.03 gm/hour. One gram makes a suitable sample for the experimental investigation.

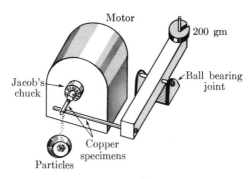

Fig. A3–1. Apparatus for producing copper wear particles.

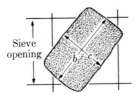

Fig. A3–2. A fragment just caught in a sieve. The width b of the particle and the sieve opening are nearly the same.

A number of methods may be used for analyzing the size distribution of the wear particles. At least two of the methods should be used. The aim of the investigation is, then, twofold. First, it is required to discover the true size distribution of the particles, and secondly, it is required to compare the different methods in terms of reliability, reproducibility, and convenience.

(a) *Sieving method.* In this method, the whole population or sample of particles is passed through a series of graduated sieves whose opening changes in geometric progression. For preference, eight sieves with openings of 500, 350, 250, 177, 125, 88, 62, 44 microns, respectively, may be used, but just four sieves, preferably 350, 177, 88, and 44 microns, will also be found satisfactory. The particles which go through the finest sieve, as well as those which are caught in each of the earlier sieves, are carefully weighed in a chemical balance.

From these data, a histogram of number of particles as a function of the size of the particles must then be drawn up. In order to do this, we divide the weight of each batch of particles by the weight of the "average particle" in the batch.

In a problem such as this, we have to consider rather carefully what we mean by "size" of a fragment. The sieving method tells us nothing about the longest dimension of a fragment, and not too much about the shortest dimension, since it is the middle dimension which mainly determines whether a particle can slip through a sieve (Fig. A3–2). In the case of wear particles, the particle shape will be found to be roughly ellipsoidal, with the longest dimension a about twice the middle one b, and the shortest dimension c about one-half the middle one. Hence, we may write the volume of the typical particle in the form

$$V = \pi \times abc/6 = \pi(2b)b(\tfrac{1}{2}b)/6 = \pi b^3/6. \qquad (A3\text{–}1)$$

From Fig. A3–2 we see that the sieve opening which will just let a particle through is very nearly equal to b, and use this fact in our calculations, so that we may estimate, from a knowledge of the sieve spacings

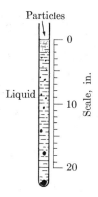

Fig. A3–3. Apparatus for measuring settling rates.

which limit the particle sizes within a sieved fraction, the average value of b for the fragments, and then the weight of the average particle within that fraction. Because the use of graduated sieves produces particle fractions which increase in size geometrically, it is expedient to plot the histogram on semilog paper, i.e., to plot the number of particles versus the log of the particle size. However, if a little care is taken to adjust for variation in size range with varying size, a direct plot of number of particles against size may also be made. The fact that the histogram is or is not normal in shape may be used to deduce whether the size of wear particles is determined by one or by a large number of independent factors.

(b) *Settling method.* When this method is used, a small representative sample of the fragments is dropped into a viscous fluid (say a lubricating oil of viscosity 100 centipoise), and the rate of fall of the various particles is measured (Fig. A3–3). The formula for the equilibrium velocity of flow of a sphere of mass density ρ in a fluid of viscosity μ and mass density ρ' is

$$v = \frac{d^2(\rho - \rho')g}{18\mu}. \tag{A3-2}$$

For particles of irregular size, this formula gives an "effective diameter" of a particle which will be nearly the same as, but not quite identical with, the diameter b of the particle as found by the sieving process.

Practical problems encountered with the settling method include selecting a small *representative* sample of fragments, and difficulties in measuring the very small, slow-falling particles and the very large, quick-falling particles as well as the medium-sized ones. In fact, most students who use the settling method to measure the size of wear particles usually arrive at histograms which seriously understate the number of the small particles.

(c) *Measurement under the microscope.* For this method, a representative sample of fragments is shaken out onto a flat surface, which may be a microscope slide (but an opaque surface is a little better), and the dimensions of some of the particles (chosen at random) are measured in a metallurgical microscope with filar eyepiece. The length and the width (i.e., dimension at right angles to the longest direction) are measured directly in the eyepiece, while the height is measured by focusing onto the top-most point on the fragment, then onto the surface on which the particle is resting, and reading off the vertical displacement of the microscope tube from the calibrated fine-focusing adjustment.

Some compromise is required in the choice of the microscope objective. If it has too large a numerical aperture, and hence magnification, many fragments will fill the field of view and cannot be readily measured. If its numerical aperture is too low, then vertical resolution drops off drastically (as the square of the N.A.). We have found an N.A. value of 0.4 as being quite suitable.

When calculating the shape of the particles, an automatic check on the correctness of the value used for the magnification of the microscope is provided by the fact that the heights of the fragments are likely to be smaller than the width, but probably not too much smaller. After about 20 particles have been measured, it becomes possible to plot a histogram of number of particles against size of particles. Since we have three measured dimensions for each particle, it becomes necessary to use a representative size dimension, either the width b, or $(abc)^{1/3}$, which will be comparable to the size dimensions used in the other two experiments. If the plot obtained with this method differs from those obtained previously, the reason for the difference should be sought, either in terms of experimental errors or approximations during the measurements or in deficiencies of the sampling techniques.

This analysis may reveal which method is the "best," or, more probably, how all the methods can be modified to yield more accurate results.

A3–2. Statistical variation of friction coefficient

In a sense, almost all experiments may be considered to illustrate the ideas of Chapter 2, although students often feel that they have a choice, when working up an experiment, between "using statistics" and "not using statistics." This is an illusion, in that statistics may be defined as the science (and art) of handling numerical data. The only choice is between "efficient" and "inefficient" statistics. In this context, it may

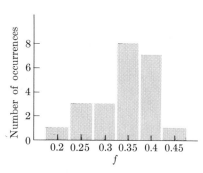

Fig. A3–4. Rotary table of milling machine set up for friction measurements.

Fig. A3–5. Histogram of static friction values: steel nut, cleaned by abrasion on fine emery paper, on a wood block, similarly cleaned.

be worth pointing out that "efficient" to a statistician does not have the usual engineering meaning of the most meaningful result for the least expenditure of effort, but rather the most meaningful result from the least amount of data. Thus, an engineer, faced with the problem of finding the slope of a straight line to a certain degree of accuracy, might make 20 observations and compute the slope by the method of extended differences, while a statistician might prefer to make 15 observations and use the method of least squares.

One class of "experiments" which can readily demonstrate the application of many of the equations of Chapter 2 is that involving the use of random numbers (see Appendix 2). Another type of experiment, which is worth carrying out from a statistical point of view, is one which leads to data which fit the normal distribution. This may involve the measurement of a simple material parameter such as hardness, or tensile strength, but perhaps the simplest experiment in this category, especially from the point of time required per data point, is the measurement of coefficients of friction.

If a block of one material is placed on a flat surface and the surface tilted until the block slides, then the static friction coefficient is merely the tangent of the angle of the flat surface with the horizontal at the instant of slip. It is quite possible to use simple apparatus in which the flat surface is tilted directly; but, in order to get closer control of the tilting, it is desirable to move the flat surface more slowly via a step-down gearing system. This can be done by mounting the flat surface on a rotary table from a milling machine, the rotary table being placed in a vertical plane (Fig. A3–4). With this device, we can obtain friction data such as that shown in Fig. A3–5.

The lack of constancy of friction coefficient in this experiment is due to a number of causes, among them vibration of the tilting surface, overshooting of the tilt position, reading errors, and last, but by no means least, local variations in the surface geometry and the surface contamination. This last source of error must be controlled, lest it becomes overwhelmingly greater than the other sources of error, and accordingly the surfaces should be carefully and uniformly cleaned before the experiments. If this is done, then fairly normal-looking histograms will be obtained.

A typical series of experiments might consist of 30 or 40 friction measurements using a smoothly sanded surface, and the same number with a rough, file-finished surface. Nominally, the aim of the experiment is to see which surface gives the larger friction, though actually the aim is to investigate the form of the histogram.

A3–3. Galvanometer response

In this experiment, we wish to determine the response characteristics of a d-c amplifier-recorder combination. We will subject the system to a step input as well as sinusoidal inputs of various frequencies. The object is to attempt to correlate the response to a sine wave with the response to a step input.

The system we will use for our tests is the Sanborn Strain Gage Amplifier and Recorder (or similar equipment), which employs an a-c carrier wave as bridge input. In the amplifier, the a-c signal is rectified

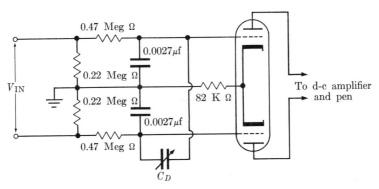

Fig. A3–6. Portion of the Sanborn strain-gage amplifier associated with Experiment A3–3. V_{IN} is input from rectifier or from audio oscillator. Damping capacitor C_D: off = 0 μf, 1 = 0.005 μf, 2 = 0.01 μf, 3 = 0.02 μf, 4 = 0.05 μf, 5 = 0.2 μf.

$$R = (0.22+0.22+0.47+0.47)\text{Meg } \Omega$$

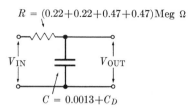

$$C = 0.0013+C_D$$

Fig. A3–7. The system response to step input is crudely approximated by that of the single-order system.

and amplified through two stages before being applied to the pens. There are filter and feedback networks in the d-c amplifier stages which are intended to improve the high-frequency response characteristics of the unit.

By balancing the Sanborn (using the plug-in resistors to complete the bridge), and pressing the "Cal." button, the system is subject to a step input. This simply shunts one arm with a calibrating resistor (see Chapter 4). If the paper is moving at high speed (25 or 100 mm/sec), the response can be observed. The response should be recorded using all five values of damping capacitance C_D (Fig. A3–6). For each value of C_D, a time constant τ can be determined, assuming the system response to be essentially that of a first-order system as shown in Fig. A3–7. The response curve for sinusoidal input at frequencies of 15, 30, 45, 60, and 90 cps can then be determined for each value of C_D by applying a constant-voltage input to the system from an audio oscillator. The input voltage should be about $\frac{1}{2}$ volt as measured on a VTVM (vacuum tube voltmeter). The measured response can then be compared with the calculated response.

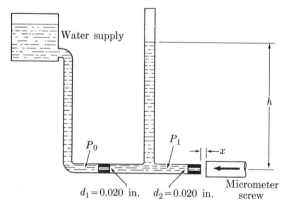

Fig. A3–8. Schematic view of flow-type displacement gage.

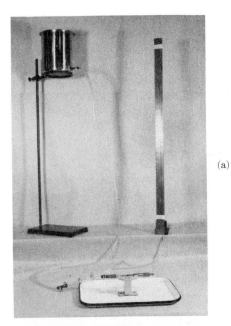

(a)

Fig. A3–9. Flow-type gage:
(a) view of entire apparatus;
(b) detail of transducer.

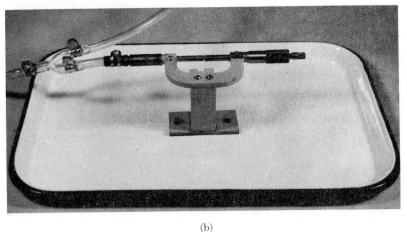

(b)

A3–4. Fluid-displacement gage

In this experiment we measure the sensitivity and linearity of a flow-type gage. A reservoir of water is used to supply the pressure, and is the source of flow media, as shown schematically in Fig. A3–8. Figures A3–9(a) and (b) show how the apparatus can be simply constructed from a discarded micrometer and a few odd parts.

By closing d_2 (making $x = 0$), the height of the column of water will indicate the supply pressure p_0. By moving the micrometer away from the orifice d_2 a small distance x (less than 0.001), a new level will be observed.

A number of readings should be taken and a plot of p_1/p_0 versus d_2x/d_1^2 made and compared with a plot made from theoretical values. Discuss any differences observed.

A3–5. Dynamic response of strain-gage dynamometer

The purpose of this experiment is to evaluate the response of an existing two-component force dynamometer to determine its suitability for measurement of dynamically varying forces. The unit to be tested is a small, sensitive, *delicate* dynamometer as shown schematically in Fig. A3–10.

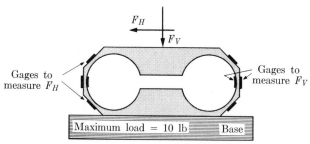

Fig. A3–10. Sensitive force dynamometer.

The dynamic response to an impulse is easily obtained when a weight of about $4\frac{1}{2}$ lb is attached to the dynamometer, so that its natural frequency falls within the useful range of a Sanborn Recorder. The impulse is applied by simply tapping the mass. The effective weight of the mass is obtained by inverting the dynamometer and noting the force reading change which will be equivalent to a variation of 2 g's, or twice the effective weight. The natural frequency and the damping can be calculated from the recording. This should be repeated with the dynamometer resting on some sort of damping material; e.g., rubber, felt, etc.

The basic dynamometer characteristics should then be computed, and the regions should be outlined where it could be effectively used to measure force, acceleration, etc. Discuss the use of damping to improve response characteristics and devise a suitable damper for at least one motion, i.e., horizontal or vertical.

A3–6. Wire-resistance strain gages

This experiment involves the use of a simple cantilever beam with strain gages attached. Assuming Young's modulus to be known, we can apply a given strain to the gages by applying known loads to the cantilever. The output of the strain gage Wheatstone bridge can be compared with a calculated value. In order to correctly determine the characteristics of the voltage source and meter system, a known resistance of the order of $\frac{1}{2}$ megohm can be shunted across one arm of the bridge. The meter deflection corresponding to this resistance change in one arm is compared with that due to strain. The report should include a discussion of measured and calculated performance.

In order to check out the calculated values, it is necessary to know the supply voltage and output voltage quite accurately.

This experiment consists of two parts. (1) A known voltage is applied to the input of the bridge and the output is measured for various values of load; the results should be plotted and compared with theoretical values. (2) A calibration resistor is placed across one leg of the bridge and a meter reading corresponding to a given strain is obtained; this permits comparison of experimental data with theory without ref-

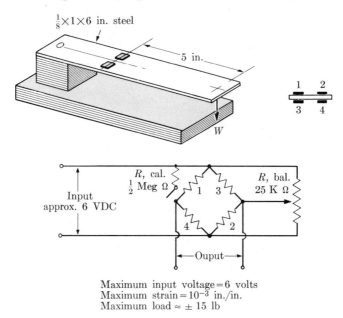

Maximum input voltage = 6 volts
Maximum strain = 10^{-3} in./in.
Maximum load $\approx \pm 15$ lb

Fig. A3–11. Schematic view of strain-gage cantilever. Four-active-arm strain gage bridge, SR4 type A–8: $R_0 = 120 \pm 0.3\ \Omega$; G.F. $= 1.85 \pm 2\%$; gage length $= \frac{1}{8}$ in.; gage width $= \frac{5}{32}$ in.

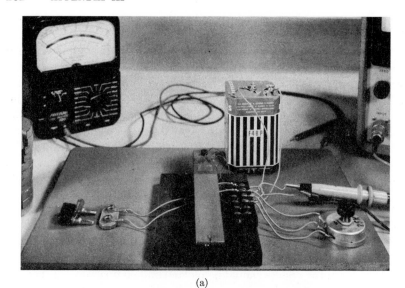

(a)

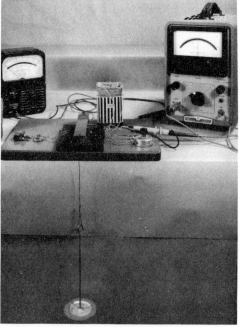

(b)

Fig. A3–12.   Photographs of strain-gage cantilever: (a) details of cantilever; (b) measuring instruments (d-c voltmeter, 10 volts full scale, d-c microvoltmeter, 10 microvolts full scale).

erence to the exact input or output voltage. Figures A3–11 and A3–12 show the physical equipment used.

Once this relationship is established and provided that the relationship between ΔV and strain is linear, a calibration can be established at any time without regard to the input voltage. The ΔV obtained when using the calibration resistor will always correspond to a certain strain, or in this case a certain applied load.

A3–7. Capacitance gage with audio oscillator and oscilloscope

The purpose of this experiment is to ascertain the properties of a simple electrical gage; its advantages and disadvantages, sensitivity, linearity, etc. When possible we want to compare the performance of the gage with performance predicted from simple theory.

The capacitance gage to be used for this experiment involves five plates, two stationary and three movable, as shown in Fig. A3–13. A micrometer screw is used to displace the upper plates relative to the lower plates and also to provide calibration over the less sensitive ranges. The gage can be used in a variety of ways so far as electrical

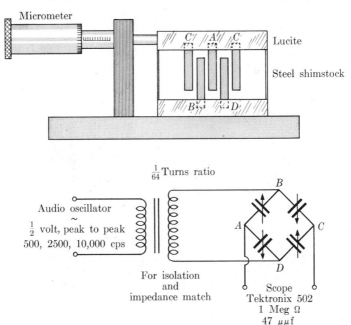

Fig. A3–13. Schematic of capacitance gage.

(a)

(b)

(c)

Fig. A3–14. Capacitance gage: (a) details of gage; (b) gage used with audio oscillator and oscilloscope; (c) gage used with Sanborn recorder. Note phase-correcting capacitance box.

circuitry is concerned. Probably one of the most practical ways of using the gage is in a four-active-arm capacitance bridge. In this fashion a simple push-pull null device is obtained. The capacitance of the gages can be simply computed, and it will be found that the individual arms have very high impedance. The sensitivity and linearity of a bridge circuit are seriously impaired if the meter impedance is not high relative to the bridge impedance. The effect of the meter impedance should be calculated and compared with test results. Figure A3–14 shows the apparatus used for this experiment.

A3–8. Capacitance gage used with a Sanborn recorder

The purpose of this experiment is essentially the same as the previous experiment. This time, however, we use a Sanborn strain-gage amplifier (or similar equipment) to provide excitation and to produce a record. With this we can obtain great sensitivity, but to do so we must pay attention to impedance matching (the Sanborn is designed for an output impedance of 100 ohms). In order to improve the impedance match, two input transformers are used. The total primary impedance of the transformer is 1000 ohms and the total output impedance is 200,000 ohms (Figs. A3–14(c) and A3–15).

Because of the phase sensitivity of the Sanborn equipment, the output voltage across AC must be in phase with the input BD. A variable capacitance across AC permits this matching. If BD is fed to the horizontal input of an oscilloscope, while AC goes to the vertical input (Fig. A3–14c), the resulting ellipse will indicate the input-output phase relationship. The capacitance is adjusted to make the ellipse collapse to

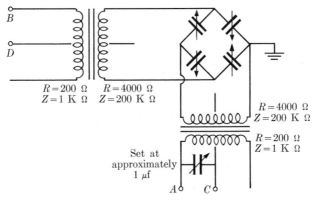

Fig. A3–15. Schematic of equipment for Experiment A3–8. *A, B, C,* and *D* refer to the input connections to the Sanborn recorder.

nearly a straight line. The sensitivity and linearity should be observed with and without the phase connection.

The characteristics of the Model 60 Sanborn Strain Gage Amplifier and Recorder are nominally: carrier wave, 3.5 volts at 2500 cps; sensitivity, 10^{-5} volt/mm pen motion; satisfactory sensitivity with input impedances from 50 to 500 ohms.

A3–9. Inductance gaging using oscillator and oscilloscope

The variable-inductance gage used to carry out this experiment is a Schaevitz Model 005MSL Linear Variable Differential Transformer. In essence, it is composed of three small coils wound side by side on a common coil form with a movable iron core. The middle coil, the primary, is excited by an a-c voltage. The flux produced by the primary induces a voltage in each of the secondaries. The gage is wired so that the two secondary voltages "buck" one another. Thus when the core is central and the opposing secondary voltages are equal, there is no output. As the core is moved from the null position, one secondary voltage increases while the other decreases, producing an output in a push-pull fashion. The nonlinearities inherent in inductance gages tend to cancel because of the two opposing secondaries, and the unit becomes fairly linear over a substantial range.

Specifications	Primary	Secondary
Resistance, ohms	56	86 (Total)
Impedance at 2 kc, ohms	59	86
Inductance, millihenries	151	nil

Sensitivity, $(\Delta V/V_0)$/in. with $\frac{1}{2}$-megohm load:

at 400 cps = 0.4

at 2000 cps = 1.88

at 20,000 cps = 4.55

Phase shift at Δx = ± 0.005 in.

at 400 cps = 87°

at 3000 cps = 59°

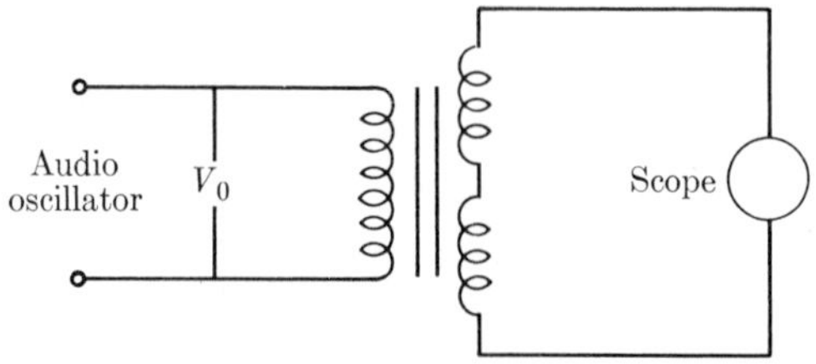

Fig. A3–16. Schematic diagram and pertinent data for Experiment A3–9. Schaevitz LVDT 005MSL.

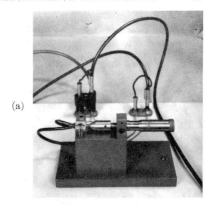

(a)

(b)

(c)

Fig. A3–17. LVDT Experiment: (a) details of transducer; (b) system using audio oscillator and oscilloscope; (c) setup for use with Sanborn equipment. Note decade capacitor and oscilloscope for proper phase shifting.

It is very unsatisfactory to attempt an analysis of the sensitivity of a variable-inductance gage. Hence, we will compare the measured sensitivity with that predicted by using the manufacturer's specifications. With this setup, using an oscillator as source and an oscilloscope as a meter, we can measure the linearity and system sensitivity.

Figure A3–16 shows the setup and provides the necessary data. Figure A3–17 shows the device set up for use. Note that the LVDT core is moved by turning a micrometer.

A3–10. Inductance gaging using a Sanborn recorder

The transducer here is the same as used in experiment A3–9. We will calculate the phase shift of secondary voltage relative to the primary voltage. Knowing this phase shift, we can calculate the capacitance required as a shunt across the secondary in order to put the input and output voltages in phase. We can also calculate the loss of sensitivity due to this shunt capacitor. We can use a Sanborn Strain Gage Amplifier and Recorder or equivalent to observe the system performance. We note that in order to make the Sanborn resistance balance control operate properly, we must shunt the primary with a high resistance and then ground the center of the resistance. Figure A3–18 shows the schematic diagram, while Fig. A3–17(c) shows the actual apparatus.

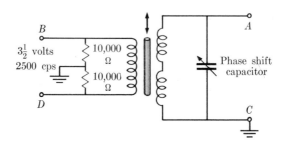

Fig. A3–18. Schematic diagram for Experiment A3–10.

A3–11. Thermocouple error

The temperature of the surface of a 100-watt electric light bulb is to be measured with several fine thermocouples. Figure A3–19 shows the location of the various couples.

The readings obtained will not agree very well. Explain as well as possible why they differ, and suggest possible ways to better define and measure the surface temperature.

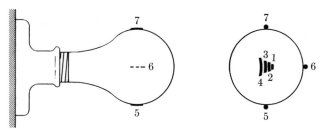

Figure A3–19

The thermocouples are chromel-alumel and are glued to the bulb with a ceramic cement.

A3–12. Experiments to illustrate radiotracer techniques

Introduction. Although problems of safety should be considered in connection with all experiments, they are worth discussing especially in a section devoted to measurements involving radiotracers. The special problems involved in work with radioisotopes are twofold. First there is the fact that the danger comes from radiation which human senses are not capable of detecting, so that a person may be irradiated to a dangerous extent without realizing it. Secondly, radiation is invariably associated in the human mind with nuclear explosions, which are known to be very dangerous to human life and health, and this attitude is transferred to radioisotopes, especially those produced artificially in nuclear piles.

It is not generally realized that the amount of radioactive isotopes required in various applications covers an enormous range, from the intensities at the kilocurie level (10^3 curies) required for producing chemical changes in polymers and for sterilizing food, down to the millicurie intensities (10^{-3} curies) used for typical tracer applications such as wear studies, down to the microcurie levels (10^{-6} curies) which are involved in simple experiments to demonstrate the properties of radiation. Owing to the large amount of radiation emitted by a source as weak as 10 microcuries, namely 370,000 particles/sec, many tests are possible with sources of this type, and their general safety is indicated by the fact that they are free of Atomic Energy Commission licensing requirements.

Many tests may be made without having a standard radiotracer source at hand, using instead a wristwatch with luminous dial. Many of these, particularly those manufactured a few years ago, are radioisotope sources of microcurie intensity. Their use obviates all problems of a legal and administrative nature.

A3–13. Operation of the geiger counter: finding the plateau

In this experiment, a constant source of radioactivity is placed near the window of the geiger counter. This source may be a specimen made radioactive in a pile, or a naturally radioactive uranium mineral fragment, or a wristwatch with a luminous dial. The geiger counter is operated at a series of voltages ranging from below the threshold, which is the lowest voltage at which any reading whatever is obtained, up to the upper end of the plateau, beyond which point the counting rate increases rapidly and almost independently of the radioactive source. (Note that the counter should not be operated for more than a few seconds beyond the plateau region, or it may be damaged.)

It is most convenient to perform this experiment using a geiger counter which has a scaling unit attached. These units generally have provision for recording the discharges of the counter over some definite preset period. When the counting rate is high (say above 1000 counts/ min), then a 1-min count will generally provide sufficient accuracy for this and other radiotracer experiments. When the counting rate is much lower, counts of longer duration are in order. It is best to keep the counting rate under 20,000 counts/min (by moving the source of radioactivity farther from the counter), or counts coming close together will frequently be missed.

If a geiger counter with scaler output is not available, then an instrument with a milliammeter output may be used. This is less accurate than a scaler output, both because the milliammeter usually has an accuracy of no better than 1%, and because the needle of the milliammeter fluctuates continuously, corresponding to instantaneous fluctuations in the rate at which particles hit the counter.

Many observers attempt to read a meter with fluctuating needle by attempting with the eye to locate the maxima and minima of the fluctuations, and then locating the mean. A better method is to use two observers, to have one of them say "now" at random intervals (say when a car is passing the road outside the laboratory window) and to have the other observer record the instantaneous positions of the needle. An averaged series of such recorded readings provides a satisfactory estimate of the true reading of the meter.

A3–14. The stopping power of matter

For this experiment it is helpful to obtain a pure β-emitting radioactive source, rather than to use the mixed radiation emitted by a luminous wristwatch dial. However, the latter can be used, although the results will be a little more difficult to interpret.

The radioactive source is placed as near the counter as is practical, bearing in mind the need to keep the counting rate below about 20,000 counts/min, and to be able to place screening material between the source and the counter. Suitable for use as screening material is steel or brass shim stock available in thicknesses from 0.001 in. up. Tests should be made with 0.001, 0.002, 0.003 in., etc., of foil between counter and source. In each case the counting rate is determined. Initially, when the counting rate is high, only a 1-min count is needed, but as the thickness of shim stock increases and the counting rate decreases, until it becomes only slightly above background, a 5-min or even a 10-min count is called for. Finally, the background is measured with the source removed.

Empirically, it has been found that the counting rate drops off with screening thickness t following a law of the type

$$I = I_0 e^{-t/t_0}. \tag{A3-3}$$

where t_0 is a constant.

Thus a plot of log I against t should be initially a straight line, though at high values of t the intensity levels off, becoming almost independent of t. From the plot, the thickness required to reduce the intensity of transmitted radiation to one-half should be determined.

Finally, we may take a thin sheet of steel of unknown thickness, measure the extent to which it stops β-rays, compute its thickness using Eq. (A3-3), and then check the results with those obtained by direct measurement.

A3-15. Investigating the statistics associated with radioactive counting

This experiment is carried out with a geiger counter connected to a scaler unit. A radioactive source is placed near the counter window and ten or twenty counts, each of 1-min duration, are made. The counts obtained are carefully recorded.

Since radioactive particle counting obeys Poisson statistics, the standard deviation of the number of events recorded should be equal to the square root of the number of events. To check this, we may compute the average counting rate of our ten or twenty counts and then compute their standard deviation. This value should be within 30% or so of the square root of the average number of counts.

We may apply a second statistical test to our data, namely that since the individual counts will cluster about their average in a normally distributed fashion, about $\frac{2}{3}$ of our data should lie within $\bar{x} \pm \sigma$. Also it is unlikely that the deviation of any individual reading from the average is as much as 3σ. If the data does seem well out of line, we would suspect malfunction of the counter.

A3–16. The inverse square law of radiation

In this experiment, the source of radiation is placed at various distances from the counter, ranging from a point where it almost touches the counter (actually touching the window of the counter is absolutely forbidden, as the next step will be the purchase of a new counter), to a distance so remote that a count hardly above background is obtained.

Figure A3–20 shows a geiger counter being used to measure the intensity-distance function for radiation from a wristwatch with a luminous dial.

Fig. A3–20. Experiment to measure the variation of intensity of radiation with distance from the geiger counter.

According to theory, the counting rate should vary inversely with the square of the distance to the counter. Hence, a plot of the log of the counting rate against the log of the distance should have a slope of -2. In practice, the slope obtained will tend to be rather lower at small distances, and higher at large distances. Explain these effects.

A3–17. Estimating the weight of wear debris: a tracer experiment

For this experiment it is necessary to obtain a piece of metal which is weakly radioactive. This may be a piece of zinc, or a rod of stainless steel (it is useful to be reminded of the fact that an object as common as a rusty nail or a teaspoon may be radioactive). The metal is carefully weighed, and then a little is abraded off onto a piece of emery paper. This is placed in front of the geiger counter and the counting rate determined, as is the loss in weight of the object by direct weighing. From the known activity of the object, the weight of the fragments may be estimated, and this estimate is compared with the value given by the weighing method.

A3–18. Autoradiography

A number of simple problems can be examined using autoradiographic techniques. For example, the distribution of abraded fragments on the emery paper, as described in the last experiment, can be obtained by

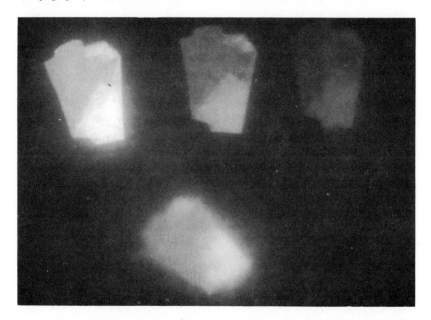

Fig. A3–21. Autoradiographic images produced on Polaroid 3000 sheet film by nickel foil of thickness 0.0005 in. (partially folded over), and radioactive intensity 500 μc/gm. Top line: exposures of 15, 5, and $1\frac{1}{2}$ min. Bottom line: exposure of 15 min, but with steel sheet of thickness 0.004 in. between the nickel foil and the film.

putting a piece of photographic film on the emery paper (in a darkroom), allowing the two to remain together for some hours, and then developing to reveal the distribution of particles.

To avoid use of the darkroom, the authors have investigated the possible use of Polaroid film in autoradiography, since with its use, processing is greatly simplified. Early tests were made using Polaroid roll film, but this proved quite inconvenient. Hence, later work was done with Polaroid sheet film, using both the negative and no-negative varieties. For our radiotracer source, nickel in the form of a thin radioactive sheet of thickness 0.0005 in., and activity of a few microcuries, was used, although other sources are suitable.

In a typical experiment, the source might be placed on the outside of a Polaroid film sheet, and exposures of $1\frac{1}{2}$ min, 5 min, and 15 min given at various points on the film. Then a 15-min exposure is given on another point of the film, with a piece of shim stock between the source and the film (Fig. A3–21). After this, the film is developed in the Polaroid camera back. If the 15-min exposure with the shim stock produces an image estimated to be of the same intensity as would have been produced by a 10-min exposure without the shim stock, then the shim stock has cut the radioactive intensity by one-third.

The Use of Analog Computers in Measurement Analysis

Since the advent of analog and digital computers, they have been used extensively to solve problems associated with the dynamics of instrument and control problems. More recently, there has been a growing use of "on line" or "in process" computation wherein raw data is fed to a computer as it is received, and operated on in some fashion. The availability of digital to analog and analog to digital converters permits the use of the most desirable aspects of each.

While we cannot consider all computational methods in a book of this size, we want to point out and illustrate, the use of simple, low-cost "student analog computers" that are just now coming onto the market. Figure A4–1 shows a set made by the Pastoriza Company of Cambridge,

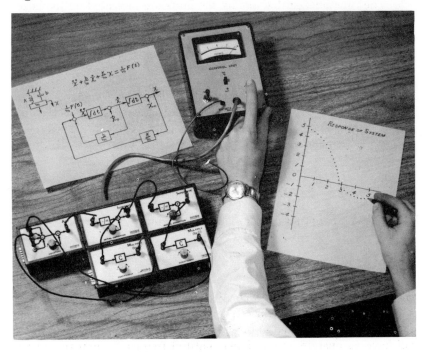

Figure A4–1

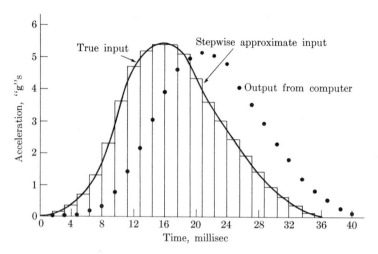

Fig. A4–2. Data for computer example.

Massachusetts, which sells for about $350 (1963) for the complete set. The functions carried out by the units are indicated on the boxes (add, integrate, and multiply). This set is capable of solving rather difficult first- and second-order differential equations. Rather than explain how it operates, we will work a problem using it. The power of the method will be realized.

EXAMPLE. Let us consider the response of an accelerometer to an impulsive input. In fact, let us consider the same problem that we labored mightily on in Chapter 3. The input is shown again in Fig. A4–2. For reference

$$f_n = 50 \text{ cps} \qquad (\omega_n = 314 \text{ rad/sec}),$$
$$\zeta = 0.7, \qquad \text{range} = \pm 10 \, g,$$

and the equation of motion of an accelerometer is

$$\ddot{z} + 2\zeta\omega_n\dot{z} + \omega_n^2 z = \ddot{y}. \qquad (A4\text{–}1)$$

From our previous work we have seen that in essence, the damping ratio ζ fixes the shape of a response curve, while the natural frequency ω_n fixes the time scale. Our computers can operate with any damping ratio, but have a limited natural frequency, i.e., $\omega_n^2 < 10$; hence, we will have to operate at a different natural frequency than the 50 cps at which the accelerometer operates. It is essential that the damping

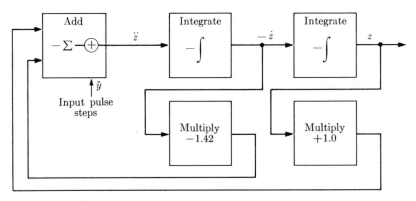

Fig. A4–3. Analog computer elements wired to work the example $\ddot{z} = \ddot{y} - 1.4\dot{z} - z$.

ratio of our computer system be held at 0.7 (same as accelerometer); hence, we can vary only the time scale. Any computer frequency will be satisfactory as long as $\omega_n^2 < 10$. However, as our input is $\ddot{y}$ and our output is proportional to z, it will be convenient to have

$$\frac{z}{\ddot{y}} = 1,$$

under steady-state conditions. This fixes $\omega_n = \omega_n^2 = 1$. We then have

$$\ddot{z} + 1.4\dot{z} + z = \ddot{y}$$

as our basic equation. It is clear that computer time is $\frac{1}{314}$ times as fast as real time. Hence, our input pulse of length 0.036 sec will have to take $0.036 \times 314 = 11.3$ sec. The Pastoriza computer has the capability of computing in $\frac{1}{4}$-second increments. Hence, we can divide the input pulse into $11.3/\frac{1}{4} = 45$ segments, or in $22\frac{1}{2}$ segments, or even 11 segments. For our purposes, we will divide it into $22\frac{1}{2}$ segments and compute for $\frac{1}{2}$ sec at each level of input. Figure A4–2 shows the input pulse so divided.

In order to use an analog computer to solve our equation, we first solve for the highest dependent derivative (i.e., $\ddot{z}$),

$$\ddot{z} = \ddot{y} - 1.4\dot{z} - z,$$

and wire the components to satisfy the equation as shown in Fig. A4–3. We note that starting with $\ddot{z}$ we integrate to $-\dot{z}$ and integrate again to $+z$. We then multiply z and $\dot{z}$ by the proper numbers and feed them back to the adder to obtain $\ddot{z}$. The input $\ddot{y}$ will simply be the steps with which we represented the input of Fig. A4–2. The table below indicates the inputs during the various pulse steps and the output at the end of each step. These data points are plotted on Fig. A4–2. If we compare this with the results of the same problem as obtained in Chapter 3, we will observe good correlation.

Time increment	Input, g's	Output, g's
1	0.05	0
2	0.12	0
3	0.35	0
4	0.72	0.2
5	1.3	0.4
6	2.3	0.8
7	3.7	1.4
8	4.7	2.1
9	5.2	3.0
10	5.4	3.9
11	5.4	4.6
12	5.1	4.9
13	4.3	5.1
14	3.6	5.0
15	3.0	4.8
16	2.4	4.0
17	1.9	3.5
18	1.4	2.9
19	0.95	2.3
20	0.60	1.8
21	0.35	1.2
22	0.1	0.8
23	0.02	0.5
24	0.00	0.25
25	0.00	0.1

Tables of Physical Quantities

In this appendix are gathered numerous data relating to the properties of a wide variety of materials. In the tables we have employed units which are not generally recognized as standard. We have simply assumed a mechanical equivalent of heat and electrical energy in order to put all energetic terms into compatible units. The obvious reason for such a presentation is the desire to avoid errors due to improper mating of units. The writers have found that when working in the general mechano-thermo-electro field, an "inch-pound-second" system proves most valuable. We should recall, of course, that in this system, the mass of a body is equal to its weight (on earth) divided by the acceleration due to gravity, 386 in./sec^2 (that is, $m = w/386$).

Many, indeed most, of the properties listed are neither *constants* nor *properties*. Rather, they are behavioral characteristics which apply to a given specimen of material, having given chemical, thermal, and physical histories. Thus the quantities listed are subject to considerable variation from specimen to specimen, and with temperature. We should also note that physical behavioral data have been obtained by many investigators, with the expected result that *different* values can be found in different references.

With these words of caution, and our apologies for any gross errors, we include the following tables:

Table A5–1. Physical Constants
Table A5–2. Metric Multiplier Prefixes
Table A5–3. Conversion Factors
Table A5–4. Properties of the Standard Atmosphere
Table A5–5. Average Properties of Solids
Table A5–6. Average Properties of Fluids (including dry air)
Table A5–7. Isotopes produced in a nuclear pile by the n-γ reaction
Table A5–8. Some other common pile-produced isotopes

REFERENCES

WESTMAN, H. P., ed., *Reference Data for Radio Engineers*, International Telephone and Telegraph Corp., New York, 1956. An extremely useful compilation of information relating to any electrical or electronic process.

"Materials Selector Issue," *Materials in Design Engineering*, Oct. 1962. An entire issue devoted to the physical properties of all metals, plastics, fibrous materials, ceramics, cements, etc. Lists of supplies as well as tabulated data.

RICHARDS, C. W., *Engineering Materials Science*, Wadsworth Publishing Co., San Francisco, 1961.

VAN VLACK, L. H., *Elements of Materials Science*, Addison-Wesley Publishing Co., Reading, Mass., 1960.

ROHSENOW, W. M., and H. Y. CHOI, *Heat, Mass, and Momentum Transfer*, Prentice-Hall, Englewood Cliffs, N. J., 1961.

TABLE A5–1

PHYSICAL CONSTANTS

Usual symbol	Name	Value
N	Avagadro's number	6.025×10^{23} atoms/gm-mole
h	Planck's constant	6.625×10^{-34} joule·sec
F	Faraday's constant	9.652×10^{4} coulomb/gm-mole
m	Electron mass (at rest)	9.108×10^{-28} gm
e	Electron charge	1.602×10^{-19} coulomb
c	Velocity of light in vacuum	2.998×10^{10} cm/sec
h/mc	Compton electron wave-length	2.426×10^{-10} cm
a_0	First Bohr electron orbit radius	5.292×10^{-9} cm
σ	Stefan-Boltzmann constant	5.669×10^{-8} watts/meter²·(°K)⁴
	Ratio: $\dfrac{\text{proton mass}}{\text{electron mass}}$	1836
k	Boltzmann's constant	1.380×10^{-23} joule/°K
R	Gas constant	8.317 joule/gm-mole·°K
T_0	Absolute zero	-273.12°C; -459.72°F

TABLE A5–2

METRIC MULTIPLIER PREFIXES

Prefix	Abbreviation	Multiplier
tera	T	10^{12}
giga	G	10^{9}
mega	M	10^{6}
myria	ma	10^{4}
kilo	k	10^{3}
hecto	h	10^{2}
deca	da	10
deci	d	10^{-1}
centi	c	10^{-2}
milli	m	10^{-3}
micro	μ	10^{-6}
nano	n	10^{-9}
pico	p	10^{-12}

TABLE A5–3

CONVERSION FACTORS

Force: 1 dyne = 2.248×10^{-6} lb
Mass (weight): 1 kilogram = 2.205 lb
Length: 1 cm = 1/2.54 in.
           1 angstrom unit (A) = 3.937×10^{-9} in.
           1 gal = 231 in^3 (U.S.A.)
Pressure: 1 kgm/mm^2 = 1420 lb/in^2
           1 $dyne/cm^2$ = 14.5×10^{-6} lb/in^2
           1 atm = 14.70 lb/in^2
           1 in. H_2O = 0.036 lb/in^2
           1 mm Hg = 0.01936 lb/in^2
Energy: 1 joule = 1 watt-sec = 8.85 in·lb
           1 calorie = 37.1 in·lb
           1 btu = 9330 in·lb
           1 kilowatt-hr = 3.185×10^7 in·lb
Power: 1 h.p. = 6600 in·lb/sec
         1 kilowatt = 8.85×10^3 in·lb/sec
Thermal conductivity: 1 $Btu/ft^2 \cdot hr \cdot °F/ft$ = 0.216 in·lb/$in^2 \cdot sec \cdot °F/in.$
                                                       (lb/sec·°F)
                 1 $cal/cm^2 \cdot sec \cdot °C/cm$ = 52.2 lb/sec·°F
Volumetric specific heat: 1 $Btu/in^3 \cdot °F$ = 9330 in·lb/$in^3 \cdot °F$ ($lb/in^2 \cdot °F$)
                        1 $cal/cm^3 \cdot °C$ = 338 ($lb/in^2 \cdot °F$)
Thermal diffusivity: 1 ft^2/hr = 0.04 in^2/sec
Temperature: $1°C = \frac{9}{5}°F$ ($°F = 32 + \frac{9}{5}°C$)

TABLE A5–4

PROPERTIES OF THE STANDARD ATMOSPHERE

Altitude, 10^3 ft	Temperature, °F	Pressure (absolute) lb/in^2	Density, lb/in^3	Speed of sound, 10^4 in./sec
0	59	14.7	4.43×10^{-5}	1.34
5	41	12.2	3.82×10^{-5}	1.32
10	23	10.1	3.28×10^{-5}	1.30
15	6	8.30	2.79×10^{-5}	1.27
20	−12	6.75	2.37×10^{-5}	1.25
25	−30	5.45	1.98×10^{-5}	1.22
30	−48	4.37	1.67×10^{-5}	1.19
35	−66	3.46	1.38×10^{-5}	1.17
40	−68	2.72	1.09×10^{-5}	1.17
45	−68	2.14	8.57×10^{-6}	1.17
50	−68	1.68	6.78×10^{-6}	1.17
60	−68	1.05	4.17×10^{-6}	1.17
70	−68	0.653	2.61×10^{-6}	1.17
80	−68	0.403	1.62×10^{-6}	1.17
90	−68	0.250	9.8×10^{-7}	1.17
100	−68	0.153	6.4×10^{-7}	1.17
150	114	0.021	5.7×10^{-8}	1.41
200	159	0.005	1.2×10^{-8}	1.46
250	−8	0.0007	2.8×10^{-9}	1.25
500	450	10^{-6}	1.8×10^{-12}	...

TABLE A5-5

AVERAGE PROPERTIES OF SOLIDS

Material	Density, lb/in³	Elastic modulus E, 10^6 lb/in²	Yield stress, 10^3 lb/in²	Melting temp. or range, °F	Thermal conduct., $\frac{\text{in·lb}}{\text{sec·in}^2\text{·°F/in.}}$	Vol. spec. heat, $\frac{\text{in·lb}}{\text{in}^3\text{·°F}}$	Thermal diffusivity, in²/sec	Coef. of thermal expansion, 10^{-6} in/in/°F	Resistivity (68°F), 10^{-6} ohm-cm	Dielectric constant (1 kc)	Dielectric strength, volts/in.
PURE METALS											
Aluminum	0.10	10	3.5	1200	29	197	0.147	13.1	2.8		
Beryllium	0.066	44	55	2340	19	284	0.067	6.4	5		
Cobalt (sintered)	0.32	30	44	2723	8.7	271	0.031	6.8			
Colombium	0.31	23	24	4380	6.8	172	0.040	4.0			
Copper	0.32	17	10	1980	51	254	0.20	9.3	1.7		
Hafnium	0.41	20	32	3800		123		3.4	30		
Lead	0.41	2	2	621	4.5	105	0.043	16.4	20		
Molybdenum	0.37	42	75	4700	1.7	193	0.0088	2.7	5.2		
Nickel	0.32	30	20	2025	7.9	356	0.022	6.6	9.5		
Tantalum	0.60	27	100	5425	7.0	185	0.038	3.6	12.5		
Titanium	0.16	15	40	3000	2.1	190	.011	5.8	55		
Tungsten	0.70	50	220	6092	26.2	204	0.13	2.4	5.5		
Uranium	0.68	30	25	2015	3.4	163	0.021	12.1	25–50		
Vanadium	0.22	22	55	3150		223		4.3	25		
Zirconium	0.25	12	16	3380	2.1	247	0.0085	2.4	40		
ALLOYS											
Aluminum 2024T4	0.10	10.6	44	1075	23.5	205	0.11	13	5.75		
6061T4	0.10	10.0	35	1080	21.5	210	0.10	13	3.8		
7075T6	0.10	10.4	83	1035	15.1	217	0.070	13	5.7		
Brass, hard yellow	0.31	15.0	74	1710	14.5	236	0.061	11.3	6.4		
Cast iron (25-T)	0.26	13	24*	2150	5–7	245		6	50–200		
Magnesium ZK51A-75	0.07	6.5	24	1175	10.3	148	0.070	16	8.4		
Phosphor bronze A, hard	0.32	16	81	1920	8.6	268	0.032	9.9	9.6		
Steel: C1018											
Hot rolled	0.283	30	48	2775	5.8	277	0.021	6.7	14.3		
Cold rolled	0.283	30	70	2775	5.8	277	0.021	6.7	14.3		
Stainless steel 302											
Cold rolled	0.29	28	75	2590	2.0	325	0.006	9.6	72		
Titanium 6A1-4V	0.16	17	135	3000	0.93	200	0.0047	5.8	176		

PRECIOUS METALS											
Gold, cold worked	0.698	12	30	1945	37.1	202	0.184	7.9	2.35		
Silver, cold worked	0.379	11	44	1761	52.0	198	0.263	10.9	1.59		
Platinum, cold worked	0.775	21	27	3224	9.1	224	0.044	4.9	14.9		
Palladium, cold worked	0.434	17	30	2829	8.9	233	0.038	6.5	10.4		
Rhodium, cold worked	0.447	42	300	3571	10.8	246	0.044	4.6	4.51		
NONMETALLICS											
Polycrystalline glass (Pyroceram 9608)	0.09	12.5	16_f–20_f	~2280	0.24	147	0.0016	0.2–1.1	10^{24} 6(680F) .3(932F)	7	2.5×10^5
Alumina (95%) ceramics	0.14	40	45_f	3686	2.2	155	0.014	3.7	10^9	8.9 (1Mc)	2.5×10^5
Fused silica glass	0.08	10.5	10_f	3050	0.17	177	0.001	0.3	10^7	3.8	1–2×10^6
Mica, natural	0.11	20–30	40_f		0.06	210	0.0003	18	10^3	5–9	
Graphite	0.06	0.5–2	0.4–2	6200	16–20	100		1.0–1.3			
CARBIDE-BASE CERMETS (variation in properties due to various binders)											
Titanium carbide	0.2–0.26	40–50	120_f–250_f		2.1			4–7	100		
Tungsten-titanium-carbide	0.38–0.47	65–90	125_f–350_f		3.5–7			3.5–4			
Tungsten carbide	0.47–0.55	60–100	175_f–460_f		5.5–11			2.5–4			
Chromium carbide	0.25–0.29		100_f–120_f					5.8–6.3			
PLASTICS											
Cellulose acetate	0.047	0.25	5_f		0.032	145	0.00022	70	10^4–10^7	3.5–7	2.5×10^5
Nylon (66)	0.041	0.41	8_f		0.03	140	0.00022	55	10^7	4.0	3.8×10^5
Epoxy	0.04–0.08	0.4–1.5	2–12		0.02–0.16	~100	0.0002–0.002	20–50	10^6–10^8	3.5–5	3.5×10^5
Teflon (Polytetra fluoroethylene)	0.08	0.04–0.07	2–3	~400	0.03	190	0.00016	55	10^{13}	2.0	4×10^5

* Subscript f indicates fracture.

TABLE A5-6

AVERAGE PROPERTIES OF FLUIDS

Material	Temperature, °F	Density, lb/in³	Thermal conductivity, lb/sec·°F	Vol. spec. heat, lb/in²·°F	Thermal diffusivity, in²/sec	Viscosity, lb·sec/in²	Prandtl number, $\frac{c_p\mu}{k}$
Water	32	0.0360	0.069	336	0.00021	2.6×10^{-7}	13.4
	100	0.0359	0.079	335	0.00024	0.0×10^{-7}	4.5
	200	0.0348	0.085	324	0.00026	0.46×10^{-7}	1.9
Light oil	60	0.033	0.017	128	0.00013	125×10^{-7}	0.38
	100	0.032	0.016	137	0.00012	33×10^{-7}	0.39
	200	0.031	0.016	147	0.00011	5.4×10^{-7}	0.42
Mercury	50	0.49	1.02	150	0.0068	2.3×10^{-7}	0.027
	200	0.48	1.30	148	0.0088	1.80×10^{-7}	0.016
	600	0.47	1.75	146	0.012	1.25×10^{-7}	0.0084
Dry air	0	5.0×10^{-5}	2.8×10^{-3}	0.111	0.025	2.4×10^{-9}	0.722
	60	4.4×10^{-5}	3.2×10^{-3}	0.098	0.033	2.6×10^{-9}	0.712
	100	4.1×10^{-5}	3.5×10^{-3}	0.093	0.038	2.8×10^{-9}	0.706
	200	3.5×10^{-5}	3.9×10^{-3}	0.079	0.049	3.1×10^{-9}	0.694
	500	2.4×10^{-5}	5.4×10^{-3}	0.056	0.097	4.1×10^{-9}	0.680
	800	1.8×10^{-5}	6.5×10^{-3}	0.043	0.015	4.9×10^{-9}	0.685
	1500	1.07×10^{-5}	8.8×10^{-3}	0.028	0.31	6.3×10^{-9}	0.709

TABLE A5-7

ISOTOPES PRODUCED IN A NUCLEAR PILE
BY THE n-γ REACTION*

Isotope	Activity, mc/gm	Half-life	Particles emitted
Antimony-122	210	2.8 d	β^-, γ
Antimony-124	20	60 d	β^-, γ
Arsenic-76	440	27 h	β^-, γ
Barium-131	0.45	11.5 d	K, γ
Bismuth-210	0.41	5 d	β^-
Bromine-82	160	36 d	β^-, γ
Cadmium-115*	1	43 d	β^-, γ
Cadmium-115	20	2.3 d	β^-, γ
Calcium-45	0.28	163 d	β^-
Cerium-141	7.1	32 d	β^-, γ
Cesium-134	37	2.3 y	β^-, γ
Chlorine-36	0.00008	300,000 y	β^-
Chromium-51	39	28 d	K, γ
Cobalt-60	47	5.3 y	β^-, γ
Copper-64	340	12.8 h	$\beta^-, \beta^+, K, \gamma$
Europium-152	280	13 y	β^-, K, γ
Europium-154	23.	16 y	β^-, γ
Gallium-72	150	14.3 h	β^-, γ
Germanium-71	40	11.4 d	K
Gold-198	3300	2.7 d	β^-, γ
Hafnium-181	55	45 d	β^-, γ
Indium-114	57	49 d	β^-, γ
Iridium-192	3200	74 d	K, γ, β^-
Iridium-194	3300	19 h	β^-, γ
Iron-55	0.15	2.9 y	K
Iron-59	0.4	45 d	β^-, γ
Lanthanum-140	500	40 h	β^-, γ
Mercury-197*	75	23 h	γ
Mercury-197	75	2.7 d	γ, K
Mercury-203	13	45 d	β^-, γ
Molybdenum-99	10	2.8 d	β^-, γ
Nickel-63	0.044	85 y	β^-

*Radioactive product and irradiated sample are the same element. Assumed time of irradiation is 28 days; flux is 5×10^{11} neutrons/cm^2/sec. Main source *Radioisotopes: Catalog and Price List*, Oak Ridge, 1957.

(Continued)

TABLE A5–7 (*Continued*)

Isotope	Activity, mc/gm	Half-life	Particles emitted
Osmium-191	65	16 d	β^-, γ
Palladium-109	220	13.6 h	β^-, γ
Phosphorus-32	44	14.3 d	β^-
Potassium-42	14	12.4 h	β^-, γ
Praseodymium-142	630	19.2 h	β^-, γ
Rhenium-186	1100	3.9 d	β^-, γ, K
Rubidium-86	31	19.5 d	β^-, γ
Ruthenium-97	1	2.4 d	γ, K
Samarium-153	1900	47 h	β^-, γ
Scandium-46	450	85 d	β^-, γ
Selenium-75	3.2	120 d	γ, K
Silver-110	7.1	270 d	β^-, γ
Sodium-24	210	15 h	β^-, γ
Strontium-89	0.12	53 d	β^-
Sulfur-35	0.52	87 d	β^-
Tantalum-182	140	115 d	β^-, γ
Thallium-204	1.4	4 y	β^-, K
Tin-113	0.14	112 d	γ, K
Tungsten-185	6.6	73 d	β^-
Tungsten-187	420	24 h	β^-, γ
Yttrium-90	93	2.5 d	β^-
Zinc-65	2.2	250 d	β^+, γ, K
Zirconium-95	0.25	65 d	β^-, γ

Note: h = hours, d = days, y = years.

TABLE A5–8

SOME OTHER COMMON PILE-PRODUCED RADIOISOTOPES*

Isotope	Half-life	Particles	Production method	Activity, mc/gm
Carbon-14	5560 y	β^-	$N^{14}(n, p)C^{14}$	0.002
Gold-199	3.2 d	β^-, γ	$Pt^{198}(n, \gamma)Pt^{199} \rightarrow Au^{199}$	8.8
Hydrogen-3	12.5 y	β^-	$Li^6(n, \alpha)H^3$	
Iodine-131	8.1 d	β^-, γ	$Te^{130}(n, \gamma)Te^{131} \rightarrow I^{131}$ (also fission product)	4.3
Magnesium-28	21 h	β^-, γ	$Li^6(n, \alpha)H^3 \quad Mg^{26}(H^3, p)Mg^{28}$ (irradiate lithium-magnesium alloy)	0.015
Niobium-95	35 d	β^-, γ	fission product	
Polonium-210	128 d	α	$Bi^{209}(n, \gamma)Bi^{210} \rightarrow Po^{210}$	0.06
Radium-226	1620 y	α	occurs naturally	1000
Silver-111	7.6 d	β^-, γ	$Pd^{110}(n, \gamma)Pd^{111} \rightarrow Ag^{111}$	1.9
Strontium-90	28 y	β^-	fission product	
Technetium-99	210,000 y	β^-	$Mo^{98}(n, \gamma)Mo^{99} \rightarrow Tc^{99}$ (also fission product)	0.000,002

* For these, target and isotope are different elements. Same irradiation time and flux as Table A5–7. Main Source: *Radioactive Materials and Stable Isotopes*, Harwell, 1957.

Note: When the radioisotopes and target are different elements, it is relatively easy to separate them chemically. This produces much higher activities than those listed.

INDEX

Accelerometers, 84, 87
Accuracy (*see* Error), 7, 15, 44
  of autoradiography, 239
  of radiotracer counting, 239, 248–250
Ahrendt, W. R., 168
Alpha particle, 230, 232, 233
Amplitude ratio, 76
Analog computers, 295
Analogous systems, 262
Argon, A. S., 56, 68
Arkin, H., 68
A.S.M.E., measurements in unsteady
    flow, 224
  power test code, 224
Atomic constitution, 225, 226
Autoradiography, 293–294
Ayre, R. S., 112

Baird, D. C., 60, 67
Balance (*see* Chemical balance)
Bears, Y., 67
Beckwith, T. G., 112, 151, 194
Beta particles, 229, 232, 233, 237, 245
Binomial distribution, 36–37
Birge, R. T., 68
Boltzmann, L., 180
Bradford, J., 258
Bridge circuits, capacitance, 143
  inductance, 138
  resistance, 128
Bridgman, P. W., 205
Brooks, C. E. P., 68
Buck, N. L., 112, 151, 194

Calibrating resistance, 132
Caliper micrometer, 16–20
Capacitance gage, 283
Capacitance plate force, 147
Capacitance transducers, 141
  linearity, 142
Carruthers, N., 68
Carslaw, H. S., 112, 185, 194
Cathode-follower preamplifier, 144
Chemical balance, 13–15, 26, 27
Chi-square (x^2) test, 49–53
Choi, H. Y., 194, 300
Colton, R. R., 68
Compensating networks, 87
Complex numbers, 74, 259
Conversion factors, 302
Cook, N. H., 160, 168
Coulomb friction, 24
Curie, 241
Curth, O. E., 224
Cyclotron, 240–241

Damping, insufficient, 93
  viscous, 25
Damping ratio, 79
Data analysis, dynamic, 106

Data elimination, 40
Decibel, 77
Depth of focus, 12
Dial gage, 114
Differential transformer, 136
Diffraction, 8
Displacement measurement, 113
  electrical means, 124
  fluid gages, 121
  mechanical means, 114
  optical means, 116
Distribution, binomial, 36–37
  nearly normal, 53
  normal, 37–51
  skewed, 53, 55
Douglas, R. D., 152
Draper, C. S., 112
Drifting of instruments, 25
Dumont Laboratories, *Transducers*, 152
Dynamics, pressure measurement, 215
  temperature measurement, 183
Dynamics of measurement, 69
Dynamometers, cross interference, 161
  design criteria, 153
  lathe, 164
  mating surfaces, 165
  multicomponent, 164
Electron microscope, 11
Electronic transducers, 148
Electrons (*see* Beta particles), 225, 226
Emissivity, 180
Eratosthenes, 4
Error, 16–26, 29–64
  dynamic, 69, 71, 72, 81
  external estimate, 30–35
  gross, 20
  hysteresis, 24
  independent, 32–35
  internal estimate, 36–38, 42–44
  parallax, 20
  personal, 20
  random, 18, 43
  reading, 19
  repeatability, 23
  systematic, 18, 43
  thermal expansion, 18
  zero, 17
Extended ring, 163
External error, 30–35
Eye, resolution, 10

First-order systems, 70
  compensation, 88
Flow coefficient, 196
Flow measurement, characteristics of
    flow meters, table, 201
  displacement meters, 196
  drag-body meters, 197
  hot-wire anomometer, 199

310

magnetic flow meter, 198
mass flow meter, 198
pitot tube, 197
sonic flow meter, 199
tanks, 195
thermal meters, 199
turbine flow meter, 199
variable-area meters, 198
variable-head meters, 196
Fluid-displacement gage, 279
Fluid measurements, 195
Force measurement, 154
    axially loaded members, 158
    cantilever beams, 159
    rings, 160
    servosystems, 157
Force and torque measurement, 153
Force transducer, example, 95
Fourier analysis, 74, 97
    phase relationships, 102
Frequency ratio, 85
Friction, 24, 44–48
Friction experiment, 275–277

Gage factor, 125
    adjustment of, 166
Galvanometer, 25, 96
    response, 277
Gamma rays, 229, 232, 233, 245
Gaussian distribution (see Normal
    distribution)
Geiger counter, 234–239, 245, 250, 254
Glasstone, S., 258

Half-life, 231, 232, 242, 243, 244
Handbook of Physics and Chemistry, 39, 68
Harmonic analysis, 97
Harris, F. K., 151
Harrison, T. R., 194
Heat transfer coefficient, 183, 199
Helmholtz resonator, 219
Histogram, 36, 48, 53
Hysteresis, 24

Illustrative experiments, 272
Impulsive inputs, 73, 81
Independent linearity, 22
Inductance gage, 286
Inductance transducers, 134
Interference, multiple-beam, 120
    optical, 116
Isotopes, 226

Jacobsen, L. S., 112
Jaeger, J. C., 112, 185, 188, 194

K-capture, 229
Kohl, J., 258

Laplace transforms, 259
Lathe dynamometer, 164
Least squares method, 60–64
Lees, S., 112

Lens, depth of focus, 12
    resolution, 9
Limit of error, 41
Linearity, 22
Lion, K. I., 194
Lion, K. S., 152
Loewen, E. G., 168
Logarithmic response curves, 76
Lukins, H. R., 258
L.V.D.T. (see Differential transformer)

McClintock, F. A., 56, 68
McKay, W., 112
Materials selector, 300
Mean deviation, 49
Mean error, 41
Measurement, 3–5
Metals, aging, 15
    thermal expansion, 15
Meter, definition (length), 119
    impedance, 129, 142
Metric multipliers, table, 301
Micrometer, 16–20
Microscope, 7–13
Miesse, C. C., 224
Millis, D., 152
Molecular mean free path, 207
Moroney, M. J., 68
Multicomponent dynamometers, 164

National Bureau of Standards, 224
Natural frequency, 79
Noise, thermal, 133
Nonparametric statistics, 56
Normal distribution, 37–51
    calculation, 44–51
Nozzle, 197
Nuclear pile, 240–244, 255, 257
Null measurements, 25
Numerical aperture, 10
Nusselt number, 184

Octagonal ring, 162
Octave, 77
Optical measuring methods, 116
Orifice, 197

Parabolic input, 72
Partridge, G. R., 152
Pastoriza Company computers, 295
Peltier, J. C. A., 174
Penetrating power of particles, 232–234
Perfect gas, 206
Periodic inputs, 74, 84
Phase angle, 75
Phase relationships, 261
Phase sensitivity, 132
Photographic film, 237–239, 252
Physical constants, table, 301
Piezoelectric constant, 147
Piezoelectric transducers, 147
Piezoelectric voltage, 148
Poisson distribution, 245–248, 256, 257

Polaroid film, 294
Positrons, 229
Prandtl number, 184
Precision, 44
Pressure measurement, dynamics, 215
  high pressure, 205
  moderate pressure, 204
Probable error, 41
  of mean, 42
Properties, of fluids, 306
  of solids, 304
Proportional linearity, 22
Pyrometry, 179

Rabinowicz, E., 252, 258
Radioactivity, safety precautions, 239, 251
Radioisotopes, 226–228
  decay, 229–232
  nontracer uses, 250–252, 256, 257
  tables, 307–309
  tracer uses, 252–253, 255, 256
Radiotracer experiments, 289–294
Ramp input, 71, 80
Random number experiments, 265–271
Random number table, 268
Random walk problem, 34
Range of data, 49
Ratio arms, mutual inductance, 145
Resistance transducers, 124
Resolution, 7
Resonance, 84
Retina, 11
Reynolds number, 184
Richards, C. W., 300
Roberts, H. C., 152, 168
Robinson, G., 38, 60, 68
Rohsenow, W. M., 194, 300
Root-mean-square error, 41
Roughness measurement, 5

Schaevitz Engineering Company, 138
Schenk, H., 28
Scintillation counter, 245
Second-order systems, 78
  compensation, 92
Seebeck, T. J., 174
Shaw, M. C., 168
Sheet thickness measurement, 6
Shepard's correction, 46
Standard atmosphere, properties, 303
Standard deviation, 38, 41
Standard error, of mean, 47
  of one reading, 41
Standing waves, 219
Statham Instruments Company, *Instrument Notes*, 112
Stationary time principle, 12
Stefan, J., 180
Step input, 71, 79
Straight line approximation of curve, 104
Straight line drawing, 56–64
Strain-gage dynamometer, 280

Strain gages, 125, 126, 127, 281
Superposition, 72
Sweeney, R. J., 194, 224

Taplin, J. F., 168
Temperature measurement, 169
  adiabatic temperature rise, 186
  bimaterials, 170
  dynamics, 183
  moving and sliding members, 187, 190
  pressure thermometers, 171
  pyrometry, 179
  radiation error, 186
  recovery factor, 186
  resistance thermometers, 171
  static temperature, 186
  thermistors, 174
  thermocouples, 147
  thermopile, 177
  velocity error, 185
Temperature-resistance coefficients, table, 172
Temperature scale, international, 169
Thermal conductivity of gases, 207
Thermocouple characteristics, table, 178
Thermoelectric sensitivity, table, 175
Thomson, W. (Lord Kelvin), 174
Time constant, 70
Timoshenko, S., 168
Topping, J., 68
Torque measurement, torque tubes, 165
Tracer experiments, 244–245, 252–253
Transducers, capacitance, 141
  electronic, 148
  inductance, 134
  piezoelectric, 147
  variable resistance, 124
Transient inputs, impulse, 73, 81
  parabolic, 72
  ramp, 71, 80
  step, 71, 79

Vacuum gages, 212
Vacuum measurement, 206
  leaks, 208
Vacuum systems, cold traps, 210–216
Van Vlack, L. H., 300
Velocity meter, 86
Venturi, 197
Vernier caliper, 20
Vibrometers, 85
Voltmeters, 21–25

Wave, elastic, 133
Wavelength, of light, 116–119
Wear measurement, 7
Wear particle measurement, 272–275
Westman, H. P., 300
Wheatstone bridge, 128, 172, 206
  linearity, 130
Whittaker, E., 38, 60, 68
Wilson, E. B., 28

Zentner, R. D., 258